# INDUSTRIAL DESIGN:

## A Practicing Professional

To Frank & family -

P. H. Stevens

# INDUSTRIAL DESIGN:
## A Practicing Professional

Philip H. Stevens, FIDSA

Foreword by Professor Ronald Beckman

Hard Pressed Publishing
a division of Philip Stevens Associates, Ltd.
Skaneateles, New York

Library of Congress Card Catalog Number 99-75588
ISBN 0-9667375-0-4

First Edition

*This book is dedicated to my late dear friend,*
*Arthur Hunt Crapsey, FIDSA*
*who personified the qualities of a modern professional*
*designer. He was a friendly critic and*
*a source of stimulating ideas.*

# FOREWORD

Industrial Design is a child of the twentieth century. It is a hybrid discipline formed from the marriage of art and engineering. Neither one nor the other; it justifies its existence by portraying the meanings of industrial products to the multitude of persons who use them. Mass production presupposes mass consumption, with all the benefits and deficits that condition implies. The industrial designer works astride compounding technologies, attempting to direct the thrust of modern industry in appropriate and constructive directions. Although it began with the task of fashioning products that would strike a consumer's fancy through appearance, by late in the century design had become much more. It deals with the interface between makers and users. In addition to the millions of objects manufactured, this interface might be the information on a computer screen, an exhibition about government service, or a hospital environment supporting care. Good designers become the conscience of their clients, assuring that the products they design are self-explanatory, safe to use, handsome to see, and friendly to the environment.

Industrial designers plan services as well as products; they create the "corporate image" of the many outcomes of an organization's activities. They investigate new materials, the potential of human labor in manufacturing, and the application of automation. Their work crosses the boundaries of architecture, interior design, graphic design, city planning, sociology, psychology, and ecology, to name a few allied fields. The industrial designer is a generalist, rather than a specialist. This alone is a novel change in our over-specialized society. And it is this uniqueness, difference and necessity that has prompted one accomplished practitioner to write this volume.

Each year Philip Stevens, the author of this book, organizes a summer competition for the third-year industrial design students at Syracuse University. In the past four years he has challenged them with significant problems such as: prefabricated house construction; the incarceration of public offenders; testing for pure water; and the historic preservation of technology. Fellow designers, recruited by Stevens, act with him as a panel of judges and sponsor substantial cash prizes for the most excellent solutions.

In the same generous spirit, this autobiography of "a practicing professional" is offered to those interested in industrial designing. In his conclusion, Stevens writes:

> Having been associated with design for almost 50 years, having grown up during the Great Depression, having served in World War II, having seen our country maintain its responsbility toward world peace, as well as having operated a successful design partnership and corporation—and designed good products, I sincerely believe there is a need for industrial design that will continue well into the twenty-first century and beyond.

It has long been clear to me that few talented art and engineering college freshmen are aware of the depth and breadth of industrial design. They and their parents may benefit from learning about what this emerging occupation has been, is now, and can become. With this chronicle of a lifetime in design, Stevens provides a definition to demystify this modern profession.

He takes us back to the formative inventions of the American Shaker movement and discusses the ingenuity of the nation's self-taught canal builders. He describes the philosophical confrontation with the disorder of the Industrial Revolution, mounted by British design critic John Ruskin and master craftsman William Morris. We see the corporate planner Peter Behrens and the educator Walter Gropius attempting, between the world wars, to integrate art and industry in Germany. He shows us how massive steam locomotives not only transformed travel and commerce on land—but were modeled in a new way to express power and motion. Design then, is a way of seeing and thinking, celebrated by the major artists and innovators of the twentieth century. His predecessors, industrial designers Walter Dorwin Teague, Norman Bel Geddes, Raymond Loewy, and Henry Dreyfuss, are a direct inspiration.

With twelve-year-old Phil Stevens and his neighborhood chums, we fly down Cortland Street hill as they pilot their soapbox racers on the steepest grade in Groton, New York. Years later, the profession has led the author into the bowels of the earth, lying on his back in an electric personnel carrier with his face inches from the roof of a Pennsylvania coal mine, observing real conditions so he can establish safety requirements for a continuous mining machine. This odyssey takes us from his schemes for lighting in Consolidated Vultee Aircraft Corporation's atomic-shielded test plane and through many subsequent case studies of projects completed in his productive career—from such diverse environments as gold mines, two miles deep into the earth, to the ceiling of a jet bomber, eight miles into the sky. Along the way we are introduced to the details of operating a design-consulting partnership and corporation, including design directing, model-making, presentation, office politics, resumes, interviews, travel and the adventures that comprise the daily flow of events in a designer's professional life.

The need for creativity is central to Stevens' discussion of education. He believes that all occupations will require a great infusion of independent thinking as world populations continue to grow and advanced technologies proliferate. Of value in this publication are the excellent illustrations that tell the history of design in visual terms. This is a collection of images chosen by one designer to parallel his commentary of events. Equally interesting are the quotations from many experts in a variety of endeavors, and timelines that have bearing on the text. These references place his work in relation to that of others who have contributed to the American experience.

The discussion in Chapter 10—"The Designer in a Changing World," fascinates me. Recently, the grandfather of one of my graduating students commented on his grandson's fifth-year thesis, dealing with water conservation. He said, "the next great war may well be fought over drinking water." Substantial changes in how we utilize the resources of this planet will profoundly impact future practice. A major adjustment in the relationship of humankind to the ecosphere will overturn many cherished beliefs and behaviors of governments, institutions and individuals in the immediate future. A new and unexpected aesthetic can evolve from our understanding of these developing realities. Rather than viewing the disruption of our past with dismay, we can see these changes as an exciting opportunity to reshape the world into a more rational, spiritual and beautiful place—as exciting a prospect as building the post-war environment was for Philip Stevens and his fellow designers.

As an experienced mentor, Stevens discusses design ethics, creativity, public service, economic realities, and the future of technology, in direct conversational language that anticipates the questions a beginner might pose. I recommend this comprehensive narrative to guidance counselors, parents, and especially to students who wish to pursue a rewarding career of creative problem-solving.

— Ronald Beckman, IDSA, *Associate Professor*
*Coordinator of the Industrial Design Department,*
*Syracuse University, retired*
Former Adjunct Professor at Pratt Institute, Rhode
Island School of Design, and Associate Professor
Cornell University College of Human Ecology

## ACKNOWLEDGMENTS

I wish to acknowledge the contributions made by the following people to the preparation of this book; Margueritte C. Stevens, my wife, for her critical eye and ear and financial encouragement; Professor Ronald Beckman, IDSA, Professor Stan Rickel, IDSA, and Professor Donald Carr, IDSA, of Syracuse University's Industrial Design Department, who never hesitated to suggest ways in which the content of the manuscript could be made more truthful and meaningful; Richard Hollerith, FIDSA, and the late Arthur Crapsey, FIDSA, my longtime personal friends, for providing endless encouragement; Tammy Murray, my secretary for many years, who provided me immense support in drafting and redrafting this book; Nancy Boyce, a freelance book designer, who has been most helpful in the page layout and book design; and, Andrew Faust, IDSA, an adjunct professor at Syracuse University, for his artistic suggestions regarding the cover design.

I wish to express my appreciation to James Ryan, FIDSA, Past President of the Industrial Designers Society of America and a partner in Henry Dreyfuss Associates, Kristina Goodrich, Executive Director and Chief Operating Officer of IDSA, Professor Craig McArt, Rochester Institute of Technology, Professor Fredrick Kuhn, IDSA, Coordinator of Industrial Design at Wentworth Institute of Technology, and Robert G. Smith, FIDSA, a practicing industrial designer, who were kind enough to critique my book and offer their professional opinion; Dr. Howard Gardner, a professor at the Harvard Graduate School of Education and adjunct professor of neurology at the Boston University School of Medicine, who graciously reviewed my chapter on creativity and allowed me to quote from his book, *Multiple Intelligences: The Theory in Practice;* and, Tom Peters, a speaker at the Forty-fifth International Design Conference in Aspen, for letting me quote his characteristics of "design mindfulness."

I also wish to thank Ernie Hinck, my friend, a retired Ingersoll-Rand engineer, for providing me support and historical data on Ingersoll-Rand; Ed Patten, Chief of Operations, Conservation, and Restoration at the National Aviation Museum in Ottawa, Ontario, Canada and Ray Wagner, an aircraft expert in San Diego, California, who assisted me with specifics on the aircraft discussed in this book; and, Atelier "Paul" Bessieres, AIA, an architect in San Francisco, for reviewing my writings on design education and curriculum.

# TABLE OF CONTENTS

## INTRODUCTION

Industrial design is an important process in the development of most products which drive our global economy. It touches us every day in discrete ways in which the average consumer is unaware. Industrial design is in the cars we drive, the appliances we use, the toys children play with, and the machinery and equipment which keep our industries and commerce thriving.

Written by a practicing professional, this book is an overview of industrial design as practiced today. I want to share with others the great experiences I have had as a practicing industrial designer. Throughout my career I felt that I was creating a valuable artifact for the twentieth century. I was also proud of the benefits my work brought to my clients and their employees who invested time and effort to help manufacture the products. The value industrial design has brought to those who use products is exciting. It is an immensely gratifying profession, and I personally have derived great satisfaction from it.

One goal of this book is to acquaint those who are unfamiliar with industrial design with the profession. Students of industrial design need very much to know more about this necessary, dynamic profession and what services it performs. Some people believe that industrial design is a skill or a craft—not a profession—and can be learned in as little as two years. In reality, it takes four or five years or longer to become a capable designer.

Chapter 1 gives an introduction to the profession along with definitions. Other professions and how they relate to industrial design are explored. Chapter 2 is a brief historical presentation on the evolution of design as we know it, from the industrial revolution to the present. These chapters will especially help those unfamiliar with the profession become acquainted with it. They will also help those who work in related fields, such as engineering, business management, marketing, and architecture understand what is often perceived as a mysterious profession. The rich history of industrial design, even though it is short compared to other professions, is important. I hope that through better understanding, better products can be developed and ways can be found whereby industrial designers will be given opportunities to contribute more effectively to our culture and develop solutions to critical world problems.

What attracts people to industrial design? Where do they first come in contact with it? Why are graphics and sculpture associated with industrial design? Chapter 3 explores the relationship of modern graphics and sculpture as it relates to industrial design.

In the interest of finding more qualified people to fill these challenging positions, we have begun to question what makes a person creative, as is an industrial designer. How do we recognize a person with the potential to become an industrial designer? Why is one person more creative than another? What qualities must a competent industrial designer possess? Chapter 4 examines creativity, particularly in children, and the critical experiences which guide them into the field of industrial design.

Chapter 5 describes the educational requirements and the process of educating industrial designers. It also discusses the various career options available to an industrial designer and the pros and cons of each.

The observations about industrial design presented in this book are those of one practicing professional. Other professionals may have similar or varied views. The objective is for all of us to stop for a moment and look around. Are we doing the best we can do? Can we see what is needed for the future? Is the quality of design today what it should be? Can we, as a profession, do better? For example, universities as well as industries have tried to box in, define limits, and confine industrial design to restricted or limited areas of service. The profession, as it matures and increases its body of knowledge, needs and wants to be challenged with greater responsibilities.

How to acquire the right job in the field of industrial design is explored. It urges design students to establish career objectives early in college and explore some of the many employment opportunities or paths that can be pursued. This chapter will help students plan and work toward the job they find themselves most suited for and want.

Chapter 6 describes a graduate's first industrial work experience.

Setting up a design consulting office is explained in Chapter 7. It discusses the pros and cons of establishing a sole proprietorship, a partnership, and a corporation and reviews the things industrial designers should consider before starting their own business. It also talks about how a new design consultancy earns clients. Ethics, recognized as a serious problem in modern industry, are discussed along with the law and design, including liability and plagiarism. Topics of professionalism and professional organizations are reviewed. I tell of my personal experience testifying, before a Presidential Commission and the United States Congressional Commerce Committee, on product safety and fire prevention.

Case studies of two large, international companies and their products are presented in Chapter 9. The purpose of these case studies is to give the reader a better understanding of what is "good design" and how environments for collaborative and creative thinking can be established. This information should be helpful to any executive in a design-related capacity.

In the last chapter, Chapter 10, I examine the question of "What is good design?" and explain how to establish a climate for continued good design development. The future of industrial design is also explored and how it can contribute to a better world. This book, for once, presents the topic of industrial design from the inside point of view of a practicing professional rather than from the outside perspective of a fine-arts critic. Finally, I sincerely hope that readers will walk away with an understanding of the following:

- What makes a good designer
- What designers do
- How designers establish themselves
- What is professionalism
- What is "good design"
- How is a climate for continued good design development achieved.

### CHAPTER ONE

# WHAT IS INDUSTRIAL DESIGN?

*Long-range planning
does not deal
with future decisions,
but with the future
of present decisions.*

Peter Drucker

Industrial design is critical to the success of today's products. What is industrial design? It means many different things to different people. Most people have no idea what industrial design entails. Some believe it is the design of industries. More people believe it relates to the function only or engineering of a product. Industrial design is much more! Even designers within the profession have differing opinions of what industrial design is. This is because the role that each industrial designer plays within the profession is varied.

While researching this book, I felt it would be interesting to see how prominent designers and writers of design define industrial design. As seen from the definitions below, the views and opinions are as varied as the profession itself.

- **Arthur J. Pulos** (*Opportunities in Industrial Design Careers*, pg. 14), 1970:
  Industrial design is the imaginative development of manufactured products and systems which satisfy the physical needs and psychological desires of people. Industrial design is not, as the name may imply to the lay person, the design of industries, nor is it the design of industrial buildings or industrial processes. It is, rather, concerned with the usefulness and beauty of the products and total environment which men create for their fellow men.

- **Arthur J. Pulos** (*American Design Ethic: A History of Industrial Design*, pg. 1), 1983:
  Design is the indispensible leavening of the American way of life. It emerged with the need of the colonists to transform the wilderness into a secure haven and expanded as a natural component of the industrial revolution in the New World. The United States was in all likelihood the first nation to be designed—to come into being as a deliberate consequence of the actions of men who recognized a problem and resolved it with the greatest benefit to the whole. America did not just happen: It was designed.

- **Charles H. Flurscheim** (*Industrial Design in Engineering, a Marriage of Techniques*, pg. 1), 1983:
  Objectives of industrial design in engineering:
  The objective of all engineers is to optimize fitness for purpose, based on market requirements and criteria of quality, performance and cost effectiveness. Industrial design, which embraces aesthetic, ergonomic and graphic techniques—or arts, for they can be considered either—provides tools that can assist in the specification of what is needed by the market and in design for the man/machine interface.

- **David Pye** (*The Nature and Aesthetics of Design*, pg. 18), 1978:
  Design—useful design, that is to say—is the business of adapting a known system so as to get at least the intended result, when energy is deliberately put in or admitted to the system.

- **Karl T. Ulrich** and **Steven D. Eppinger** (*Product Design and Development*, pg. 3), 1995:
  The design function leads the definition of the physical form of the product to best meet the customer needs. In this context, the design function includes engineering design (mechanical, electrical, software, etc.) and industrial design (aesthetics, ergonomics, user interfaces).

- **John Heskett** (*Industrial Design*, pg. 10), 1980:
  …[I]ndustrial design is a process of creating, invention and definition separated from the means of production, involving an eventual synthesis of contributory and often conflicting factors into a concept of three-dimensional form, and its material reality, capable of multiple reproduction of mechanical means.

- **Christopher Lorenz** (*The Design Dimension, Product Strategy and the Challenge of Global Marketing,* pg. vii), 1986:
Creating products whose shape, feel and appearance give satisfaction and pleasure to the consumer is certainly an element of the industrial designer's work; feel and appearance are part of the function of most manufactured products. But are they the limits of the industrial designer's contribution? …[I]ndustrial design is a process of creation, invention and definition. The idea that industrial designers might be just as capable as marketing experts and technologists of conceiving new products, and of playing a full and sometimes leading part in their successful development, provoked much initial skepticism in the breast of a hardened observer of the "heavy" sides of management: corporate strategy, planning, finance, research, production and marketing.

- **Thomas Hauffe** (*Design,* pg. 9), 1996:
Today the question, "What is design?" is almost as difficult to answer as the question, "What is art?" And because design is influenced in both theory and practice by the most varied factors, it is no longer possible to come up with a single definition. In spite of this, or perhaps because of it, the attempt to mark out the territory of design is important.

- **Katherine McCoy** (*Design Discourse,* pg. 7), 1989:
[Industrial design] is a "forward-looking" focus…When people look to the future, they are more open to new ideas, to innovation. They are more open to industrial design's contribution.

- **Abraham Moles** (*Design Discourse,* pg. 15), 1989:
In short, designers are no longer creators of *objects* but of *environments.* The design task is to reconceptualize the various shells that surround human beings in order that a means of deriving the greatest possible satisfaction from their position in the world and the possibility for attaining a specific quality of life is not made more and more remote.

- **Herbert Simon** (*Design Discourse,* pg. 3), 1989:
Everyone designs who devises courses of action aimed at changing existing situations into preferred ones. The intellectual activity that produces material artifacts is no different fundamentally from the one that prescribes remedies for a sick patient or the one that devises a new sales plan for a company or a social welfare policy for a state. Design, so construed, is the core of all professional training: it is the principal mark that distinguishes the professions from the sciences.

All of the above definitions are correct, but incomplete. The Industrial Designers Society of America (IDSA), the national non-profit organization for professionals who design products and provide related services, offers its *Comprehensive Description of Industrial Design* (2002):

> Industrial design is the professional service of creating and developing concepts and specifications that optimize the function, value and appearance of products and systems for the mutual benefit of both user and manufacturer. Industrial designers develop these concepts and specifications through collection, analysis and synthesis of data guided by the special requirements of the client or manufacturer. They are trained to prepare clear and concise recommendations through drawings, models and verbal descriptions.

> Industrial design services are often provided within the context of cooperative working relationships with other members of a development group. Typical groups include management, marketing, engineering and manufacturing specialists. The industrial designer expresses concepts that embody all relevant design criteria determined by the group.

The industrial designer's unique contribution places emphasis on those aspects of the product or system that relate most directly to human characteristics, needs and interests. This contribution requires specialized understanding of visual, tactile, safety and convenience criteria, with concern for the user. Education and experience in anticipating psychological, physiological and sociological factors that influence and are perceived by the user are essential industrial design resources.

Industrial designers also maintain a practical concern for technical processes and requirements for manufacture; marketing opportunities and economic constraints; and distribution sales and servicing processes. They work to ensure that design recommendations use materials and technology effectively, and comply with all legal and regulatory requirements.

In addition to supplying concepts for products and systems, industrial designers are often retained for consultation on a variety of problems that have to do with a client's image. Such assignments include product and organization identity systems, development of communications systems, interior space planning and exhibit design, advertising devices and packaging and other related services. Their expertise is sought in a wide variety of administrative arenas to assist in developing industrial standards, regulatory guidelines and quality control procedures to improve manufacturing operations and products.

Industrial designers, as professionals, are guided by their awareness of obligations to fulfill contractual responsibilities to clients, to protect the public safety and well-being, to respect the environment and to observe ethical business practice.

The above IDSA description is embraced by most professionals. I might add that this description of industrial design will change over time as the profession evolves. The role of the industrial designer is changing and will continue to change over the next century and beyond as the needs of our society change.

Three important aspects of the above IDSA definition need emphasis. First, where human factors are applied to a product, it is critical that the designer is sure the design satisfies and can be used by the maximum number of people. Careful market research must be conducted to determine the exact market where the product will be used and the design must satisfy the maximum number of users possible. For example, a power tool used in building construction has a very different market and, therefore, different anthropometric requirements than kitchen tools. Designers should realize that many products will be used by children, the elderly, or the physically-challenged. Their individual needs must be addressed.

Second, thought must be given as to how a product can be made more valuable than previous or competitive products. Value to a product means the following: more useful; appealing to look at and feel; less costly; and easier to use and/or more dependable. The design must provide pride of ownership.

Third, designers need to consider the impact of their work on the environment. The design profession should protect and preserve our natural resources.

Many design scholars and experts today call for the development of design as a science. In the book *Design Discourse,* Victor Margolin (page 4) describes one of the problems in design:

> We presently divide design in the narrowest sense into discrete forms of practice such as industrial design, graphic design, stage design, interior design, or fashion design. This tends for the most part to separate more artistically oriented ways of designing from those connected with engineering or computer science, which are technologically based. It also segregates the design of objects from the design of immaterial products like techniques and services, which are the province of fields such as industrial engineering and urban planning.

Is industrial design an art or a science? Gyorgy Kepes, formerly at the Institute of Design in Chicago and a professor of visual design at Massachusetts Institute of Technology, addresses the relationship between the visual arts (painting, sculpture, graphics, etc.) and science in his book, *The Visual Arts Today* (page 6):

> Because our modern specialization so often separates artists and scientists, neither has been always fully aware of the profundity of the other's work. Scientists and artists both reach beneath the surface phenomena to discover basic natural pattern and basic natural process. Yet, there is a tendency for the scientist to expect the artist to interpret literally, like some unthinking sensitive device, and for the artist to expect the scientist to think coldly and mechanically, like some unfeeling technical appliance. …[T]he creation of a visual image in the arts is not the instinctive act of certain individuals but rather a fusion of their deepest inner workings with the messages of society, including information from the realm of knowledge and rational thought. Like the scientist, the artist uses the learning of his times in a basic way. And, again like the scientist, the artist profoundly affects our world outlook.

I agree with Kepes' feeling that social issues such as mass poverty, social unrest, urban blight, population growth, and environmental issues force today's artists to do "more than…respond strongly to aesthetic fact." Kepes also believes that artists teach us "how to see and how to enjoy." In *The Visual Arts Today,* Kepes further explains this belief (page 6): "We rely upon them [artists] to help us make our perceptual grasp of the world functional, meaningful, satisfying, and communicable—even though there is often a considerable time lag between the artist's grasp and ours, for the artist's high degree of sensitivity tends to make him something of a prophet."

The industrial designer (or architect, for that matter) is an important link between art and science. What good is a beautiful building if it is not structurally sound? On the other hand, what good is a strong building, built with the newest technological advances and materials, if it is ugly to look at? The same is true in product design. If a product works well and is safe to use, but is distasteful and unattractive to look at, it is not a good product. If the product has poorly designed graphics, it will not be successful. The industrial designer must take advantage of every development and advance science has to offer in order to design truly successful products. Scientists must take advantage of what visual artists have to offer. Separately, art and science are ineffective and abstract, but together they can deliver a powerful message. Some artists have understood this important connection, such as, Fernand Leger and Herbert Bayer who are discussed later in Chapter 3. Additionally, a few scientists and engineers have understood this important connection. For instance, Admiral Rickover showed this understanding in the development of the atomic submarine *Nautilus* as well as Ferdinand Porsche with the design of the Porsche 911 automobile.

## The Product Development Process

One of the first questions people ask regarding industrial design is, "How is it done?" The 10 general steps in the product development process are as follows:

**1. Conception of a need or idea**    This conceptualization usually comes from the product planning department of a corporation. The product planning department, which is usually closely allied with marketing and management, determines that a new product is wanted to meet an important need. A written description of what this product might look like, visually, is generated. With this description, engineers and industrial designers are asked to begin thinking about the product.

**2. Research**    To begin the design project, usually a corporation's marketing department, engineering department, design department, or all three, will join together to develop a market research activity. This research effort involves going into the market place, studying competitive products and interviewing users or potential users of such a product. The idea is to attain a good description of what is needed from those who will buy and use the product.

**3. Product Specification**

With the data acquired from the research phase, a careful word picture or specification is developed. This is a written description of what the ultimate product should be. Such factors as controls, instrumentation, safety considerations, size, shape, color, cost, function, materials, etc. are identified in this specification.

**4. Product Development Team**

About this time in the development of a new product, a product development team is formed. This team consists of representatives from management, product planning, marketing, engineering, design, and manufacturing. Members of this team review the product specification, contribute to and modify it to meet what they consider realistic expectations. Engineers are very concerned with the mechanical, electronic, and/or electrical aspects of the design as well as manufacturing cost.

**5. Concept Development**

With approval of the product specification, the industrial designer(s) and engineer(s) may begin developing the design. The industrial designer generates a form or collection of forms to embody the product's shape. Such concepts are usually presented in perspective drawing(s) form or may even be simply wooden or cardboard shapes which help everyone appreciate the size and function of the product. Sometimes a rendering is developed of the concept(s) at this time.

**6. Concept Refinement**

Criticism of the proposed concept(s) is made by the product development team. Compromises are made and the best concept is refined. With acceptance of a concept, engineers and industrial designers are free to begin work on the design. The industrial designer(s) gives much thought to the human factors of the product. Research may be continued to identify any problems that exist with the concept.

**7. Mock-up and Model Development**

The next meeting of the product development team takes place when the engineering department has completed a bread-board model or mock-up which proves the feasibility of the engineering concept. At this time, the industrial designer has also developed a mock-up or appearance model. This model defines placement of controls and feedback instrumentation, size of the product, cost, and justification for the design. The engineering team now knows how much space it has for its mechanism to fit within and may refine the product's engineering. The industrial design team then develops a housing or cover system to wrap around and protect the mechanism and the user.

**8. Prototype Development**

Once the engineering and appearance models have been approved, a working prototype model is developed and presented. This becomes a joint effort between engineering and industrial design.

**9. Test Production Run**

Upon completion of the first working prototype and approval of the product by the development team, a limited number of units are fabricated. Once this is achieved, products are sent into a test area where they are used and evaluated in their working environment to be absolutely certain that the product specification has been achieved. Problems are addressed and refinements to the design are made if necessary.

**10. Full Production Begins**

If the product performs satisfactory, it is released for full-scale production.

Before understanding the complexity of industrial design and the industrial design process, people need to appreciate related fields and how they compliment and overlap the industrial designer's work. It is important to understand the differences among an industrial designer, an engineer, an architect, an inventor, a stylist, an artist, etc. While they have similar objectives, each approach the problem differently.

| PROFESSION | DESCRIPTION | PROFESSIONAL(S) |
|---|---|---|
| **Industrial Designer** | The industrial designer creates something and it is his or her responsibility to make it beautiful to look (aesthetics) at and comfortable and safe to use (human factors). *Webster's Dictionary* says "to plan, to construct, contrive." The word "industrial" simply means the designer has been trained to have his or her designs duplicated by manufacturing and industrial processes. | Raymond Loewy Walter Dorwin Teague Norman Bel Geddes Henry Dreyfuss |
| **Engineer** | An engineer creates something. *Webster's Dictionary* defines an engineer as "to plan, to construct, to contrive." An engineer makes a product work and is usually only concerned with the internal mechanisms of a product. | R. Buckminster Fuller Clarence Kelly Johnson |
| **Architect** | An architect is defined by *Webster's* as "one who designs buildings and superintends their construction." | Frank Lloyd Wright I.M. Pei |
| **Inventor** | An inventor creates something. *Webster's* defines an inventor as "to think up, to make a new contrivance." The inventor strives to create something that has not existed before. | John Browning Thomas Edison |
| **Stylist** | A stylist is described by *Webster's* as "one who develops, designs, or advises on styles." See the comments below regarding styling versus industrial design. | Yves St. Laurent Laura Ashley |
| **Artist** | An artist is described by *Webster's* as "one who professes and practices an imaginative art; a person skilled in one of the fine arts." | Picassio Henry Matisse |
| **Graphic Artist** | A graphic artist is described by *Webster's* as one who is involved with "the fine and applied arts of representation, decoration, and writing or printing on surfaces together with the techniques and crafts associated with them." | Herbert Bayer Saul Bass |

| PROFESSION | DESCRIPTION | PROFESSIONAL(S) |
|---|---|---|
| **Human Factors Specialist/Ergonomist** | Sometimes referred to as "human engineering," this term is defined by *Webster's* as "a science that deals with the design of mechanical devices for efficient use by human beings." Barry H. Kantowitz and Robert D. Sorkin define human factors in their book, *Human Factors, Understanding People-System Relationships,* as "the discipline that tries to optimize the relationship between technology and the human." An ergonomist is described by *Webster's* as "a specialist in biotechnology," which is "the aspect of technology concerned with the application of biological and engineering data to problems relating to man and the machine." This is where the term "ergonomic design" comes from and is closely related to human factors. | Frank and Lillian Gilbreth Alphonse Chapanis, Ph.D. |
| **Illustrator** | An illustrator is described by *Webster's* as someone who "makes clear by giving or by serving as an example; to provide with visual features intended to explain or decorate." | Norman Rockwell A.M. Cassandre Gyorgy Kepes Paul Rand |
| **Painter** | *Webster's* describes a painter as "an artist who paints." | Paul Klee Henry Matisse |
| **Sculptor** | *Webster's* describes a sculptor as "an artist who produces works of sculpture." These works are three dimensional. | Alexander Calder Henry Moore |
| **Craftsman** | A craftsman, defined by *Webster's* as "one who creates or performs with skill or dexterity especially in the manual arts." A craftsman primarily uses his hands or hand tools to make something. | Gustav Stickley Elbert Hubbard |

Obviously, there is much overlap among these different professions. Many engineers believe that industrial designers are only concerned with the appearance of a product and refer to them as "stylists." Industrial design does include the appearance or style as part of the problem, but there is much more to an industrial design service than appearance! Industrial designers must do competitive product research including feature analysis, safety and human factors analysis, cost analysis, market research where necessary, and ultimately provide a product specification. A product specification helps describe the design in detail before the design process begins. A design is then developed incorporating human factors, appearance (style), a mock-up or bread-board model illustrating the mechanical mechanism, followed up with an appearance model or prototype (working) model to prove the design. Sometimes working drawings with critical dimensions are developed, including materials and manufacturing process specification, packaging and corporate identity. This is industrial

**FIGURE 1.1.** Airstream "Caravan" trailer with light-weight riveted aluminum body, c. 1950. This is an excellent example of the use of streamlining. Photograph courtesy of Airstream, Jackson Center, Ohio.

staggered lines, and called it streamlined. A streamlined shape reminiscent of a raindrop or a bullet was the rage.

Streamlining has had an important effect on product design for many years. As defined, streamlining is the shaping of a form such that when air passes over or around it, the form presents the minimum resistance to the air. Also, the form can be moving like an automobile in a race, or a racer on a bicycle in a head wind, or a downhill ski racer (Figure 1.1). The form can also be stationary such as a building. A building's form must resist wind forces or else it gives in and blows away. The term "streamline" suggests a teardrop form. Most people picture a drop of liquid as a round ball-like body with a pointed tail. However, scientists tell us a ball with no tail is the actual shape of a falling drop of water.

Applying a wind-resisting shape to products started in 1894 when J.J. Heilman proposed a locomotive with a pointed nose and rounded corners in front. Around 1900 the rigid airship assumed the shape of a cigar for greater efficiency in the air. Automobiles used a rounded front and a pointed back as early as 1899. Aircraft found a use for such shapes just prior to World War I.

When the big four American design consulting firms (Teague, Loewy, Geddes and Dreyfuss) were active in the 1930s in trying to help industries out of the depression, streamlining was proven effective on a moving product. Why not apply streamlining to stationary products likewise? Streamlining has been applied to all sorts of domestic appliances, all to stimulate sales. For a long time it was felt

design, *not* styling. An industrial designer can provide the fine arts of a stylist, but he is also a researcher, a model maker, a draftsman, a renderer, a businessman, a sculptor, etc.

During the Great Depression of the 1930s and early 1940s, the federal government encouraged product consumption to help the economy. Manufacturers applied a "modern" style or appearance to the face of their products, usually in the form of three parallel but that industrial design had hit a new low when streamlining was applied in this fashion. Today, however, streamlining is an essential science in the design of aircraft, automobiles, trains, and ocean cruise ships. After World War II the railroad industry, recognizing the inefficiency of streamlining because of the complexity of the cover system, dropped its use of streamlining on steam-powered trains.

Streamlining also helps products like automobiles. Automobile owners of the1940s and 1950s were being deceived. The automobiles they drove, with their useless tail fins and streamlined appearance, seemed to function as an extension of their owners' personalities and what they perceived as fast and important. People joked that drivers wanted to give the impression that they were "traveling fast while standing still."

Streamlining suggested speed, progress and the new age. Car designers who applied streamlining to the appearance of vehicles were called stylists. Those, then in the auto industry, who used industrial design often believed all that a product needed to enhance sales was a "styling" job. A pretty rendering or picture of what the product might look like and what their engineers could easily interpret was all that was needed. For complex products this approach usually fails, and in some cases is ridiculous. It is not that stylists have bad intentions or unethical plans to take advantage of their clients. It is more a lack of ability to appreciate what is needed to make the product more valuable or enhance the product in the eyes of the consumer. Many stylists collect their fees, believing that they have done what is expected of them and leave the design execution up to a client who, in many cases, has little idea of what the stylist had in mind. The result is that those who are not stylists find it very difficult to convince clients who need design service that industrial design can really help them and will not be wasting their money.

The words "create" or "contrive" are common among people regardless of their label, time or discipline. In this book I will use the word "designer" to include all creative people. In the past, say 70 years ago, a person who created a product or design was called an engineer or inventor. The expertise required in fields like civil, structural, and mechanical engineering has become more and more specialized and complex—very similar to the diverse specialties in the medical profession. They are still all called "doctor." Many engineers advance in their profession by taking professional engineering exams which qualify them to tackle more complicated problems, often involving safety and public welfare. They are then referred to as P.E.'s or professional engineers. Industrial designers do not take formal testing, but perhaps they should.

The process of getting some products to work has become extremely complicated and demanding for engineers. They cannot also be responsible for a product's industrial design needs. They do not have the time required for the additional education necessary to meet these needs. As a matter of fact, many engineers have become specialists in order to stay abreast of materials and production developments in their own fields where they find themselves best qualified and enjoy the greatest rewards.

A specialist, the industrial designer, has stepped in to assist in conceiving, designing and finishing the product development process. While industrial designers are not formally instructed in depth about the function of the engineering profession, they do become familiar with engineering services through their practice. Conversely, engineers are not trained in industrial design but are sometimes made aware of industrial design services, usually through schooling and by working with designers. This problem is a big weakness in both professions. Ignorance builds suspicion and distrust. It is regrettable that engineers and industrial designers do not have more opportunities to work together in school before entering their respective professions. Usually it becomes a learning experience and is sometimes difficult when they must work together for the first time. The designer and engineer must appreciate the fact that both are dependent upon, and indispensable to, each other and must work in concert to achieve a successful, appealing product. Many progressive manufacturers today are overcoming this problem by using a team approach, developing products as discussed in IDSA's *Comprehensive Definition of Industrial Design* (see page 5). Engineers, industrial designers, marketing personnel, etc. are all involved in a product's development from its inception. The result is that the product develops faster and the concerns of each member are respected and taken into consideration early in the development process. A better product can be the result.

Compare some of the development tasks listed in the box for both engineers and industrial designers. These responsibilities are presented as typical but by no means are sacred. Different product assignments demand different emphasis and arrangement of the tasks listed.

An engineer has four or five years of college education, and the pressure to acquire even more education seems to be building every year. An industrial designer must have a bachelor's degree for completion of an industrial design program. Some programs are four years long while others are five. There are now about as many different types of industrial design specialists as there are engineering specialists. For example, there are interior designers, packaging designers, human factors specialists, furniture designers, toy designers, appliance designers, jewelry designers, interior designers, auto designers, stage designers, graphic designers, safety design specialists, expert witnesses, etc. A designer can become an expert or a specialist in one particular field, or become a generalist and work in a variety of areas. A designer can, as I have, focus on the human factors requirements demanded within the extremes of unusual environments, such as high-altitude military aircraft or low-roofed mines.

It is interesting to note that half of the industrial designers in this country are employed by large manufacturing companies. Others may work as independent consultants, or as employees of a consulting

### Typical Responsibilities of the Engineer vs. Industrial Designer

| ENGINEER | INDUSTRIAL DESIGNER |
|---|---|
| 1. specification development | 1. product planning |
| 2. solution to the design problem (inside workings) | 2. specification development |
| 3. component materials | 3. research |
| 4. safety | 4. user habits and preferences |
| 5. cost | 5. solution to the design problem (outside form) |
| 6. design life or durability | 6. human factors—ease of use and control, levers, switches, warning lights, gauges, etc. |
| 7. structure | |
| 8. maintenance | |
| 9. mechanical function | 7. color, texture, and material of the product's exterior |
| 10. electrical function | 8. product graphics |
| 11. electronics | 9. aesthetics or beauty |
| | 10. safety (warnings, how to use, etc.) |
| | 11. cost |
| | 12. packaging |
| | 13. corporate identity |

firm, or even work for architects, graphic and interior design companies, and so forth. Some designers, like those employed by large manufacturing firms, spend their entire career designing one type of product, for instance, office machines or automobiles. Others, such as generalists, may be competent in many areas and work in several fields.

Most industrial designers enjoy art and sculpture. Many can cross over to paint and sculpt. There are differences, however, between the artist and the industrial designer. The educational requirements for an industrial designer are far different from that of an artist, although in some schools the first year or so may be the same. Artists are not prepared and cannot simply cross over to industrial design and begin designing products. When artists work, they are creating a form to satisfy their own internal image or feelings and no one else's. The sky is the limit when it comes to artistic expression with minimum restrictions.

The industrial designer, on the other hand, must work closely with the client to arrive at a detailed specification describing the needs of the design just to start the design process. This specification is important since it communicates to everyone involved what the design will be, including many design requirements stipulated by others. It is a picture of the design in words. The design specification is then refined with the input and critique of others and the product becomes more clearly defined. The designer then worries the design to its finished mass-producible form hoping it will be liked and desired by many others (client, consumers, etc.), enjoys successful sales, and ultimately leads to the creation of jobs. Thus, the responsibility of the industrial designer is much broader than that of a painter or sculptor. The designer must be sure he has a safe and appealing form which can be easily manufactured. The designer is also responsible to his colleagues to conduct himself with ethical responsibility. Misconduct by the designer reflects negatively on the entire profession. An artist has little or no such concerns. An artist may be concerned with the toxicity of his paints or whether or not his picture will hang securely on the wall, but the magnitude of this responsibility, particularly in the area of safety design, is no where near as complex as that of an industrial designer's.

This chapter has defined industrial design and described the role of the industrial designer. The history of design and the development of technology in America and abroad will be explored next.

### CHAPTER TWO

# HISTORY OF
# INDUSTRIAL DESIGN

*Is it not our duty to find a symphonic
means to express our time,
one that evokes the progress,
the daring and the victories of modern day?
The century of the aeroplane
deserves its music.*

Claude Debussy

*Have nothing in your house
that you do not know to be useful
or believe to be beautiful.*

William Morris

*When we build, let us think
that we build forever.*

John Ruskin

15

Where are we going in the future if we do not know where we have been? To fully appreciate where the world is today in design philosophy and technology we must be aware of their roots. With this knowledge we can avoid the mistakes and learn from the successes of the past. A few of the philosophies which have been influential in bringing efficient, high quality design to the world are discussed in this chapter. While it would be impossible to cover all design advances leading up to design as it is known today, several different areas are explored in detail, such as the design of early American furniture and trains. Many other products could have been discussed, for example, automobiles, ocean liners, or aircraft, but space prohibits it. Although this is not a book about industrial design history, those who are not familiar with its past, as well as some of those currently in the industrial design profession, need a simple presentation of its history. We should know it and be proud! According to *Discovering Design: Explorations in Design Studies,* edited by Richard Buchanan and Victor Margolin (pages 27-8), "the origins of design are usually traced to one of only four beginnings." Buchanan and Margolin explain:

> Some argue that design began in the twentieth century with the formation of new disciplines of design thinking. Others argue that design began in the early days of the Industrial Revolution with the transformation of the instruments of production and the social conditions of work. Still others argue that design began in the prehistoric period with the creation of images and objects by primitive human beings. And, finally, some argue that design began with the creation of the universe, the first act of God, who represents the ideal model of a creator which all human designers, knowingly or unknowingly, strive to imitate.

The following events, philosophies, or movements will be examined in this chapter:

1. The influence of the designs of the Shakers is explored. They designed and manufactured with a will to survive and a religious commitment to perfection in design. Little is known about individual Shaker designers, but the results are beautiful.

2. With the construction of the Erie Canal following the American Revolution one can see how the workers unknowingly educated themselves to become world leaders in design and engineering.

3. English philosophers John Ruskin, William Morris, and Christopher Dresser are credited with founding industrial design.

4. American bicycle manufacturers, brothers Wilbur and Orville Wright from Dayton, Ohio, built the first powered aircraft. The Wright brothers, while not trained as engineers or designers, used sophisticated engineering procedures to accomplish their designs and developments.

5. The power and influence of one individual, American designer Gustav Stickley, will be reviewed. Stickley strongly believed in good design and quality through craftsmanship. He understood the virtue of combining simple, practical, comfortably designed furniture blending manufacturing methods and craftsmanship.

6. Peter Behrens was a talented, energetic German designer in the late nineteenth century. He was a generalist (painter, designer and architect) and the first to comprehend the value of a "corporate image" and how its identity could be enhanced through a comprehensive design policy.

7. The heinous politics of Adolf Hitler forced upon the Bauhaus design school and the efforts of Walter Gropius to save it are investigated. The Nazis drove Bauhaus teachers from Germany. The result was the spreading of the Bauhaus philosophy. Ultimately the entire modern design world would benefit.

8. The influence of design on trains, particularly engines, in Europe and the United States is explored. By studying trains

one can see the value of design generated through evolution, not revolution.

9. The "big four" modern American consultants—Walter D. Teague, Norman Bel Geddes, Raymond Loewy, and Henry Dreyfuss—understood how design can help product manufacturers. These designers set the stage for industrial design as we know it today.

Notice that the designers discussed in this chapter are primarily male. This is simply true because the industrial design field, like engineering, architecture and medicine, has been a male-dominated profession in the past. This is definitely not the case today and there are equal opportunities for both men and women in industrial design. For further information about these opportunities, contact IDSA (Appendix A).

## HISTORY AND EVOLUTION OF INDUSTRIAL DESIGN

### The Shakers

One success story can be seen by studying the Shaker movement in America. The Shakers came from their home in Manchester, England in 1774 to escape religious persecution and establish the first American settlement in Niskayuna in 1776, near Albany, New York under the leadership of Mother Ann Lee. They first built a log cabin and then larger dwellings to accommodate all "believers." Shakers were a religious sect related to the Quakers and they were known for their efficiency in every aspect of life, such as farming, home chores, and creativity of arts and crafts. Mother Ann's philosophy was, "put your hands to work and your hearts to God." The Shakers lived by, "Do your work as though you had a thousand years to live, and as if you were to die tomorrow." They rejected the thoughtless, useless clutter of ugly, ungodly things and believed that Godliness was brought about by reducing the tools and chores of life to their base

---

**Elements of Shaker Designs**

Four basic elements flow through their designs:

1. the joy of industry
2. design to satisfy a need
3. simple and economical designs
4. quality products with aesthetically-pleasing shapes

---

essentials. They felt that performing this essential act of life was God's wish.

In 1795 in New Lebanon, New York, a Shaker society was established and was the model society for all others to follow. They lived in a community called a "family" consisting of 30 to 90 members, sharing a common dining hall. Each community was given a name by order, such as First Family, Second Family, or by geographical location such as East Family, West Family, Hill Family, etc. The Shaker movement spread west. At their peak prior to the Civil War, they numbered 6,000 and consisted of 18 communities.

Harsh reality forced these religious people to work to survive. They did what they knew best, planted gardens and processed seeds, designed and manufactured furniture, fabrics, rugs, baskets, etc.

What do the Shakers have to do with industrial design? Their work did inspire inventions among themselves. Their designs on the whole were a result of a group effort, not one single person. The Shakers organized themselves in a corporate-like structure when facing challenging competition. Architects and designers were impressed with their work. The Shakers designed without decoration or trivia, and found beauty in the honest, simplest form of a functional product.

The Shakers began designing products out of necessity. As their numbers grew, they needed money to buy more land and to build shops and dormitories. They processed and sold seeds from their farms, and printed almanacs, journals, and labels for their products such as herbs and prepared foods. Shakers also designed and built label printing presses, started advertising, and distributed pamphlets. From their herbs grew the business of natural medicines such as rose water and "soothing syrup." Superfluous decoration cannot be found on Shaker designs. Their religion rejected it. Their market was simple, rural consumers like themselves. Only useful and helpful items were made and sold. Everyone in the community, even the children, worked and contributed, and jobs were rotated to prevent fatigue and relieve boredom.

The Shakers were not against using time-saving devices if using them did not hamper the quality of a product. For instance, in 1812, Sister Tabitha Babbitt of the Shaker community in Harvard, Massachusetts, watched her spinning wheel whirl its spindle. From this she invented a circular saw blade spun by a water wheel. Because the Shakers did not believe in patenting, this invention was freely given to the world to use. The concept was adopted by sawmills, and the invention led to the development of other, more complex rotary cutters.

Most people are aware of Shaker-designed and -manufactured furniture. The Shakers believed that their sect would continue forever. Thus, they made quality furniture to last. As Marian Klamkin observes in the book *Hands to Work, Shaker Folk Art and Industries* (page 119): "Constructed of simple design with superb materials and excellent workmanship, Shaker furniture is now recognized as being the best quality of American country furniture ever made."

Function and simplicity together with fine workmanship were their design philosophy. Nothing was wasted. Drawers were put into any piece that could accommodate them. Careful thought was put into all of their designs. For example, chests and beds were made with legs high enough to make dusting under them easy. Children's furniture was appropriately scaled down to accommodate their small stature. The Shakers designed the first institutional furniture made in America.

---

### Shaker Principles and Developments

In his book, *Design: An illustrated historical overview* (pages 23-4), Thomas Hauffe describes the Shakers:

**Guiding Principles of the Shakers:**
- Regularity is beautiful.
- The highest beauty lies in harmony.
- Beauty arises from practicality.
- Order is the origin of beauty.
- That which is most practical is also most beautiful.

**Inventions and Developments Attributed to the Shakers:**
- The circular saw
- A basket-weaving machine
- Clothes pins
- Threshing machine
- The cheese press
- Rotating harrow
- Pea sheller
- A scale with sliding weights

---

They were innovative out of necessity, and also were the first to develop the chest with drawers and the drop leaf table.

No piece of Shaker furniture is as well known as their chair (Figure 2.1). The Shakers were probably the first people in America to commercially manufacture chairs. They used product planning to expand their line, adding armchairs, rocking chairs, and swivel chairs. In *Hands to Work* (page 131), Marian Klamkin says, "They [Shakers] continued to manufacture chairs almost solely for Shaker use until 1867, when the chairs were made to be marketed to the world."

The South Family exclusively manufactured and marketed many chairs through mail order. As time progressed, most of the chairs went to department stores in the large cities such as New York, Boston, and

**FIGURE 2.1.** Two-slat Shaker dining chair, maple-stained, light brown, splint seat, c. 1830. The low back made a neater appearing dining room and allowed the table to be set and cleared easily. Photograph courtesy of Shaker Museum and Library, Old Chatham, New York.

Chicago, to furniture dealers and their own shops. By studying the Shakers, designers can see how important product planning and marketing are to a product's success. They were intelligent business people and augmented and expanded their product line by selling related accessory items such as chair cushions and foot stools. Shakers even developed product advertising and literature showing different styles and sizes of chairs.

---

**Shaker Philosophy**

What can be learned from the Shakers? Their philosophy can apply to any modern business:

1. conservative, sound business,
2. efficient corporate management,
3. quality, spirituality, and economy in design,
4. useful, valuable products,
5. humane working conditions,
6. diversity and product planning, and
7. progressive marketing practices.

---

The Shaker concept was great except they did not believe in sex, marriage, and the creation of children; thus no propagation. Slowly this religious sect has vanished. Today, their workshops and creations have been carefully preserved in museums and visitors can see the clean, uncluttered, efficient and inventive environments where Shakers nurtured the production of furniture, processed and packaged seeds, wove baskets, and fabricated other useful crafts and products.

## Early Industry

For whatever reason, great products aimed at efficiency and low cost were developed throughout the nineteenth century in America. The list seems endless, for example, furniture, firearms, sewing machines, the telegraph, bridges, submarines, rock drills for mining, dental chairs, agricultural equipment, boats, trains, and toward the end of the century, automobiles and electrical products. Concurrently, the country was moving westward. There was a need for tools, from axes to weapons to plows. By the late nineteenth century communication improved greatly throughout the country, so it seemed everybody became aware of and was fascinated by new, labor-saving tools. The

## TIMELINE

**B**elow is a timeline of important and significant events which impacted the history of the design world. I believe it is important for readers to be aware of these events and understand why they are significant and how they relate to industrial design. When wars come about, creativity usually ceases or is heavily curtailed. As time progressed, however, as in the case of the Civil War, World War I and World War II, the demand for technology grew. For example, during the Civil War, the machine gun, the rifle, and the submarine were all developed. During World War I, the machine gun and submarine were refined and perfected. In World War II the aircraft was perfected and aircraft carriers and the atomic bomb were developed. Great technological advances have been made since World War II. All of this has impacted the designer's work.

1774  The Shaker Movement begins in America near Albany, New York.

1775  Revolutionary War begins.

1776  Declaration of Independence is signed.

1783  Revolutionary War ends.

1812  Sister Tabitha Babbit, a Shaker, designs a circular saw.

1825  The Erie Canal is completed.

  John Quincy Adams (1767-1848) becomes the sixth president of the United States.

  Eli Whitney (born 1765), developer of the cotton gin and techniques of modern manufacture, dies.

1828  Andrew Jackson (1767-1845) is elected seventh president of the United States.

1830  Peter Cooper (1791-1883) develops the first locomotive in the United States.

1831  Cyrus McCormick (1809-1884) develops a reaper.

1832  Andrew Jackson re-elected president of the United States.

1836  Samuel Colt (1814-1862) develops a pistol.

1837  Samuel Morse (1791-1872) develops a magnetic telegraph.

  John Deere (1804-1886) develops an iron plow.

1860  The Steel Age begins.

1869  Celluloid, the first synthetic plastic, was made by American inventor John Wesley Hyatt.

1874  Remington Arms manufactures the first Sholes typewriter.

1896  William Morris (born 1834), British artist, designer and philosopher, dies.

1900  John Ruskin (born 1819), a noted philosopher, dies.

1902  Wilbur (1867-1912) and Orville Wright (1871-1948) constructed an improved glider and flew it hundreds of times.

1903  The Wright Brothers added an engine to their glider and developed the first powered airplane.

1909  Leo H. Baekeland develops phenol-formaldehyde, called Bakelite, which led to the development of polyethylene, acrylics, and polyvinyl chloride (PVC).

1912  Woodrow Wilson (1856-1924) elected as twenty-eighth president of the United States.

1913  First assembly line starts at Ford Motor Company.

1914  World War I begins.

  Walter Gropius (1883-1969) designs building "Werkbund" Exhibition, Cologne, Germany.

  Lillian Gilbreth (1878-1972) uses motion pictures to study time and motion.

  Panama Canal opens, linking the Atlantic and Pacific Oceans.

1915  Alexander Graham Bell (1847-1922) in New York and Thomas Watson in San Francisco complete a telephone call.

1916  Arts and Crafts movement in the United States fades away.

1917  The United States becomes involved in World War I.

1918  World War I ends.

1920  Warren Harding (1865-1923) becomes twenty-ninth president of the United States.

1921  Adolf Hitler's (1889-1945) storm troops terrorize political opponents.

1923  United States President Harding dies; succeeded by Calvin Coolidge (1872-1933).

1924  Ford Motor Company produces 10 millionth car.

  German airship, *Zeppelin's Z-R-3*, flies across Atlantic to Lakehurst, New Jersey.

1925  Walter Gropius moves the Bauhaus to Dessau from Weimar, Germany.

1926  Walter Gropius designs Bauhaus building in Dessau.

  Admiral Richard E. Byrd (1888-1957) makes first airplane flight to the North Pole.

  Ludwig Mies van der Rohe (1886-1969) designs the "cantilever chair."

1927  Charles A. Lindbergh (1902-1974) flies the monoplane, *Spirit of St. Louis,* nonstop from New York to Paris in 33.5 hours.

1928  Herbert Hoover (1874-1964) elected president of the United States.

  Charles Rennie Mackintosh (born 1868), Scottish artist, architect and designer, dies.

*(continued on page 22)*

challenge to make a product better was there, as well. There were handsome rewards to be earned.

From 1776 until 1830 industries in America began to come alive. Eli Whitney was probably the one man who best understood what would become modern product design utilizing mass production techniques. While he is best remembered for his work in designing the cotton gin, his idea for the development of interchangeable product parts was an even greater contribution.

Whitney won a contract in 1798 from the government to manufacture a musket. Instead of every musket having its own unique parts exclusively customized for that gun as traditional manufacturing required, he insisted that each fabricated part be adaptable to a master jig or fixture which would accept only properly manufactured parts. This allowed all parts adapting to their jigs to perform equally. Ultimately this provided for interchangeability of parts between the muskets and ensured the future replacement of damaged or worn parts. Thus, the concept of using jigs and fixtures led to successful mass production in the twentieth century. Samuel Colt must have been aware of the manufacturing procedures established by Eli Whitney because he also implemented the production of his famous revolvers using the jigs and fixture tooling techniques.

## The Erie Canal

The United States military was the first to recognize the need for engineers. In June 1775, Colonel R. Gridley became the first chief engineer of the Army. He and two assistants were charged with securing the United States' ports. In March 1802, the U.S. Military Academy at West Point was established for the purpose of using engineers to teach soldiers engineering for fortification of our coastline. West Point was the first school to teach engineering in North or South America.

FIGURE 2.2. This aqueduct located over the Genesee River at Rochester, New York and completed in 1823 was one of the longest on the Erie Canal. Notice the barge on the aqueduct. Courtesy of The Gayer Collection/Canal Society of New York State.

The most significant engineering development since the Revolutionary War and single endeavor to generate pride in America as a new independent nation was the building of the 360-mile Erie Canal, running from the Hudson River west across New York State to Buffalo and Lake Erie (Figure 2.2). This undertaking demanded sophisticated engineering, and aside from a handful of West Point graduates, America lacked native experts. Building the Erie Canal was the first on-the-job "school of engineering" in America. The engineers did not have the proper tools and the canal had to be dug painstakingly by hand. At first, the canal managers wanted the engineering advice of men experienced in designing and constructing large civil projects. They believed they could only acquire this expertise from England. No Americans seemed to have the necessary skills, abilities,

(continued from page 20)

**1929** Museum of Modern Art opens in New York City.

Construction begins on the Empire State Building.

Ludwig Mies van der Rohe designs the Barcelona Pavilion Chair.

United States stock market crashes; Great Depression begins.

**1930** Comic strips, such as "Dick Tracy" and "Terry and the Pirates," grow in popularity in the United States.

**1931** Rohm and Haas Company first manufactures Plexiglas.

**1932** Amelia Earhart (1898-1937) is the first woman to fly across the Atlantic Ocean solo.

Franklin D. Roosevelt (1882-1945) elected president of the United States.

Work begins on the San Francisco-Oakland Bay (Golden Gate) Bridge.

**1933** Hitler granted dictatorial powers; the first concentration camps are erected by the Nazis in Germany.

Great teachers of the Bauhaus like Vasili Kandinski (1866-1944) and Paul Klee (1879-1940) leave Germany for France and Switzerland.

Sir Frederick Henry Royce (born 1863), British engineer and a founder of Rolls-Royce Ltd., dies.

Nazi government closes the Bauhaus.

**1934** Winston Churchill (1871-1947) warns British Parliament of German air menace.

DeSoto automobile *Air Flow* introduced.

The *Burilington Zephyr* passenger train designed by a team from the Budd Manufacturing Company.

**1935** *S.S. Normandie* crosses the Atlantic in 107 hours.

The Saarland is incorporated in Germany.

Nazi repudiate Versailles Treaty.

German Luftwaffe formed.

The German *Bf 109*, designed by Willy Messerschmitt (1898-1978), first flew.

The *Hawker Hurricane* first flew.

**1936** German troops occupy the Rhineland.

R.J. Mitchell (1895-1937), British aircraft designer, develops the *Supermarine Spitfire* fighter, perhaps the best fighter aircraft in World War II.

Frank Lloyd Wright (1869-1959) designs Kaufmann House (Falling Water, PA) and Johnson Wax Company.

Walter Dorwin Teague (1883-1960) designs Kodak Bantam Special.

**1937** Ford Motor Company introduces the Lincoln *Zephyr*.

Walter Gropius immigrates to the United States and builds Gropius residence in Lincoln, Massachusetts.

Norman Bel Geddes (1893-1958) designs General Motors "Futurama" exhibit at the New York World's Fair.

**1938** United States and Germany recall ambassadors.

Volkswagen *Bug*, developed by Ferdinand Porsche, is introduced.

Howard Hughes (1905-1976) flies around the world in three days, 19 hours and 17 minutes.

Nylon is introduced.

**1939** Britain and France declare war on Germany.

Lockheed *P-38 Lightening* aircraft first flies.

Television debuts in America at New York World's Fair.

Ludwig Mies van der Rohe designs campus of Illinois Institute of Technology in Chicago, Illinois, called Armor Institute at the time.

After 1938 recession, U.S. economy begins to recover.

**1940** Battle of Britain begins; Germany occupies Paris and invades Norway and Denmark; 180 German planes shot down, August 15.

Peter Behrens (born 1868), noted early 20th century designer, dies.

North American *Mustang P-51* aircraft first flies.

**1941** United States declares war on Germany, Italy and Japan; Germany invades Russia; Japan bombs Pearl Harbor.

First jet airplane takes flight.

**1942** 400,000 American troops land in French North Africa.

Gustav Stickley (born 1857), furniture designer, dies.

**1943 -56** Frank Lloyd Wright designs Soloman Guggenheim Museum in New York City.

**1944** Franklin D. Roosevelt is re-elected to a fourth term as president of the United States.

**1945** President F.D. Roosevelt dies; is succeeded by Harry S. Truman (1884-1972).

World War II ends.

Atomic bomb tested in New Mexico.

**1946** Le Corbusier (1887-1965) designs an apartment block at Marseilles

**1947** Studebaker introduces a new line of cars designed by Raymond Loewy (1893-1986) and Virgil Exner.

**1948** Harry S. Truman elected president of the United States.

**1949** Walter Gropius designs Harvard Graduate Center, Cambridge, Massachusetts.

**1950** Frank Lloyd Wright designs Johnson Wax Tower.

United States sends troops to defend South Korea.

**1951** Color television is first introduced in the United States.

Marcel Breuer (1902-1981) designs dormitory at Vassar College, Poughkeepsie, N.Y.

**1952** Dwight D. Eisenhower (1890-1969) elected President of the United States.

**1954** Henri Matisse (born 1869), dies.

**1956** Eisenhower reelected President of the United States.

(continued on page 24)

## Eighth Wonder of the World

The Erie Canal was actually called "the eighth wonder of the world" during the time of its completion! In 1972, Elting E. Morison, the then-Killian Professor of History at Massachusetts Institute of Technology, was invited to give the Messenger Lectures at Cornell University. In Morison's book, *From Know-how to Nowhere, The Development of American Technology* (pages 44-5), he uses an excerpt from his lecture about the canal:

Never before in this country, save in the revolutionary armies, had so large a force of men been put together to achieve a common end. And these men, with little more to sustain them than muscle, native wit, and an organizing purpose—which many people thought an idle dream—built an ordered structure conceived from rational premises through 363 miles that were for the most part a trackless wilderness.

In so doing, they built a good deal more than a canal. For one thing, of course, they changed the history and condition of life throughout a considerable section of the new country. For another, they freed men who wanted to build and make things in this country from their dependence upon European advisors and European rules of thumb.

Finally, in constructing the canal, they opened the first—and quite possibly the best—school of general engineering in this country. Acting under the direction of the remarkable chief engineer, Benjamin Wright, scores of untutored men learned how to think and work their way through unfamiliar problems. From this experience these scores of men went out to build with ingenuity and confidence many different kinds of things in many different parts of the country.

or experience. The managers were tired of relying on Europe, particularly England, for help, thus with initiative they decided to educate themselves. Challenging as it was, they succeeded on their own and built this magnificent, all-American waterway. The stone work is beautiful and quite appealing in the central New York environment. Out of necessity, Americans learned fast as Joseph and Frances Gies comment in *The Ingenious Yankees* (page 139):

The first task for the "American engineers" who were learning their profession by doing it was to establish the proper level for the middle section. [James] Geddes ran a series of test levels for a distance of more than a hundred miles around Oneida and Onondaga Lakes while [Benjamin] Wright laid off the canal line west of Rome. When Geddes's survey returned to the line laid off by Wright, the difference at the junction was less than one and a half inches.

By 1825, the canal was complete. Then-Governor DeWitt Clinton of New York State praised their accomplishment (*The Ingenious Yankees,* page 148), "[The Engineers] have built the longest canal, in the least time, with the least experience, for the least money, and to the greatest public benefit."

It is easy to envision the new local designers upon completion of the canal, who had learned civil-mechanical engineering, floating up and down the length of the canal, selling their services. They saw the world for the first time and recognized the need for their abilities. With the completion of the great Erie Canal and for the next 100 years, interesting and important technological advances took place not only in the design world but in the world in general.

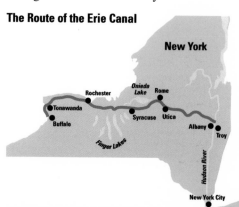

**The Route of the Erie Canal**

# TIMELINE

(continued from page 22)

**1957**   U.S.S.R. launches Sputnik I and II, first earth satellites.

**1958**   Guggenheim Museum, designed by Frank Lloyd Wright, opens in New York City.

Explorer I, United States' artificial earth satellite is launched from Cape Canaveral; first moon rocket launched and traveled 79,000 miles from earth.

**1959**   American scientists patent the computer chip.

First United States nuclear-powered merchant vessel *Savannah,* is launched.

**1960**   John F. Kennedy (1917-1963) elected President of the United States.

United States scientists develop laser device.

First weather satellite, Tiros I, launched by the United States to transmit TV images of cloud cover around the world.

**1961**   Alan Shepard (1923-1998) makes first United States space flight.

**1962**   Rachel Carson's "Silent Spring" stimulates environmental protection movement.

**1963**   President Kennedy assassinated; Lyndon B. Johnson (1908-1973) sworn in as president of the United States.

First use of an artificial heart to take over the circulation of a patient's blood during heart surgery.

**1964**   Lyndon Baines Johnson elected President of the United States.

**1965**   United States combat troops arrive in South Vietnam; United States bombs North Vietnam.

**1966**   United States spacecraft *Surveyor I* makes soft landing on moon and transmits more than 11,000 TV images of the terrain.

**1968**   Richard M. Nixon (1913-1994) elected President of the United States.

Rev. Martin Luther King, Jr. (born 1929), winner of 1964 Nobel Peace Prize, is assassinated.

*Apollo 7* spacecraft, with three astronauts aboard, launched from Cape Kennedy, Florida,

11-day orbiting flight with splashdown in Atlantic Ocean; *Apollo 8,* with three astronauts aboard, orbits moon.

**1969**   Walter Gropius (born 1883), German architect, dies.

Ludwig Mies van der Rohe (born 1886), German architect, dies.

The *Concorde* supersonic aircraft makes its first test flight.

*Apollo 11* lands lunar module on the moon's surface; astronaut Neil Armstrong walks on the moon (many designers thought the lunar module was ugly!).

**1972**   Richard M. Nixon is reelected President of the United States.

**1973**   Pablo Picasso (born 1881), Spanish artist, dies.

Watergate investigation begins.

**1974**   President Nixon resigns; Vice President Gerald R. Ford (born 1913) becomes President of the United States.

**1975**   United States ends two decades of military involvement in Vietnam War.

**1976**   James Earl Carter, Jr. (born 1924) is elected President of the United States.

Alexander Calder (born 1898), American sculptor, dies.

**1977**   First mass market personal computers launched.

United States space shuttle *Enterprise* makes its first manned flight.

**1980**   Ronald Reagan (born 1911) elected President of the United States.

**1981**   International Business Machines (I.B.M.) launches its personal computer .

**1982**   The Vietnam Veterans' War Memorial, designed by Maya Ying Lin, is dedicated in Washington, D.C.; the names of more than 58,000 dead are inscribed on the black granite memorial.

**1983**   United States space shuttle *Challenger* is launched on its maiden flight.

Six thousand United States troops invade and institute civil rule in Grenada after Prime Minister Maurice Bishop is killed in a military coup.

The compact disc is launched.

**1984**   Ronald Reagan is reelected President of the United States.

The Apple Macintosh microcomputer with mouse is launched.

**1986**   Dick Rutan and Jeanna Yeager in the aircraft *Voyager,* designed by Burt Rutan, make the first nonstop flight around the world in nine days without refueling.

**1988**   The first transatlantic optical fiber telephone cable to enter service links France, the U.K., and the U.S.; it can process 40,000 simultaneous conversations .

George Bush (born 1925) is elected President of the United States.

A silicon microchip that stores four times more data than previously possible is developed.

The *B-2 Stealth* bomber is unveiled.

**1989**   Berlin Wall falls as East Germany lifts travel restrictions.

N.A.S.A. launches the *Galileo* space probe to Jupiter.

**1990**   Iraq invades Kuwait and the United States and allies send military troops to Saudi Arabia.

**1991**   U.S.S.R. dissolves; Mikhail Gorbachev (born 1931) resigns; Boris Yeltsin (born 1931) takes over.

**1992**   William Jefferson Clinton (born 1946) is elected President of the United States.

**1996**   Clinton is reelected President of the United States.

**1997**   *Pathfinder* lands on Mars, sending back astonishing photos.

**2000**   George Bush (born 1946) is elected President of the United States.

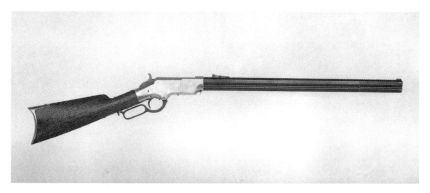

**FIGURE 2.3.** Henry rifle, .44 caliber receiver with brass frame, made by New Haven Arms Company, 1861 and 1862. *Photograph courtesy of Buffalo Bill Historical Center, Cody, Wyoming.*

## Industry After the Canal

Small industries and mills popped up everywhere. In Illinois during July of 1831, Cyrus McCormick demonstrated his reaper, harvesting six acres of wheat in the time it took to harvest one acre by hand. John Deere developed his plow in 1837. Deere's first big contribution was developing a smooth, shiny plow beam. The plow beam, being smooth, prevented the sod from sticking to it like it did to a wooden plow beam. Joseph Henry developed the telegraph device in 1832 in Albany, New York. Samuel Colt received a patent in 1836 for the first of his famous revolvers. Rifles like the Benjamin Tyler Henry, later known as the Winchester, with its metallic cartridge designed by Daniel Wesson of Smith & Wesson, were being developed (Figure 2.3). In fact, it is believed that the Civil War would have been shortened if the Northern Army had embraced this rifle and modernized its infantry tactics. The ranks then could have been opened up and spread out with equal fire power, resulting in fewer casualties. Targets would have been more difficult for the enemy to see and hit.

The Civil War brought on even more advances in weapons. The north had sewing machines and was able to make uniforms much faster than the south could by hand. Land mines, "booby" traps, the iron-clad warship, the submarine, and the machine gun were all developed at this time.

From the Civil War until World War I, great bridges and highways were built. Steel making was refined and expanded to meet the country's growing needs in building construction. The railroad system continued to expand. It is interesting to note that following each major American war, transportation grew dramatically. After the American Revolution the Erie Canal was developed. The Civil War brought upon an impressive expansion in an already excellent railroad system which the north possessed. Some claim that the north's ability alone, to move men and equipment about more efficiently than the south through their rail system, won them the war. Between the Civil War and World War I, automobiles and trucks came on the scene.

Following the Civil War, developments in communications and electrical systems were dynamic. One important invention was the typewriter. In 1867 the first single-key typewriter was developed by Christopher Latham Sholes. Just a year later Sholes and his partner, Carlos Glidden, developed a multi-key typewriter, an early ancestor to those used today (Figure 2.4). It was also during this time, in 1876, that Alexander Graham Bell invented the telephone. Thomas Edison invented the phonograph just a year later, and in 1880 he devised the first practical electric lights.

Until the 1890s, world design was heavily influenced by decoration rather than the shape itself as

**FIGURE 2.4.** Remington typewriter, derived from designs by Christopher Latham Sholes and Carlos Glidden, 1874. Notice the flowers painted on the body. *Photograph courtesy of Remington Arms, Ilion, New York.*

expressed by a product's function and form. In other words, it was believed that heavily engineered products could be made beautiful by covering the mechanisms with superfluous decoration, thus making the product more valuable. It seemed that everything, from type-writers, china, clocks, furniture, and firearms to teaspoons, was covered with rosebuds. As time progressed, people were getting tired of these overly-decorative designs. In part, industrial design grew from this ostentatious era. Less decorated products cost less to manufac-ture, thus lowering the selling price. During and following World War I, truck manufacturing growth was dramatic. A surplus of trucks left over from war activities was available, and probably at low cost. Civilians and soldiers could see how efficient truck transportation was compared to the horse and wagon. After World War II there was an expansion of air and space travel. Our magnificent highway systems were developed. Automobiles became faster and more economical to operate. Goods could move to market faster and touring about the country was much more efficient. Truck transportation grew, taking advantage of the new road networks.

## John Ruskin (1819-1900) and William Morris (1834-1896)

Returning to the nineteenth century, one can see the influence of John Ruskin, the mid-century English philosopher, and William Morris, the great British fabric designer and philosopher (Figures 2.5 and 2.6). This period is often thought of as the beginning of industrial design. In *Avantgarde Design: 1880-1930* (page 9), Torsten Brohan and Thomas Berg describe the movement this way:

> The origins of modern design history are to be found in 19th-century England. With the rise of industrialization and the social changes it wrought, the call for a new unity of art and life was voiced here earlier than elsewhere. The leading figures of this movement were the writer, reformer and painter John Ruskin and the painter and social critic William Morris. It was William

**FIGURE 2.5.** John Ruskin, 1819-1900.    **FIGURE 2.6.** William Morris, 1834-1896, by London Stereoscopic Co., 1877. Courtesy of the National Portrait Gallery, London.

Morris, in fact, who was the first to make the decisive crossover from fine artist to craftsman and designer. The Arts and Crafts movement founded by Morris attracted many young artists and craftsmen who, in turn, made major contributions to this refor-mative style.

Morris was against over decoration and put great emphasis on the beauty of natural forms in his designs. Morris was an early supporter of Ruskin. In Morris' *Hope and Fear for Art,* a collection of essays first published in 1882, he says:

> … [A]rt which is to be made by the people and for the people, as a happiness to the maker and the user. These virtues are honesty, and the simplicity to life. To make my meaning clearer I will name the opposing vice of the second of these—luxury to wit.

Morris' design philosophy can be best understood by the advice he gave to his employees (from *Gustav Stickley, The Craftsman,* by Mary Ann Smith, page 12):

1. Never forget the material you are working with ... the special limitations of the material should be a pleasure to you, not a hindrance.
2. Don't copy any style at all, but make your own; yet you must study the history of art, or you will be nose-led by the first bad copyist of it that you come across.

Ruskin and Morris had trouble with the industrial revolution, finding it repulsive and threatening to workers and users. Together, these men felt that a machine should not apply decoration to products but should help express the structure and functional elements. Ruskin was against the use of machines altogether. Frank Whitford amplifies on these points in *Bauhaus* (page 16):

> [Ruskin] damning the introduction of any device in the crafts which did more than aid "the muscular action of the human hand" both believed that the effects of industrial production were spiritually damaging to craftsman and customer alike: the machine had no soul; it would render mankind soulless. It robbed the craftsman of the joy in work well done and denied the public the life-enhancing pleasure of living in an environment that had been shaped with both skill and love.

Ruskin and Morris both felt that it was dishonest for machine goods to pretend to be handmade. Both the craftsman and the customer could be spiritually hurt by machine-made products. Handmade products gave the craftsman the satisfaction of good work and the customer the satisfaction of owning an original, handmade article. This philosophy is not too far from the Shakers' thinking.

John Ruskin wrote *Stones of Venice,* published in three volumes between 1851 and 1853, which formed a basis for the Arts and Crafts theory. In *Stones of Venice,* Ruskin identifies three rules for the design and manufacture of products of any kind:

1. Never encourage the manufacture of any article not absolutely necessary, in the production of which invention has no share.
2. Never demand an exact finish for its own sake, but only for some practical or noble end.
3. Never encourage imitation or copying of any kind except for the sake of preserving records of great works.

These ideas seem strange today and are hardly practiced. However, these men influenced early industrial design up until the beginning of this century.

## Christopher Dresser (1834-1904)

Christopher Dresser was the first modern product designer, advocating equality of the designer with the manufacturer. He had enthusiasm for machines, unlike others of his time such as William Morris and John Ruskin. Dresser paved the way for others like Peter Behrens by marrying design and industry. Torsten Brohan and Thomas Berg discuss Dresser's contribution to industrial design in *Avantgarde Design: 1880-1930* (page 9):

> He [Christopher Dresser] may be regarded as Europe's very first industrial designer, a forerunner of Peter Behrens. In his designs, Dresser consciously catered to industrial needs, thereby contributing to the aesthetic and technical improvement of industrially produced goods.

Christopher Dresser was born in Glasgow on July 4, 1834. Living most of his life in London, he joined the Government School of Design at Somerset House in 1847, where the idea of linking art and industry had been a topic. He is said to have been the most talented of all the students there. Upon his graduation in 1854 he married Thirza

Perry and together they had 13 children. In 1959, he published *The Rudiments of Botany* and *Unity in Variety.*

Dresser spent the first five years of his design career struggling before he earned enough money to support his family with his designs, lecturing and writing to supplement his income. He became an expert in plant morphology (the study of the external form of the plant) and botany, and was sympathetic to John Ruskin's belief in nature as a basis of ornamentation. In 1862, Dresser wrote *The Art of Decorative Design,* where he shows his interest in plant forms: "The designer's mind must be like the vital force of the planet, ever developing itself into forms of beauty, yet while thus free to produce, still governed by unalterable laws."

Dresser established a modern design office, calling it a "studio," with about 12 assistant designers and a support staff. Many of his children worked with him doing various duties.

Dresser, an ornamentalist, denounced the separation of the beautiful from the useful. When lecturing at the Pennsylvania Museum and School of Industrial Art, he concluded his first lecture by saying: "If your art-manufacturers are to prosper, if the fabric which you weave and the objects which you make are to satisfy the educated … apply to them an ennobling art. Taste was not a matter of intuition, but a matter of cultivation."

Dresser was the first European designer to visit Japan, and in 1877 spent four months there studying art and architecture. In fact, in 1879, Dresser formed a partnership with a Mr. Holme with the intention of importing Oriental manufacturers. He wrote and lectured on Japanese art and architecture and later, Frank Lloyd Wright did so as well.

Dresser never allowed technical constraints to restrict his designs. His knowledge of machines and technology was expansive and well respected among his associates. Dresser's ideas were far ahead of William Morri's and John Ruskin's. Although he was an

**FIGURE 2.7.** Christopher Dresser's soup tureen, model no. 12780, 1885-86. Photograph courtesy of The Mitchell Wolfson, Jr. Collection, The Wolfsonian-Florida International University, Miami Beach, Florida.

ornamentist, Dresser believed that a product's form should speak for itself and devalued the importance of decoration, saying that ornamentation should be acquiescent to form.

He designed carpets, wallpaper, pottery, furniture, ceramics, glass, and metal works (Figures 2.7 and 2.8). The last 10 years of his life he spent designing mostly textiles and wallpapers. Unlike Morris, Dresser never established a studio to manufacture his designs. He commanded

**FIGURE 2.8.** Artist's drawing of a Christopher Dresser chair, manufactured by Chubb & Sons, London, c. 1880.

**FIGURE 2.9.** Wilbur (l) and Orville (r) Wright on the back porch of their home in Dayton, Ohio, June 1909. Photograph courtesy of CORBIS, New York.

**FIGURE 2.10.** Wilbur Wright aboard the *Flyer*, outfitted with a motor and propellers as it runs aground on takeoff during its first test, December 14, 1903. Photograph courtesy of National Air and Space Museum, Smithsonian Institution, Photo No. A-38618-A.

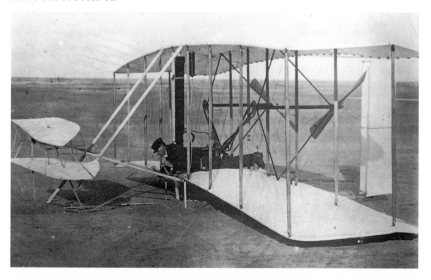

as much as 20 pounds for a design from French and German manufacturers, yet was always hard pressed for money and felt tremendous competitive pressures. In his later years, he developed a drinking problem and died in his sleep on November 24, 1904. He had very little capital except his studio and his designs. He worked for over 50 clients in his lifetime—a goodly number. One can only wonder about the depth and breadth of his influence on design in the emerging design world.

## Wilbur (1867-1912) and Orville (1871-1948) Wright

Wilbur Wright and Orville Wright and their development of the first flying machine must be looked at in detail (Figure 2.9). Neither brother was an engineer or designer by training. They had a successful bicycle manufacturing shop and were considered good businessmen. They started their development as a challenge to themselves and began to act very much like modern-day engineers. For example, the Wrights discovered that they had to do a great deal of research to understand what others had already accomplished.

In 1902, they built a glider which would support a person, which was a great accomplishment. Achieving their designs required constructing models and careful analysis and revisions to the designs following each failure. To determine the most efficient airfoil, they built a miniature wind tunnel and tested innumerable shapes. The Wrights developed a turning control called "wing warping" but it was later abandoned in favor of a simple rudder.

Once the Wrights had made hundreds of glider flights, they moved to the next logical step, developing a satisfactory power source to fly the glider as an airplane. No existing engine met their requirements so they were compelled to design and develop their own. In late 1903 they flew the glider as a powered aircraft (Figure 2.10). From then on they encountered the heartbreaking experience of combating others who claimed to be the first to develop and fly an aircraft.

## The Wright's Design Process

What was unique about the way the Wrights developed their designs? They generated their designs using the following process:

1. They researched what others had accomplished and how and why.

2. They studied the mathematical calculations of others to best understand the dynamics of their designs. Not many noncollege educated designer/engineers did this at that time. Now they could communicate intelligently with other aeronautical engineers around the world.

3. To determine the correct wing shape, the Wrights made many wing cross sections and studied them carefully in their home-made wind tunnel.

4. They sought the correct environment to test their designs by seeking the advice of the weather bureau to find a place in the United States with a constant wind speed.

The development of aviation is probably the most significant achievement in the twentieth century. In his book, *Warpaths: Travels of a Military Historian in North America,* John Keegan notes that Major Baden Powell, a British War Office observer, says (page 344) "that Wilbur Wright is in possession of a power which controls the fate of nations is beyond dispute." Events of the past 100 years have proven this true. Keegan also states that on the Wright's aircraft, the *Flyer,* on display at the National Air and Space Museum, Smithsonian Institution, a note identifies their achievements. The brothers:

1  developed the airplane,
2. taught man to fly, and
3. opened the era of aviation.

## Gustav Stickley (1858-1946)

One great American furniture designer came much later in history than the Shakers, but today his influence is just as great. Syracuse, New York furniture designer, philosopher and manufacturer Gustav Stickley has attracted the attention of the modern design world (Figure 2.11). Stickley wanted to manufacture furniture that was well designed, comfortable, and easily mass-produced. He had been a leader in the Arts and Crafts movement in America since 1900 when he first started manufacturing and selling his furniture.

**FIGURE 2.11.** Gustav Stickley (1858-1946), c. 1909. Photograph courtesy of Dover Publications, Inc., New York, from *Gustav Stickley: The Craftsman* by Mary Ann Smith.

The Stickley family came to the United States from Germany and settled in Osceola, Wisconsin. Gustav was born in 1858, the eldest child in his family. At age 12 he went to work for his father as a stone mason. Stickley started out as a "tender" (a novice) and by the age of 14 was earning a journeyman's wage. He learned to hate stone masonry. His father, after excessive drinking and unhappiness, abandoned the family, leaving Gustav as head of the household.

About 1875 the family moved to northern Pennsylvania to be with his mother's brother, who owned a small chair factory. Gustav left school after eighth grade and began his career in the furniture industry. He learned to love wood and experienced the joy of furniture manufacturing. While he was in and out of assorted furniture manufacturing and sales ventures, he was impressed by the furniture manu- factured by the Shakers. In 1892 through 1894, he took a position working in the state prison at Auburn, New York, supervising the manufacture of simple chairs which were sold to the public.

Gustav found time to start a new company in Eastwood, New York, later to became the home of the Stickley Craftsman Workshops. Stickley become successful in his work and slowly developed a vision for himself and his craft. Besides manufacturing, he displayed an interest in other influences relating to furniture, such as interiors and accessories, and a magazine called *The Craftsman,* reporting on the subject of arts and crafts. In the early 1890s he made his first trip to Europe. When he returned, his furniture designs began to change reflecting the Art Nouveau (Henry van de Velde's influence) and the English Arts and Crafts (William Morris' influence) movement. Stickley went to Europe with an idea of what he wanted to experience. Mary Ann Smith tells of this trip in *Gustav Stickley, The Craftsman* (pages 9-10):

> Since childhood he had been an admirer of the work of John Ruskin and William Morris. As a young man in Brandt, Pennsylvania, Gustav had access to a small library which contained a number of Ruskin's books as well as work by Thomas Carlyle, another popular Victorian reformer whose work he admired. It is not difficult to imagine what particular Ruskinian theories inspired Stickley. Ruskin's *Seven Lamps of Architecture,* first published in 1849, stressed the importance of good crafts- manship and honesty in the use of materials. Ruskin's belief in a world made better by morality in craftsmanship was essentially a reaction against the abuses of the Industrial Revolution in England. In the *Seven Lamps of Architecture* Ruskin discussed the virtues of Gothic architecture, but the comments he made could often apply to furniture as well. In one chapter, "The Lamp of Truth," he categorized "Architectural Deceits" as follows:

1st   The suggestion of a mode of structure or support, other than the true one; as in pendants of late Gothic roofs.
2nd   The painting of surfaces to represent some other mate- rial than that of which they actually consist (as in the marbling of wood), or the deceptive representation of sculptured ornament upon them.
3rd   The use of cast or machine-made ornaments of any kind.

Stickley was impressed with the daily philosophy of both John Ruskin and William Morris. For instance, Ruskin once said "What we like determines what we are, and is the sign of what we are. To teach taste is inevitably to form character."

After returning from Europe, Stickley approached his designs with a new kind of energy and philosophy. Ruskin and Morris abhorred the use of machines to build objects of art which possess decoration. Americans realized that machines were necessary to make products affordable to the everyday family. Stickley showed the way. In *Gustav Stickley ... His Craft,* by A. Patricia Bartinique, Stickley mused about the field's beginnings (page 73):

> I did not realize at the time that in making those few pieces of strong, simple furniture, I had started a new movement. Others saw it and prophesied a far-reaching development. To me it was only furniture; to them it was religion. And eventually it became religion with me as well.

Bartinique further discusses Stickley's style (page 11):

> He [Stickley] acknowledged "the present tendencies ... toward simplicity" and selected his material for "potential beauty." He defined "style" as "an indefinable quality" which in terms of art "must be a part of the very conception." Style is therefore the quality and rightful possession of one individual, or class of individuals. In other words, style comes from within and should be an outgrowth of the environment from which the

**FIGURE 2.12.** Gustav Stickley dining chair from the author's private collection.

creation originated. Ultimately style should be based in "artistic truth" and should "represent ... [the] dominant thought of the period."

Stickley strove to make quality undecorated furniture with typical wood manufacturing equipment (Figure 2.12). He believed that his creations should add to the ease and convenience of life. His factory produced simple, low-cost oak furniture for any family. The furniture could be plain or stained. Also, the furniture was durable and comfortable when compared with what Frank Lloyd Wright or Charles Rennie Mackintosh designed.

Gustav Stickley demonstrated that design and manufacturing can go hand-in-hand to mass produce beautiful, warm and useful products. Mary Ann Smith describes some of the characteristics of Stickley's furniture in *Gustav Stickley, The Craftsman* (page 165):

> Gustav Stickley's Craftsman furniture, solid, sturdy, "primitive," and "structural," might be considered among the earliest modern designs in the United States. He eliminated the machine-made ornamentation of late-nineteenth-century American furniture and created furniture which depended on honest expression of structure for its characteristic design qualities.

Stickley developed designs which used a craftsperson to complete its assembly and finish yet used power tools to do the drudgery of manufacture. This illustrated that beautiful products can be made by machine and finished by hand. Stickley demonstrated concern for his employees in the arts and crafts tradition as expressed by William Morris. He tried profit sharing with his employees. Additionally, he developed designs that the middle class could afford

and demanded quality of manufacture and quality of design. It is said that he continually reviewed his designs to be sure all design details were the best.

During the 1940s and 1950s, the American Arts and Crafts style experienced a devaluation and change in taste so severe that major museums in Cincinnati, Philadelphia, and St. Louis sold or gave away noteworthy objects. One Salvation Army center which had gathered a quantity of Stickley's creations had its employees destroy all of the furniture because of lack of room or demand. By the 1960s, however, the first steps to salvation began. In the 1980s the demand for such pieces was fierce and a flood of books were written on the subject. Barbara Mayer writes of this phenomena in her book *In the Arts and Crafts Style* (page 23):

> In December 1988, for example, at Christie's auction house in New York City, a successful bid of $363,000.00 for a ten-foot-long Gustav Stickley sideboard announced to the world that there was such a thing as the Arts and Crafts movement in America and that it had produced unique and desirable objects.

Stickley's designs have withstood the test of time. In fact, as illustrated by the above example, they have appreciated considerably in value over the past 100 years. Today Stickley's philosophy of furniture design is still being practiced. The Stickley Furniture Company in Manlius, New York manufactures reproduction pieces to the original specifications of Gustav Stickley. It also has incorporated new pieces into the Stickley line, all using the same quality manufacturing, purpose, and appeal.

The end of Stickley's success during his lifetime came when he:

1. overexpanded his showroom in New York City,
2. remained inflexible in his furniture designs when styles changed,
3. overextended his projects by working in architecture and interior design rather than sticking to furniture,

4. did not vigorously protect the name "craftsman" which was infringed upon by many.

There were others in America and England who extolled the virtues of craftsmanship and the concept of corporate harmony. Elbert Hubbard established the Roycroft community in East Aurora, New York. Roycroft was the most commercially successful American arts and crafts community ever, employing more than 400 people by 1906. Hubbard was a salesman and philosopher first, a furniture manufacturer second. His furniture, made from oak, was simple, square, slightly Gothic in style, and very similar to Stickley's with little ornamentation except for the Roycroft symbol of an orb and cross. His shops also did metal working, leather goods, souvenirs, and stained glass lighting fixtures. He was active in publishing his philosophy through *The Philistine,* a journal published by his Roycroft Press. After his death in 1915 aboard the *Lusitania,* his son Bert took over and successfully ran the community.

## Peter Behrens (1868-1940)

Industrial design is a relationship between the designer and industry. Peter Behrens exemplified this philosophy. Peter Behrens came from Hamburg, Germany and studied painting in Karlsruhe and Dusseldorf (Figure 2.13). In the late 1800s, Behrens and other artists/architects who had been functioning in isolation as free spirits changed their thinking and became more socially obligated. They began to move away from heavily decorated products and reduced engineered designs to their simplest mass-producible forms. This concept, developed by Josef Hoffmann and called "right angle design," was a welcome change to many from the repugnant, excessively adorned designs of the previous century (Figure 2.14). This reflected the impact of William Morris' philosophy.

From 1899 until 1903, Behrens worked at the Darmstadt artists' colony, founded in 1898. This colony somewhat emulated the American Arts and Crafts movement. Among those at Darmstadt it became customary to design their own homes. This became almost an obligation and proof that the designer was master of all design disciplines. Behrens house, designed in 1901, was unique in shape and color. Although not trained as an architect, he did a superb job. Even his interior was elaborate but tasteful—very reminiscent of Charles Mackintosh, the famous Scottish designer/architect. From 1903 to 1907, Behrens served as director of the Dusseldorf School of Industrial Arts. He did various work including graphics, architecture, and interior design.

An important design movement, founded in Germany, was referred to as the "Werkbund." In 1896 the German government established a post at its embassy in London for architect Hermann Muthesius (1861-1927). He was looking for products that expressed the quality of materials from which they were made. The architect wanted products free of decoration that would be appealing

**FIGURE 2.13.** Peter Behrens (1868-1940) in 1911. Photograph courtesy of A.E.G. Company Archives, Frankfurt.

**FIGURE 2.14.** Behrens dining chair, c. 1902. Photograph courtesy of The Mitchell Wolfson, Jr. Collection, The Wolfsonian-Florida International University, Miami Beach, Florida.

## Peter Behrens

What is significant about Peter Behrens' work?

• Behrens was the first to train himself to be proficient in the arts, crafts, product design, and architecture. Today he would be referred to as a "generalist."

• He was one of the first to convince industry that it needed a comprehensive designer who could enhance the corporate image by working to demonstrate good design through product design, corporate and product graphics, and architecture.

• By working with engineering, he became involved in product planning. He mixed and matched assorted existing product parts to form new products.

• Behrens attracted superior talent (Gropius, Le Corbusier, Mies van der Rohe) and stimulated them with his diverse thinking regarding the arts and design. This stimulation helped Gropius in defining his philosophy for the Bauhaus school.

**FIGURE 2.15.**
A.E.G. "Synchron" clock designed by Peter Behrens in 1929. Photograph courtesy of A.E.G. Company Archives, Frankfurt.

and affordable to the general public. When Muthesius returned to Germany, he was appointed the superintendent of schools of arts and crafts by the Prussian Board of Trade. He contacted Peter Behrens and others and persuaded them to head art schools in cities such as Dusseldorf and Berlin. He attempted to persuade German industries to use good design. In 1907 Muthesius brought together 12 artists, including Peter Behrens, and 12 industrialists to form the organization called the Werkbund. By 1908 the Werkbund had 492 members, and at its peak in 1929, its membership exceeded 3,000. Frank Whitford, in his book *Bauhaus* (page 20), describes the Werkbund:

> The Werkbund was to arrange for the employment of designers in industry, and sustain a publicity campaign directed at the improvement of manufactured goods. Its aim was the reconciliation of art, craft, industry, and trade, and a subsequent improvement in the quality of German products.

Peter Behrens seemed to have developed a comfortable relationship with industry. In 1907 he was appointed "an artistic advisor" to the electrical manufacturing giant AEG (Allgemeine Elektrizitats Gesellschaft) in Berlin. This company was like our modern General Electric. His diverse work at Darmstadt made him competent to handle the responsibility of a corporate assignment. This was, at last, a very significant step in industrial design history toward linking art and industry.

Peter Behrens was given control over "visual image" and products, from letterheads to buildings at AEG (Figures 2.15, 2.16 and 2.17). Behrens and AEG's talented in-house design engineer, Michael van Dolivo-Dobrawolsky, worked together to interchange product parts to make new products. Of 81 possible combinations, 30 were marketed.

In 1909, three important designer/architects joined Behrens staff: Ludwig Mies van der Rohe, who later became influential in American architecture; Walter Gropius, founder of the Bauhaus; and the great Swiss/French architect of the twentieth century, Le Corbusier.

**FIGURE 2.16.** A.E.G. hanging lamp designed by Peter Behrens in 1907. Photograph courtesy of A.E.G. Company Archives, Frankfurt.

**FIGURE 2.17.** Electric teapot designed by Peter Behrens in 1921. Photograph courtesy of A.E.G. Company Archives, Frankfurt.

**FIGURE 2.18.** Walter Gropius as a practicing professional in 1920. Photograph courtesy of Bauhaus-Archiv Museum, Berlin.

**FIGURE 2.19.** Gropius mahogany dining chair, c. 1913. Photograph courtesy of Bauhaus-Archiv Museum, Berlin.

It is believed that this alliance helped establish the ground work for Gropius' Bauhaus movement.

## Walter Gropius (1883-1969) and the Bauhaus

Walter Gropius was born into a family of artists and architects. In fact, his father was an architect and his great-grandfather a prominent painter. A great-uncle of his designed the Berlin Museum of Arts and Crafts. Between 1903 and 1907, Gropius studied architecture in Munich and Berlin. His studies were interrupted when he joined the fifteenth regiment of Hussar. In 1907 Gropius joined the staff of Peter Behrens where he must have met Mies van der Rohe and Le Corbusier.

Three years after joining Behrens, Gropius opened his own office and designed the Fagus factory at Alfeld on the River Leine (Figure 2.18). From *Bauhaus* (page 33), "The building … was star-tlingly ahead of its time, especially in its novel use of steel and glass as substitutes for conventional load-bearing wall."

In 1912 Walter Gropius joined the Werkbund, taking an active role in its organization and policy making. Gropius believed that arts like painting, graphic arts, product design, and architecture could evolve from the same school through cross stimulation. The bringing together of many different art disciplines such as crafts (weaving and pottery), furniture making, painting, sculpture, product design, and architecture was exciting.

Around 1913 Gropius tried his hand at designing a diesel loco-motive, railroad carriage, wallpaper and furniture (Figure 2.19). He was pursuing the same path that Peter Behrens did seven years earlier at AEG. Gropius functioned as a generalist designer but his work was for different clients. The diesel locomotive-passenger car is worth reviewing. Gropius' office was retained by the Prussian State Railway to develop this design and he was given a free hand. The external front view of the locomotive is significant. Its curved contour helps

**FIGURE 2.22.** Gropius diesel-locomotive, side view with cover slid forward providing easy access to the engine. Photograph courtesy of Bauhaus-Archiv Museum, Berlin.

**FIGURE 2.20.** Gropius diesel-locomotive for the Koenigsberg factory, 1913. Its slanted and streamlined hood is well designed for visibility and removal of exhaust fumes. Photograph courtesy of Bauhaus-Archiv Museum, Berlin.

**FIGURE 2.21.** Gropius diesel-locomotive, side view. Photograph courtesy of Bauhaus-Archiv Museum, Berlin.

**FIGURE 2.23.** The operator's compartment of the Gropius diesel-locomotive. Notice the panoramic front view provided for the engineer and fireman by the extensive use of glass.

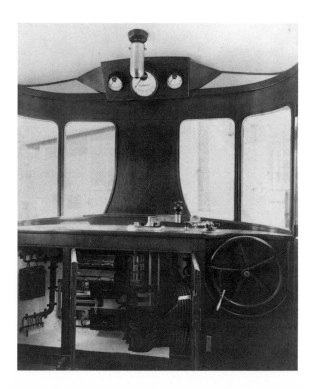

**FIGURE 2.24.** Henry van de Velde (1863-1957, center) discussing design, c. 1947. Antonin Heythum (right) was one of my professors at Syracuse University. Photograph courtesy of Arthur Hunt Crapsey.

the on-rushing air to flow, up and over the top of the train. This flow carries any objectionable exhaust away from the passenger compartments (Figures 2.20, 2.21 and 2.22). Gropius uses glass extensively on the front of the train, thus providing the engineer and fireman with an unobstructed view (Figure 2.23).

Another member of the Werkbund was Henry van de Velde, 1863-1957 (Figure 2.24). Van de Velde, a superb generalist designer, architect, and artist, was the original founder of the Art Nouveau movement. Art Nouveau was an important art movement for a short time. Art Nouveau is exemplified by the writings of Henry Van de Velde. He felt everyday objects, such as automobiles, bathroom fixtures, lamps, and medical products, could be made beautiful to look at as well as mass produced. He did not exclude ornamentation and thought it could help design. Unfortunately, its products, while high quality, could not be easily mass produced and were expensive, so the movement faded away (Figure 2.25).

Van de Velde held considerable influence in Germany even though he was a native of Belgium. Ironically, in 1914 Van de Velde found himself living and working in a country that was invading his homeland. Van de Velde, a leading figure trying to reconcile art with industry (the Werkbund), could see the beginning of cooperation among the artist, craftsman, and industry. In 1907 his school, the Arts and Crafts Seminar, became public. Hermann Muthesius established the Werkbund to put emphasis on formal standards (standardized sizing for everything) and commerce. This was interpreted as a threat to the artists' independence. Van de Velde opposed Muthesius' proposal, believing most of the members to be artists first. The Werkbund, while a great idea, failed to reconcile a precise program regarding the role of the designer.

About 1914 the German government decided it wanted to reform art education. The government felt it was vital for economic reasons. It relied heavily on skilled labor and the ability for its industries to produce high-quality, sophisticated products. The Germans felt that in order to continue to achieve high production, there was a growing need for more designers. During World War I negotiations went on between the government and Gropius about reopening the Arts and Crafts Seminar as soon as the war ended. In 1915 Gropius was one of three candidates recommended by Van de Velde as a possible successor for director of the Weimar Kunstgewerbeschule. The interviewer asked him to write a paper identifying his view of the future of the school. In the paper he proposed a partnership with the artist,

**FIGURE 2.25.** Van de Velde dining chair, 1898. Photograph courtesy of Hessiches Landesmuseum, Darmstadt.

industrialist, and technician and subsequently was awarded the position of director. The school had three objectives:

1. Rescue all artists from isolation. Help them learn and train together. Ultimately, the aim was to have all creative activities in one building.
2. Elevate the status of craftsman to that of a fine artist. Gropius believed there was no difference.
3. Develop a close contact with the leaders of crafts and industries of the country. Bauhaus wanted to be independent of the state.

By 1918, Gropius had seen combat in World War I and was badly wounded, receiving two iron crosses. Mentally and physically scarred by war, he wrote to Weimar authorities and said, "I have immersed myself for a long time in the idea of giving Weimar a new kind of artistic life, and have very specific plans for doing so." On April 1, 1919 Gropius was appointed director of the Academy of Fine Art. On April 12 he obtained permission to unite that institution with the reopened Arts and Crafts Seminar. He named the new school the Bauhaus. The word Bauen means "to grow a crop." He chose the name Bauhaus to signify sowing, nurturing, and bringing to fruition a design philosophy.

In a document entitled *Principles of Bauhaus Production,* written in 1926, Gropius says:

> The Bauhaus workshops are essentially laboratories in which prototypes of products suitable for mass-production and typical of our time are carefully developed and constantly improved.

There are some questions regarding the feasibility of mass-production of many of the Bauhaus designs. However, the furniture designed by Mies van der Rohe and Marcel Breuer were outstanding,

FIGURE 2.26. A chromed steel and cane arm chair designed by Ludwig Mies van der Rohe in 1927. Cane work was designed by Lily Reich, a close associate of van der Rohe. Photograph courtesy of Carnegie Museum of Art, Pittsburgh; Dupuy Fund.

FIGURE 2.27. Marcel Breuer (1902-1981) in 1927. Photograph courtesy of Bauhaus-Archiv Museum, Berlin.

FIGURE 2.28. Marcel Breuer dining chair from the author's private collection.

simple, and beautiful (Figures 2.26, 2.27 and 2.28). These pieces could be manufactured and in some cases are still offered for sale today.

Gropius was a good administrator, politically shrewd, and an adept manipulator of people and events. His work was the center of his life. He had problems in the school, but political opposition to the Bauhaus was severe from the outside. The state (Weimar) owned the

**FIGURE 2.29.** Ludwig Mies van der Rohe (1886-1969), c. 1933. Photograph courtesy of Bauhaus-Archiv Museum, Berlin.

**FIGURE 2.30.** Hannes Meyer (1899-1954) at the Bauhaus in 1928. Courtesy of Bauhaus-Archiv Museum, Berlin.

school and provided money for its support. Both political parties—the extreme right, the Nazis, and the extreme left, the communists—tore at the fabric of the school. Bickering inside and outside the school impacted the resources so necessary for survival of this teaching environment. On top of these problems Germany was wrestling with out-of-control inflation. Gropius always had his students working, but now he had the students shoveling coal to heat the school. Other students worked in theater groups to entertain the community. They built products for the shops and worked the vegetable gardens, all to help support themselves and the school. Finally, Gropius had enough of the political pressure and resigned in January of 1928. He asked Mies van der Rohe to succeed him, but he refused (Figure 2.29). He then offered the position to his former architectural partner and fellow educator, a communist named Hannes Meyer, who was head of the architectural department at the Bauhaus (Figure 2.30). Meyer accepted the post.

Meyer made several changes when he managed the Bauhaus. He divided the architecture department into two sections: building in theory and practice, and interior design. He established a photography workshop and allowed painting classes as part of the architecture curriculum. A new course called "Man" was added which consisted of human biology, psychology, and philosophy along with life-drawing. Regular gymnastics classes were offered to students. Meyer turned his attention to making the school profitable, as Whitford describes in *Bauhaus* (pages 186-7):

> Meyer also did his best to persuade the various workshops to think first of producing designs and goods for sale to industry, not supplying the luxury market but making cheap, mass-produced essential items like furniture. And he made his architectural students concentrate not on individual dwellings but on the problems of mass-housing.
>
> … The best example of how some of the workshops became profitable during Meyer's directorship is provided by the mural-painting department. Emil Rasch who had inherited a wallpaper factory at Bramsche near Osnabruck, and whose sister was a student at the Bauhaus, suggested to Meyer that the school might like to produce some designs for him. … [H]is suggestion was enthusiastically received. Staff and students in the mural-painting department designed a series of textured and quietly patterned papers quite unlike anything commercially available at the time. They proved very popular and made more money for the school than anything else. In the first year alone four-and-a-half million rolls were sold. They are still available today and are produced by the same company, Emil Rasch of Bramsche.
>
> At the same time the weaving and furniture workshops also proved capable of earning considerable funds for the school. A few of the commissions secured by the Bauhaus during the last quarter of 1928 demonstrated how successful the workshops had become. …

**FIGURE 2.31.** Bauhaus students being led away by Berlin police on April 11, 1933. Photograph courtesy of Bauhaus-Archiv Museum, Berlin.

... For the first time the school was achieving what it set
out to do.

Political influences forced Meyer and communist students out of the school and in August 1930 he was replaced by Mies van der Rohe. By 1931 political developments outside the school were intense and threatening. On September 30, 1932, the Dessau government closed the Bauhaus. Sometime around October 1932 the Nazis moved in, smashing windows, destroying files, tools, and throwing furniture out into the streets below.

The Bauhaus ideals were still not dead. Mies van der Rohe tried to salvage the school. He rented an old telephone factory in a Berlin suburb and set up shop. By then the Nazis had come to power. The final end for the Bauhaus came on April 11, 1933 when the Berlin Police arrived in trucks and took students away and closed the doors forever (Figure 2.31).

The influence that the Bauhaus teaching philosophies has had upon the world of design is undeniable and profound. Many members of the faculty, besides Gropius, moved to the United States bringing the Bauhaus design philosophy with them. It is interesting to speculate what the quality of design throughout Germany and all of Europe might have been had the Weimar and Dessau governments and the Nazis left the school alone to pursue its teachings. Here was a classic illustration of a government whose image at first was bolstered and enhanced by new and exciting designs (aircraft, locomotives, weapons, automobiles, buildings, and graphics) and design thinking. It then turned around and attacked the school and its teachings. The Nazis could sense the power of new art and design thinking but refused to try to understand it and preferred to live in ignorance and fear. They hated anything and everything that was the slightest bit foreign or contrary to Hitler's doctrine. The Bauhaus was new and exemplified a different and free expression.

In *Industrial Design* (page 104), John Heskett discusses the influence of the Bauhaus:

> Whatever reservations may be expressed about the Bauhaus, the fact of its enormous influence is undeniable. The varied community of talent gathered together by Gropius was highly individualistic, but developed, too, a strong corporate identity. When scattered by emigration from the Third Reich, the members of this community carried with them a deep sense of conviction that had a profound impact wherever they worked and taught, and was reaffirmed by large numbers of students and adherents. What the Bauhaus was, appears to have been less important than what its members and followers believed it to be. Its influence, far greater than the sum of its practical achievements, is above all a testimony to the power of ideas.

Contrary to what many people still believe, Gropius did not want a Bauhaus *style*. He wanted the students to evolve into the best

## The Bauhaus

When reflecting on the Bauhaus, the following conclusions and questions come to mind:

1. Walter Gropius must have been aware of the success Peter Behrens had with AEG, the German electrical giant. Why didn't he use the Bauhaus to promote the generalist approach to design to other industries throughout Germany? Why didn't he bring industries in and get them involved with the Bauhaus?

2. There was a crisis in Germany following the first World War. Industry had a need for good product design. Why didn't the state encourage industry to bring design students into its factory environments? We have only heard of one German design engineer and he worked closely with Behrens at AEG to expand its product line. Were there other German design engineers?

3. The concept of equating the artist with the craftsman is fine in school but is impractical in real industry. Both the artist and craftsman have slowly disappeared in this context. The designer has prevailed embracing the artist's aesthetic judgment and taste while harnessing the craftsman's knowledge and use of materials and tools. In *Walter Gropius: Work and Teamwork* (page 43), author S. Giedion discusses this trend:

On the basis of this systematically sound foundation new prototypes for mass production were now developed. The origins of their design must be sought in the seemingly sequestered work of the art studios. Now this became absorbed into industrial production and distributed around the world. An outstanding example is the tubular steel chair first designed by Marcel Breuer in 1925. Many other examples come to mind including typography, lamps and textiles.

The kind of work that was coming out of this German educational institution is called in the U.S.A. "product design": in other words, giving form and shape to mass-produced objects, which has become one of the most important problems of highly mechanized industry.

4. Gropius' concept of encouraging each student to progress to his fullest potential is perhaps his greatest legacy.

Unfortunately, Gropius did not or was not encouraged to continue the Bauhaus concept here in America at Harvard. Perhaps he chose to limit himself only to teaching architecture. Regardless, his insight on design, architecture, and the teaching process has influenced world design.

---

designers possible with their own unique styles and abilities. He wanted them to be free and stimulated by others. Students were not expected to follow, imitate or copy their teachers.

Walter Gropius finally emigrated to the United States in 1937. His philosophy was carried on when he became director of the architectural school at Harvard University.

S. Giedion describes the Bauhaus in his book *Walter Gropius: Work and Teamwork* (page 27):

… One of the clearest expositions of the secret of the Bauhaus was given by that taciturn authority, Mies van der Rohe, when he rose to speak after a dinner in honor of Gropius at the Blackstone Hotel in Chicago on May 18, 1953.

"The Bauhaus," he said "was not an institution with a clear program—it was an idea, and Gropius formulated this idea with great precision … As I said before, it was an idea. The fact that it was an idea, I think, is the cause of this enormous influence the Bauhaus had on every progressive school around the globe.

**FIGURE 2.32.** The *Northumbrian 0-2-2,* Liverpool & Manchester Railway, Great Britain, 1830. Illustration courtesy of Salamander Picture Library, London.

**FIGURE 2.33.** The *American Type 4-4-0,* Western & Atlantic Railroad, United States, 1855, nicknamed The General. This photograph taken in 1939 at the New York World's Fair. Photograph from the collection of Harold K. Vollrath.

You cannot do that with organization, you cannot do that with propaganda. Only an idea spreads so far …"

It is regrettable that Germany did not examine itself, and assess its strengths following World War I, before Hitler's take over. Germany was on the forefront of world design. Could Germany have won the world peacefully through design, industrialization and honest, aggressive marketing? If it could have, should it have tried?

## Trains

Interest in all kinds of transportation began to flourish in the early nineteenth century. England had the famous English engines designed by George and Robert Stephenson, the *Planet Class 2-2-0* (1830) and the *Northumbrian 0-2-2* (1830) (Figure 2.32). In the 1830s the United States became keenly interested in locomotive design. Among the objectives were great traction and pull, efficient power, and safe boiler construction. Both England and the United States seem to have been highly innovative and motivated, but it was the English who began to focus seriously on the machine's aesthetics. Their shapes, proportions, colors, and trims were outstanding.

One distinguished American design which most movie goers are acquainted with is the *American Type 4-4-0* (1855) (Figure 2.33). Authors Brian Hollingsworth and Arthur Cook make the following observations about what made the American a success (from *The Great Book of Trains,* page 46):

The General was built by Thomas Rogers of Paterson, New Jersey in 1855 and it is a wholly appropriate example of the most numerous and successful locomotive design ever to have been built. The reason is that Rogers was responsible for introducing most of the features which made the true American the success it was. The most significant development, so far as the U.S.A. was concerned was the general introduction of Stephenson's link motion, which permitted the expansive use of steam. This was in place of the "gab" or "hook" reversing gears used until then, which permitted only "full forward" and "full backward" positions.

In other aspects of design Rogers gained his success by good proportions and good detail rather than innovation.

One English locomotive, the *Stirling 8ft Single Class 4-2-2* (1870), was considered an exceptionally beautiful engine (8 ft. being the diameter of the drive wheels, Figure 2.34). In fact, Hollingsworth and Cook discuss the appearance of the Stirling in *The Great Book of Trains* (page 49):

> The Stirling 8-foot single is considered by many to be the epitome of the locomotive regarded as an art form. The graceful lines set off by lovely paint- and brass-work combine to produce a sight that has few rivals for beauty.
>
> Patrick Stirling, Locomotive Superintendent of the General Northern Railway had the first of them built in 1870 at the line's own Doncaster Locomotive Plant.
>
> … The domeless boiler was very apparent to the onlooker; it was both unusual for the time as well as being a Stirling trademark. Mechanically the engine was as simple as can be, with outside cylinders but inside valve chests, the slide valves being driven direct by sets of Stephenson's link motion.
>
> … Many authentic recordings were made showing speeds around 75 mph with surprisingly heavy loads being hauled by these locomotives, but the coming of such developments as eight- and twelve-wheeled bogie stock, corridor carriages and dining cars spelt their removal to lesser tasks. All had been withdrawn by 1916 except the legendary No. 1 which survives at what was the boundary of her home territory at the National Railway Museum at York.

In 1893, the New York Central Railroad, not wanting to be outdone by the British, developed a unique engine, the 999 4-4-0 (Figure 2.35). This train became known as *The Empire State Express.*

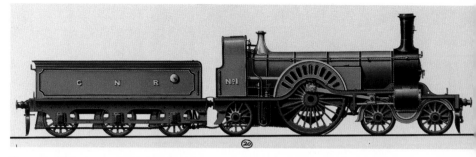

**FIGURE 2.34.** The *Stirling 8-ft. Single Class 4-2-2,* Great Northern Railway, Great Britain, 1870. Illustration courtesy of Salamander Picture Library, London.

**FIGURE 2.35.** The *Empire State Express, 999 4-4-0,* New York Central and Hudson River Railroad, 1893. Illustration courtesy of Salamander Picture Library, London.

**FIGURE 2.36.** New York Central's *J3a 4-6-4 Hudson,* 1926, designed by Paul W. Kiefer of American Locomotive Company (ALCO). Illustration courtesy of Salamander Picture Library, London.

**FIGURE 2.37.** *Six-car diesel-electric train, No. M-10001,* Union Pacific Railroad, 1934. Photograph from the collection of Harold K. Vollrath.

**FIGURE 2.38.** The Burlington *Pioneer Zephyr,* Chicago, Burlington & Quincy Railroad, 1934. Photograph from the collection of Harold K. Vollrath.

The engine had 86" diameter drive wheels, and at 112 miles per hour, it provided its passengers with both speed and comfort. Its simplistic aesthetics are its trademark.

Railroads are a conservative industry where products evolved slowly and aesthetics flowed more naturally from the product's form. This is similar to the evolution of ocean liners. In the late 1800s and early 1900s, American locomotive designs had engines of beautiful proportions. However, they had pipes wrapped over the form like the protruding veins of a weightlifter. It was not until the 1930s that aerodynamics, or streamlining, began to be appreciated and applied to ground vehicles. For instance, New York Central Railroad, with its *J3 Hudson* trains, designed by Paul Kiefer of ALCO, at 65 miles per hour enjoyed 20 percent more power than the previous model, the *J1,* with smooth sides (Figure 2.36). This knowledge ushered in the streamlined designs of the 1930s. Covers began to be integrated into the form of the train from the beginning of a design effort. Examples of careful integration of the cover system into the total design and engineering can be seen in the Burlington Railroad's *Pioneer Zephyr diesel-electric Three-car train* by Edward G. Budd (Chicago, Burlington & Quincy Railroad, 1934 ) and the *M-10001 Six-car trainset* (Union Pacific Railroad, 1934), also a diesel-electric train (Figure 2.37). The Burlington *Pioneer Zephyr* is described in *The Great Book of Trains* (page 258) (Figure 2.38):

> On May 26 a brand new stainless steel articulated streamlined self-propelled train (Zephyr) reeled off the miles between the two cities (Denver and Chicago) in just over 13 hours at an average speed of 78 mph. As the little train triumphantly ran into its display position at the Century of Progress Exhibition in Chicago, US railroading had changed forever.

Around 1937 Henry Dreyfuss designed a streamlined jacketing system for a New York Central *J3 Hudson* train. The new train was called the *Twentieth Century Limited* (Figure 2.39).

Raymond Loewy designed the *"T1" 4-4-4-4 duplex locomotive* for the Pennsylvania railroad in 1942 (Figure 2.40). This design had all kinds of problems and was later dropped. While most railroad's loved the image streamlined designs presented for its trains, the streamlined covers created a nightmarish maintenance problem. A New York Central engine that traveled from Harriman, New York to Chicago and back would spend a full day in maintenance before it went back on the road. This meant the removal and replacement of streamlined covers at least once a week. The added work was time consuming and expensive.

Another great American design was the *Niagara Class 4-8-4* (1945), manufactured by American Locomotive Company (ALCO) and designed by Paul W. Kiefer (Figure 2.41). It had a smooth and uncluttered appearance. In *The Great Book of Trains* (pages 172-3), the Niagara is described:

> … [E]xcellent organization allowed quick and thorough servicing. The power production part of the locomotives had to be just so to give such a remarkable performance on the road and to achieve this the fire [box] was first dropped with the engine in steam. [Then] a gang of "hot men" in asbestos suits entered the firebox—the size of a room—and cleared tubes and flues, did any repairs required to the brick arch, grate, etc. … On many railways steam locomotives were allocated one "shed day" each week for these things to be done, but running the 928 miles from Harriman to Chicago or vice versa each night, the Niagaras needed to do a week's work in one 24-hour period.

There is an interesting story about the chief engineer who helped develop this beautiful locomotive (From *The Railroad Encyclopedia*, page 74):

> One of the key secrets to the power of the Niagaras lay in their excellent steam flow circuit. This came about following

**FIGURE 2.39.** *Twentieth Century Limited* with a Hudson engine and tender, New York Central Railroad, 1938, designed by Henry Dreyfuss. Photograph (c) 1998 Kalmbach Publishing Co., reprinted with permission from the April 1988 issue of Model Railroader Magazine.

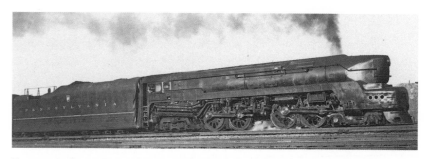

**FIGURE 2.40.** *"T-1" 4-4-4-4 Duplex Locomotive,* Pennsylvania Railroad, 1942, designed by Raymond Loewy. Photograph from the collection of Harold K. Vollrath.

**FIGURE 2.41.** The *Niagara Class 4-8-4,* New York Central Railroad, 1945. Illustration courtesy of Salamander Picture Library, London.

# History of Trains

Interesting design conclusions can be drawn by studying trains:

1. The aesthetics of railroad engines has evolved with time, and it seems that the best design has flowed from the engine form itself in small, incremental steps. With corporate management's desire to add cover systems to enhance the aerodynamics and corporate image in the 1930s, designers like Raymond Loewy and Henry Dreyfuss soon discovered that their clients' maintenance shops were facing difficult problems. The smooth streamlined shape of their designs, while appealing when compared with the complex, irregular form of the traditional steam train, proved difficult to service.

2. American industry and the public at large discovered that there were designers talented and capable of enhancing the design and marketability of products. Industrial design could not have had better public relations as these trains crossed the country heralding the arrival of a new profession.

3. Two kinds of products in need of design seem to emerge. Small, everyday, high-volume consumer products such as furniture, china, housewares, appliances, sporting goods, and automobiles need design. On the other hand, large, low-volume complicated products like railroad engines with their cars, stationary engines used in power houses, and engines and pumps used in industry by themselves, could and should be enhanced by careful industrial design. Most people find these large, complicated products mysterious and difficult to understand, but these products need design and intelligent design criticism. These products receive little public exposure and most design critics know little about how they work or their great challenge to the designers. Yet some dramatic designs are achieved when industrial design is used on such products. This can be attributed to the effort of designers in trying to understand mechanisms and with the close cooperation between the engineers and designers. Industrial design had arrived at last. It was the New York World's Fair that thrust these designs and their designers upon the world stage. The "big four" design consultants (Teague, Bel Geddes, Loewy, and Dreyfuss) knew the value of such exposure for their clients and themselves and went all out with industrial design. In the book *Streamlined, A Metaphor for Progress* (pages 72-3), author Barbara Hauss-Fitton describes the New York World's Fair:

> … As a result, the New York World's Fair became a "designer's fair" nonpareil: Teague, Norman Bel Geddes, Raymond Loewy, Henry Dreyfuss, Donald Deskey, Russell Wright, Gilbert Rohde, Egmont Arens, George Sakier—the list of men responsible for the Fair's main exhibits reads like a compilation of the most influential designers of the '30s and '40s. Both commercial and civic exhibitors had something to sell to the crowds, be it a new product or a social idea, and both employed the abilities of industrial designers for this purpose.
>
> … Nowhere was the expanded notion of streamlining more evident than in the work of Norman Bel Geddes. His "Futurama" exhibit (Figure 2.45) for General Motors is a quintessential example of the development that took place between 1933 and 1939. After pursuing radical designs for streamlined automobiles, train, ships, aircraft, and buildings during the early thirties, Bel Geddes increasingly recognized the pertinence and potential of a streamlined society. His attention shifted from teardrop-shaped automobiles and exotic airliners to efficient traffic systems and large-scale city planning. GM's "Futurama" gave him the opportunity to translate his vision of motorized America in 1960 into a vast working model that became the most popular attraction at the New York Fair.

4. It is interesting to note that these same industrial designers sensed a need and joined hands to form a professional organization which was later referred to as IDI (Industrial Design Institute) and ASID (American Society of Industrial Designers). Slowly, a movement toward professionalism in industrial design began to emerge. These designers demonstrated that they, their clients, and the products they manufactured, could benefit from industrial design through greater sales.

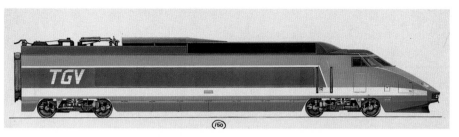

**FIGURE 2.42.** *TGV Ten-car Electric Trainset,* French National Railways, 1981. Illustration courtesy of Salamander Picture Library, London.

discussions between Paul Lipetz, the chief consulting engineer at Alco, and the outstanding French engineer Andre Chapelon.

Lipetz was a Pole who had been sent by Lenin to the US as Technical Representative of the USSR, to learn about American railroad technology. When Lenin died, he was asked by Stalin to return to Russia. Lipetz wisely refused and joined Alco instead.

The *Niagara* class engines were about the last of the great steam passenger engines. The engine had 30 percent more adhesive weight and traction than the *Hudson* class and could run at high speeds, hour after hour. Notice the smooth surface treatment along the sides of the engine and tender. At last, close to the ultimate in steam engine design was achieved without covers.

With the growing threat of coal strikes, diesel oil as a fuel became very appealing and diesel-electric engines are now preferred over steam powered engines. From approximately 1955 until today the French, German, Swedish, British, and Japanese all developed sophisticated electric motor coaches and passenger trains. Many different profiles and front ends were experimented with but the Burlington *Pioneer Zephyr's* frontal treatment prevailed. At last, the engineer and fireman had an unobstructed, panoramic view across the front of the engine's path. Speeds of 160 to 186 miles per hour were achieved on a regular basis. The French *TGV Ten-car trainset* (French National Railways), developed in 1981, is an excellent example of a

modern high speed train (Figure 2.42). This electric train has a maximum speed of 236 miles per hour. Its appearance is uncluttered and its engine is beautifully integrated into the carset.

## Modern American Design Consultants

Four of the many pioneer industrial design consultants were Walter Dorwin Teague, Norman Bel Geddes, Raymond Loewy, and Henry Dreyfuss. These men, referred to as the "big four," seem to have become the most successful American designers in the early- and middle-twentieth century. These men came not from the Ruskin-Morris background, but from a different media—advertising and stage design. Ruskin and Morris wrestled with the impact of the industrial revolution upon the worker and the consumer. The Bauhaus idea of industrial design coming from art rather than engineering was questioned. Some of the chairs designed by Marcel Breuer and Mies van der Rohe were enthusiastically accepted. Likewise, the disciplined features of the architectural designs of Hannes Meyer were accepted. Economics were considered as an important part of the design process. Quality materials and prefabricated components were accepted and practiced. The Bauhaus did not seem to have much influence on the "big four." However, the Bauhaus did impact our schools of architecture and industrial design, including graphic design, as the Bauhaus faculty emigrated to the United States, taking up key teaching positions at our universities. Their influence has been felt for generations.

American designers became consumer oriented, probably as a result of their clients' design requirements. Richard Weston describes the contributions of the "big four" to the design community in his book *Modernism* (page 193):

The profession of industrial designer appeared first in America, as a response to desperate sales figures during the Depression. Designers such as Raymond Loewy, Norman Bel

Geddes, W.D. Teague and Henry Dreyfuss worked closely with engineers, market analysts and sales managers to redesign—or more often simply restyle—products. Loewy made his mark by restyling the Gestetner duplicating machine and thus extending its life cheaply: "streamlines the sales curve." With economic growth depending on a rapid turnover of money, obsolescence became a valuable "design" feature, rendering products "out of style" long before they were technically obsolete—so much for the ... Bauhaus' commitment to form follows function.

The futuristic designs (for ships, cars, airplanes, etc.), featured in Norman Bel Geddes's book *Horizons* (1932), did much to popularize streamlining, and Loewy's Coldspot refrigerator of 1932 and Hoover Model 150 vacuum cleaner evoked a feeling of speed and efficiency in housework and were widely emulated.

... The "Building the World of Tomorrow" theme pavilions of the 1939 New York World's Fair, which was seen by forty-five million visitors, were designed by the "big four" American designers. They proved immensely popular, although an architectural critic berated them as "over-streamlined pseudo-modern" (see the soft corners and fungoid bulges on the buildings by some of our most celebrated industrial designers).

Perhaps these four designers became outstanding because they were all based in the same vicinity, New York City. Because of their geographic closeness, they could meet, communicate, and encourage each other. While they were competitors and had very different personalities and lifestyles, they bonded and helped establish industrial design as a profession. They each had a strong design philosophy and wrote books and articles about industrial design and their work. Maybe the most significant reason they were successful was that they served their clients and achieved results. They knew that for them to survive and flourish, their clients must be successful from the design service they provided. These men inspired young designers and their offices proved to be training grounds for many up and coming con-

sultant designers. I call attention to them because modern design service is patterned after their practice.

In my particular case, I did not know any of the "big four." I never met them or heard them speak. They all were practicing before I completed college. However, I had studied them in school and was very much aware of their design activities. The "big four" were anxious for others to become aware of their work. Designers who studied their work were influenced by their design research and philosophy. As a young practicing designer, I took these prominent designers as my role models. Below is some background information on each of the "big four" designers.

### Walter Dorwin Teague (1883-1960)

Walter Teague, the son of a Methodist minister, came from a small town (Figure 2.43). Trained in advertising, he became known as a seller of dignified products and services. He also studied French history and was enamored by European culture.

In 1926 Teague traveled to Europe and studied the work of Le Corbusier and Walter Gropius. Teague was the same age as Walter Gropius. He subsequently returned to the United States with new ideas for commercial high-class interiors. Next he worked on consumer goods and automobiles.

**FIGURE 2.43.** Walter Dorwin Teague (1883-1960), working at his drawing board. Photograph courtesy of Walter Dorwin Teague Associates, Inc., from "Industrial Design" magazine.

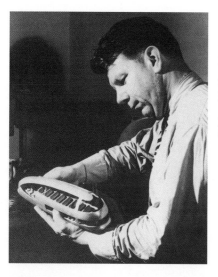

**FIGURE 2.44.** Norman Bel Geddes (1893-1958), holding aerodynamic bus, c. 1935. Photograph from The Norman Bel Geddes Collection, The Theatre Arts Collection, Harry Ransom Humanities Research Center, The University of Texas at Austin by permission of Edith Lutyens Bel Geddes, Executrix.

**FIGURE 2.45.** General Motors "Futurama" exhibit for the New York World's Fair of 1939, designed by Norman Bel Geddes. Photograph from The Norman Bel Geddes Collection, The Theatre Arts Collection, Harry Ransom Humanities Research Center, The University of Texas at Austin by permission of Edith Lutyens Bel Geddes, Executrix.

Teague believed that better design could be achieved through simplification. He wrote a sensitive book called *Design This Day* in 1940. Teague's book was one of the first written in detail about design and the experiences of a designer. As the eldest of the "big four" designers, he perhaps focused on building a healthy industrial design profession. Teague is often thought of as the "Dean of Design."

### Norman Bel Geddes (1893-1958)

Of the "big four," Norman Bel Geddes was the designer with vision (Figure 2.44). He was born 10 years later than Teague, but was the same age as Raymond Loewy. Bel Geddes, like Teague, came from a small town. His father died when he was only 13 but his mother instilled in him a strong sense of purpose, a desire to succeed, and a deep appreciation for the arts. He had a strong interest in the theater, set and stage design.

Bel Geddes left school after the ninth grade and entered industrial design through the theater. He became very much interested in streamlining in the 1930s and designed boats, trains, cars as well as a gigantic airplane. Bel Geddes wrote a book called *Horizons* in 1932 which was the most influential publication on industrial design at that time. He designed the "Futurama" Building of General Motors at the 1939 New York World's Fair (Figure 2.45).

### Raymond Loewy (1893-1986)

Raymond Loewy, was born in 1893, the same year as Norman Bel Geddes (Figure 2.46). He emigrated to the United States from Paris, France. Loewy exhibited an interest in transportation vehicles and at age 17 studied at a school devoted to helping students entering the engineering profession. During World War I he decorated his dugout with drapes, pillows, and recent periodicals, helping him to maintain his sanity.

**FIGURE 2.46.** Raymond Loewy (1893-1986), atop a Penn Railroad *S-1 Locomotive,* 1937. Photograph courtesy of Raymond Loewy Collection, Cooper-Hewitt, National Design Museum, Smithsonian Institution/Art Resource, New York.

Loewy was flamboyant and dramatic besides being extremely talented. Beginning his career in the United States as a fashion illustrator, he is most remembered for designing trains and automobiles. He, like Teague and Dreyfuss, grasped the importance of helping his clients experience success and profitability from their designs. Like Bel Geddes, Loewy was intrigued by streamlining and used it on many stationary products. Later in his career, in 1979, he wrote a comprehensive book called *Industrial Design.*

In 1927 Dreyfuss visited Europe to study. Returning to the United States, he joined Macy's and was able to suggest changes to products used in the store's window displays. Dreyfuss wanted to be independent and not an employee so he opened his own consulting office. He wrote a book in 1955 called *Designing For People.* While running his own office, Dreyfuss never forgot three important ideas necessary for success:

- He aimed for simplicity in his designs.
- He never forgot the user. Dreyfuss went on

**FIGURE 2.47.** Henry Dreyfuss (1904-1972). Photograph courtesy of Henry Dreyfuss Associates, New York.

to pioneer the use of anthropometric statistics and psychological nuances in human factors as they apply to products.
- He never forgot that his clients must make a profit from his designs.

By now the philosophies of Ruskin and Morris had been set aside. Industrial design revolved around what a corporation perceived the consumer as needing and wanting. Industrial design as it is practiced today has steadily evolved, not only with design consulting offices like the "big four" but also through corporate design departments and design entrepreneurs who design, manufacture, and sell their own products.

### Henry Dreyfuss (1904-1972)

Henry Dreyfuss, born in 1904, was the youngest of the "big four" designers (Figure 2.47). His family owned a theater supply company in New York City. After his father died when Henry was 11, he had to help support his mother and younger brother as a sign painter.

At age 16, Dreyfuss entered an arts high school on a scholarship. The school tried to develop people who would, through competence and a sense of responsibility, enhance their environment. He studied under Norman Bel Geddes in a stage design class in 1922 and was then subsequently hired to design sets for the Strand Theater.

## Where is the industrial design profession going?

In the late twentieth century we are beginning to see new challenges and opportunities for industrial design. Here are some facts:

1. There are more schools than ever before offering industrial design, thus more students graduating. Is this good? This may be good for the schools, but is it good for the students and the profession?

2. The profession of industrial design must find ways to think "one world" yet respect and honor all countries' and our country's politically democratic traditions.

3. We cannot think "one world" if we are consumed with race prejudice and intolerance. Studies indicate that there is not much that can be done about this in the college classroom. If not there, then where and how other than meeting and trying to get to know other students? Perhaps more collaborative design problems are needed with schools from other countries. If we come to our relationship with foreign clients with distrust and suspicion, then our clients will sense this and distrust us in return. Thus, we will lose work opportunities and will contribute to a negative image of our country and our way of life.

4. There needs to be continued sensitivity to our deteriorating environment. While design problems for students are always necessary in the area of transportation, domestic appliances, construction, etc., what is the long range impact from these products on our lives and the lives of our children? What good does it do to design new products that make jobs now if the products slowly pollute the world and harm our grandchildren?

5. There are problems and a need for design solutions to criminal incarceration. Can design help change the criminal behavior of a borderline felon or someone who commits repeated misdemeanors?

6. There is a growing need to protect and save our national shrines. What can designers do to help?

7. Designers need to have better working relationships with other professionals, especially engineers. While there are many more engineering students graduating each year than industrial designers, we owe it to ourselves and our future clients to try to build bridges to these people. How can the best designs emerge and be developed if each player in a product's development team is continually worried about his turf?

8. There needs to be better ways to find potentially responsible, creative industrial designers while they are in their teens and help guide them to and through the educational process.

An important event took place in New York City in 1944. The "big four" discovered that they had become the target of the New York State Department of Taxation. All businesses except professional services are expected to pay an unincorporated business tax. The "big four" designers claimed that they were like architects or lawyers who provided a service, not goods. Walter Darwin Teague stepped forward and was named in the suit. Teague won. The result of this action was that industrial design, like architecture, was classified as a profession, not a trade. The significance of this decision was that industrial design from thereafter was thought of as a profession. These four designers joined together for the common good of all industrial designers, displaying "professionalism" which all other industrial designers could pursue.

Industrial design is often looked upon as a form of fine arts. True, it is somewhat similar, but it is not the same. The next chapter explores art, graphics, and sculpture and their interrelationship with industrial design.

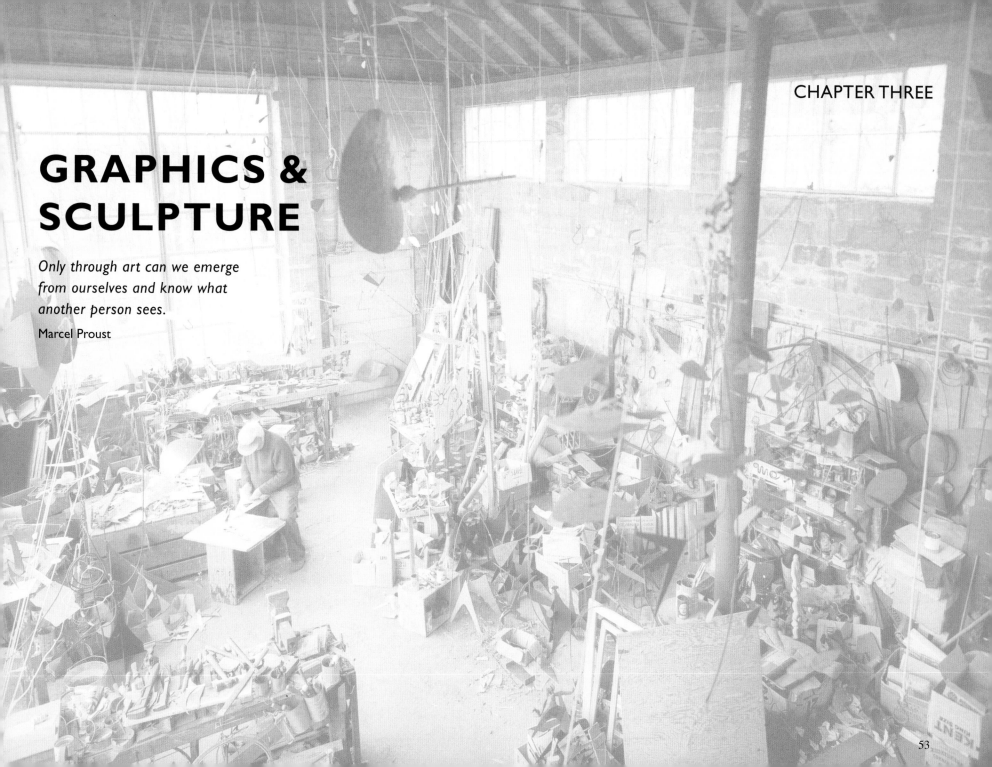

### CHAPTER THREE

# GRAPHICS & SCULPTURE

*Only through art can we emerge
from ourselves and know what
another person sees.*

Marcel Proust

Many early industrial designers were artists who became intrigued by the advancement of mechanization, efficiencies of production, and wonders of technology. Perhaps a more appealing factor to the artist was that sometimes beautiful shapes could be conceived and refined and be applied to products. This was something that had never been done before and was rewarding for the designer. Artists found it easy to move from painting and sculpture to creating and specifying graphics, laying out interiors, designing stage sets, developing packaging, designing furniture, and in some cases, designing products.

There are common characteristics between the artist and industrial designer. They both have an appreciation for aesthetics—how something appears and appeals visually. Painters trying to work in the three-dimensional world of product design today would find it more complex because of modern material selection and manufacturing techniques, which involves production efficiencies, providing adequate human factors, and appreciating modern marketing necessities. However, it would be much easier for a designer to move over and become an artist, sculptor, or painter, and some eventually do. Designers also appreciate graphics. In this chapter I will look at graphics and sculpture as they relate to each other and industrial design in the twentieth century.

## GRAPHICS

People with strong kinesthetic and visual talents are stimulated by two-dimensional and three-dimensional images. Photography and its advancements have helped bring images closer to us. Many are attracted to the images offered by magazines such as *Popular Mechanics* and *Fortune*. People interested in these publications find the images clinging to their mind. Not all industrial designers find themselves introduced to design in this way. It is worth noting, however, because some people who were attracted to these two- and three-dimensional forms later became industrial designers.

## Popular Mechanics

*Popular Mechanics* and its companion periodicals, *Popular Science* and *Scientific American*, have made a huge impact on design and engineering here in America. The use of graphics and photography along with good copy have made these magazines successful. These magazines:

1. dramatically illustrate technological developments through the use of colored illustrations which appeal to readers of all ages,
2. sense when exploded section views are needed and show in x-ray fashion the inner workings of a design,
3. are expert at explaining complex engineering so that the layperson can understand, and
4. will not hesitate to discuss and compare several different and competitive products in the same article and elaborate on their differences and features.

Effective industrial design requires that designers be able to express and show their designs in a similar fashion.

## Fortune Covers

For me, in trying to grasp modern graphics, I found that studying *Fortune* magazine covers was a good place to start. I had first done this in high school when a neighbor let me borrow her back issues of *Fortune*. These covers stuck in my mind for years and motivated me to return and look again at these beautiful images from the 1930s, 1940s, and 1950s. The following *Fortune* covers are impressive by their unrealistic beauty:

- **May 1939 by John O'Hara Cosgrove, II**
  This cover is a realistic presentation of a portion of a refrigerated railroad car. The graphics on the side of the car use a typestyle typical of the period. A desert scene can be seen

underneath the car in the distance. Colors used are authentic railroad colors.

- **November 1941 by George Giusti**

  This cover by Giusti suggests transportation with a perspective view of a tank tread and sprocket with an idler wheel. In the background is an automobile wheel, tire, and hubcab.

- **December 1941 by Fernand Leger**

  Leger presents an industrial scene showing smoke stacks, link chain, wheels, and rivets. The colors are primary but subdued. Plenty of black was used to enhance the industrial mood.

- **August 1942 by George Giusti**

  A military aircraft wing on top of a torpedo is depicted. Very careful air brush work is used. Colors are subdued.

- **October 1942**

  This cover, by an unknown artist, is probably the most beautiful cover of the lot. Its colors are subdued and form abstract, while suggesting modern production. A collection of wheels, perforated metal, and assorted hand tools are portrayed.

- **February 1943 by Herbert Bayer**

  This *Fortune* issue is entitled "Moving the Stuff of Production." The scene is probably a shipyard with an authentic presentation of a deck gun being lowered from a crane. Above it, a crane supports a bulkhead as it is slowly lowered into position.

- **April 1944 by Taro Yashima**

  One of the simplest covers that *Fortune* shows is a drab brown fabric background, perhaps silk. Two Japanese characters in black are in the center. A brilliant red JAPAN is underneath the characters.

Due to copyright restrictions, I am unable to show these covers here. However, readers can visit most public libraries and view these covers. It is interesting that the degree of abstraction does not detract from the visual objective of the illustration, in a collective way, the contents or theme of the magazine. Magazine issues at that time explored in depth, with many articles on such topics as energy, scrap materials, world transportation, communications, or our national defense. Such covers tied the magazine issue together. For some, modern art may be a complex mystery which needs to be ignored. However, the *Fortune* magazine covers were leaders in this century's modern graphics.

Reviewing each *Fortune* cover, I soon discovered that two graphic styles seemed to prevail. I was struck by the simplicity of Fernand Leger's paintings and in contrast, the artistic depth of the presentations by Herbert Bayer, formerly a professor at the Bauhaus. Both artists should be appreciated for their skill and sensitivity in presenting the mechanical and technological world of the time. In Bayer's work, we see complex and symbolic ideas superbly juxtaposed, thus communicating a simplified idea. Besides Bayer and Leger, there were other great *Fortune* cover artists, such as George Giusti, Peter Peining, Herbert Matter, and A. Petroccelli to mention a few.

## Fernand Leger, 1881-1955

Fernand Leger was a most unusual twentieth century artist because he had a good grasp of how to present industrialization in a way that was understandable to everyone (Figure 3.1). In her book *Leger,* Katharine Kuh describes Leger as follows (pages 6-7):

> No artist has ever grown out of his times more completely than Fernand Leger. He is unquestionably one of the great protagonists of twentieth century life, a man so steeped in the world around him that his art cannot be separated from contemporary vision. In a sense, he is a folk artist of our scientific and

**FIGURE 3.1.** Fernand Leger in New York City, 1941. Photograph ©Arnold Newman.

**FIGURE 3.2.** Fernand Leger's *Constructeurs au cordage (Builders with Rope),* 1950, oil on canvas. Photograph courtesy of Solomon R. Guggenheim Museum, New York, David Heald, photographer.

**FIGURE 3.3.** Herbert Bayer in 1926. Photograph courtesy of Bauhaus-Archiv Museum, Berlin.

**FIGURE 3.4.** *Great Ideas of Western Man… one of a series* by Herbert Bayer for Container Corporation of America. Photograph courtesy of The Herbert Bayer Archive, Denver Art Museum.

mechanistic age, but he does far more than report and reflect; he makes painting an integral part of the life it comes from. Though he is indebted, as are all artists, to the past, his true source material is drawn from his immediate surroundings.

… Throughout his life his main interest has been and still is centered on color (often flat, pure, and complementary) on the object (sometimes magnified, usually isolated and monumental) and on the most careful properties. His paintings are apt to be large, objective, and bold. …

Leger spoke widely on art in both Europe and the United States and even lectured at Mills College and Yale University. He was intrigued with the "architecture of the mechanical." This theme led to a series of paintings, which established him as an expert painter in this area (Figures 3.2).

## Herbert Bayer, 1900-1985

Herbert Bayer called himself an artist, yet he came to the Bauhaus school to study art, graphics, and architecture (Figure 3.3). Later, he taught graphics at the school, and in the 1930s emigrated to the United States, becoming quite renowned. He is best known in America for his graphic communication skills and his Aspen, Colorado architecture. One of his most distinguished clients for graphics was Container Corporation of America (CCA), especially the visual presentation of *Great Ideas of Western Man* (Figure 3.4). This work for CCA used a collage of photographic images to mix complex ideas to achieve certain feelings or statements.

## TYPOGRAPHY

Another necessary component to graphics is the development of typestyles. Advertising posters were popular in the late 1800s and early 1900s. Advertising is not a new phenomena. The objective of many manufacturers, Volkswagen for instance, was to engineer, manufacture, and sell products as quickly as possible. Communicating to its potential customers was important. The message in the illustration was brief and to the point—"Buy me; I am the best." First, the idea had to be clear and easily understood. The typestyle had to be straightforward and easily read. The illustrations had to be simple and free from distracting detail. What previously was thought of as a realistic graphic illustration needed to be "cleaned-up" to allow the emphasis to focus on what the manufacturer considered special and unique about his product or idea.

Today, it is easy to understand the emphasis that has been placed on high-speed communications. A variety of companies may all be competing for the eye and resources of the consumer. In their book, *The Language of Graphics,* Edward Booth-Clibborn and Daniele Baroni discuss the phenomena (pages 281-6) of advertising posters:

The most popular kind of graphic art comes not from books but from posters, which according to a middle-class conception are not only the source of a message but also an essential completion of an urban decor, one in which streets should be transformed into drawing rooms or art galleries.

It is not difficult to envision the German poster designer of the 1900s trying to design with the heavy Gothic type that was used at the time. This typestyle left little room for an artistic expression. It made the poster so complex that the idea was often missed or it took too much time to interpret and digest. Herbert Bayer recognized this problem and set about to design new, simplified typestyles. Each character was reduced to its simplest form (Figures 3.5 and 3.6). Bayer even devised his own technique of writing which eliminated capital letters. For example, here is what Bayer says about typography in the book *Herbert Bayer: painter, designer, architect* (page 75): "Typography

**FIGURE 3.5.** Adrianol Emulsion nose drops advertisement by Herbert Bayer, 1935. Photograph courtesy of The Herbert Bayer Archive, Denver Art Museum.

**FIGURE 3.6.** Catalog cover done for the first Bauhaus exhibition in 1923, by Herbert Bayer. Photograph courtesy of The Herbert Bayer Archive, Denver Art Museum.

**FIGURE 3.7.** Laszlo Moholy-Nagy in 1926. Photograph taken by Lucia Moholy, courtesy of Bauhaus-Archiv Museum, Berlin.

**FIGURE 3.8.** Leaflet publicizing a publication by the Weimar Bauhaus, layout by Moholy-Nagy, 1923. Photograph courtesy of Bauhaus-Archiv Museum, Berlin.

is a service art, not a fine art, however pure and elemental the discipline may be. The graphic designer today seems to feel that the typographic means at his disposal have been exhausted. Accelerated by the speed of time, a wish for new excitement is in the air." Everything was aimed at speeding up and simplifying the communication process. In the book, *The Language of Graphics,* the authors discuss the growing demands for efficient communication (page 281):

> With the growth and intensification of urban structures together with breathtaking industrial and commercial developments, and with the strengthening of a progressive bourgeoisie that did not exist in previous centuries, demands by communications circuits spring up that undoubtedly go beyond the internal ones of a group or tribe. Thanks also to a period during the last decade of the nineteenth century that was relatively free of belligerent activities and revolutionary tensions, even graphic art—as well as related activities, such as the development of the decorative arts—enjoyed a particularly fervid creativity and became charged with new stimuli and new meanings.

## Laszlo Moholy-Nagy, 1895-1946

In 1922, Walter Gropius of the Bauhaus met a Hungarian, Laszlo Moholy-Nagy, and was impressed with his art and reformative ideas (Figure 3.7). Gropius invited Moholy-Nagy to join the Bauhaus staff in 1923. Moholy-Nagy agreed with Gropius' plan for the Bauhaus. Gropius' vision is described in *The Patricia and Phillip Frost Collection, American Abstraction 1930-1945* as follows:

> In his plan, students would contribute to improving the modern world by designing beautiful, functional objects that could be easily and inexpensively produced. New materials, made possible by technological advances, would be used in architectural plans as well as in functional objects, and contribute to raising the standard of life for mankind.

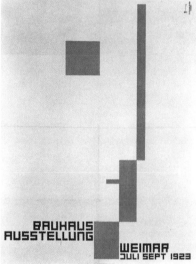

**FIGURE 3.9.** Poster for an exhibition held at Weimar in 1923 by Joost Schmidt. Photograph courtesy of Bauhaus-Archiv Museum, Berlin; Atelier Schneider, photographer.

**FIGURE 3.10.** A print done for the Weimar Bauhaus for the exhibition of the summer of 1923, to which both students and teachers contributed. The poster is composed with the symbol of the school, a head made up of strictly geometric elements, design by Oskar Schlemmer. Layout by Fritz Schleifer. Photograph courtesy of Bauhaus-Archiv Museum, Berlin.

**FIGURE 3.11.** One of the forerunners of modern graphics, Lucian Bernhard, created this ad for Adler. Bernhard created the so-called Sachplakat (poster about an object). Photograph courtesy of Kaiser Wilhelm Museum, Germany.

Moholy-Nagy was a painter, prolific writer, photographer, film maker, and builder of exotic light-space machines. He excelled as a teacher and began to promote new ideas and attitudes toward graphic design (Figure 3.8). His philosophy is described by author Joseph Harris Caton in the book *The Utopian Vision of Moholy-Nagy* (page xvii):

> Moholy-Nagy, like Gropius, saw the machine as potentially dehumanizing and argued that the artist was uniquely capable of ameliorating its harmful potential. Yet Moholy-Nagy took an essentially positive view of technology. He believed it offered opportunities for changing the world through mass production, distribution, and communication. He further believed that since art is rooted in society, the artist had a deep and abiding responsibility to address social issues. He saw the artist as a visionary—one who would provide the forms and ideas necessary for the understanding of future societies.

Moholy-Nagy survived the early Nazi repression, as did Bayer, Gropius, Breuer, and Van der Rohe. Like his fellow faculty members, he emigrated to America in 1937. When he tried to form a "new Bauhaus" in Chicago, it failed due to lack of financial support. However, early in 1939 he opened the School of Design. This school was later called the Institute of Design and affiliated itself with the Illinois Institute of Technology. Upon his death in 1946, Moholy-Nagy had left a strong impression on his students.

The Bauhaus's influence on graphics is undeniable (Figures 3.9, 3.10, 3.11, and 3.12). In *The Language of Graphics,* authors Booth-Clibborn and Baroni comment on this tradition (page 308): "The generation of German and Swiss graphic artists that received its training from the Dessau workshops, mainly during the years between 1926 and 1928, and whose masters were Herbert Bayer, Joost Schmidt, and Laszlo Moholy-Nagy, subsequently organized their knowledge and developed a tradition which is with us today."

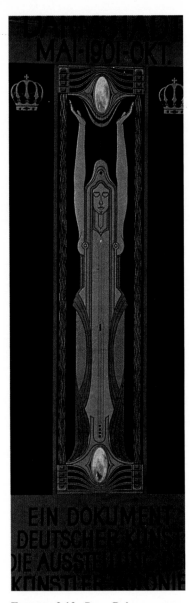

**FIGURE 3.12.** Peter Behrens poster for the Darmstadt Kunstler Kolonie, 1901.

## Corporate Identity

One outgrowth or extension of graphics is corporate identity. Companies want their names easily recognized and remembered. There may be a sense that a corporation is changing through product diversification, acquisitions, and mergers. Corporate identity is necessary to express this change. To achieve this, it often means the corporate name must be written more phonetically in a new fashion. Sometimes graphic symbols are used, in the form of a trademark (like Nike) and logotype, which represents this change. Other times the name is simplified or reduced in characters for better recognition (Esso to Exxon), sound, and especially possessing greater retention value. A company wants its name and product image retained and remembered from a television screen or magazine page to the store shelf. Attention to corporate identity extends from the product and its package as well as to the corporate name over an office or factory's front door, delivery trucks, calling cards, stationery, etc. Industrial designers skilled in graphics provide this service to their clients.

During my college years, I followed the graphic work of Saul Bass. Bass (1920-1996), educated in the United States, was renowned for his work in cinema graphics (film title design). For example, he did the film credits and movie posters for *The Man with the Golden Arm, Exodus, Storm Center, Vertigo,* and *Psycho.* These posters had visual impact resulting from the superior graphic design. The symbolic value of the graphics was its core strength. Bass was also active in corporate identity, working on programs for AT&T, United Airlines, and ABC.

The impact of graphics is becoming more significant. The images one sees on a daily basis must make an impact! Our world is changing faster than ever around us. We see more images today—largely due to the television and computer—than ever before. Industrial designers are aware of this fact because they have an appreciation for both three-dimensional (possessing depth) and two-dimensional forms. As more and more designers become proficient in the use and efficiencies of the computer; graphics can be easily developed to assist in more efficient communications.

Just as graphics have provided a tremendous impact upon us; the influence that television and film also has on modern man cannot be ignored. Many television viewers spend four hours or more a day watching news, sports, advertising, documentaries, and distractive entertainment, including science fiction. Much of what appears on television and in films is fantasy. This is the way many people like to let their mind relax after a hard day. All kinds of images are allowed to enter one's brain while watching television. It seems impossible to eliminate unwanted images. When it comes time for designers to design and they seek new forms for new environments, these images are part of their repertoire. Even radio imparts images. Somehow what we hear we arrange with other images to make the "theater of

**FIGURE 3.13.** Constantin Brancusi in his studio in 1955. Photograph courtesy of George Braziller, Inc.

**FIGURE 3.14.** Brancusi's *Sleeping Muse,* worked on from 1909 to 1926. Photograph courtesy of George Braziller, Inc

the mind" more realistic. Designers assume that users of products have similar images within their minds. By implementing these images into products, the designer establishes a link between the product and the user.

## SCULPTURE

Today sculpture means one of two things. First, it can be a realistic presentation in the form of a statue. The outgrowth of this endeavor

has led many artists to want to simplify their forms. The second presentation is abstract or a collection of nonobjective forms, often synthesized from realistic shapes. As this simplification and abstraction is refined, artists discover beauty in the emerging new forms, which has little to do with the traditional concept of sculpture.

Sculpture is probably more like industrial design than painting or graphic design. As I stated in Chapter 1, scientists (engineers) must take advantage of what visual artists have to offer. Separately, art and science are ineffective and abstract, but together they can deliver a powerful message. Both industrial design and sculpture have evolved into three-dimensional forms, rather than two-dimensional as in painting. The shapes of products need to be appealing in form. Sculpture made great strides in the early part of the twentieth century. Realistic shapes, which had been so readily accepted for centuries, slowly began to be broken down by their artists into manageable geometric forms which could be communicated quickly and efficiently. It was discovered that new sculptural forms could be displayed for their unique, artistic appeal.

## Constantin Brancusi, 1876-1957

Constantin Brancusi, the son of a peasant in Rumania, is one of the most important modern sculptors of the twentieth century (Figure 3.13). He is probably memorable to me because of his ability to synthesize his sculptured forms into basic simple shapes. His work symbolized simplicity, perfection, and the simplicity of form in motion (Figures 3.14, 3.15, 3.16, 3.17 and 3.18). He attended the Academy of Fine Arts in Bucharest and in 1904 moved to Paris, which became his home. He had many exhibitions starting in 1906. His sculpture was exhibited throughout the world and his final presentation was in 1955-56 at the Guggenheim Museum in New York City. Brancusi was profoundly gifted. Here are some of his favorite

**FIGURE 3.15.** *Mlle Pogany* (version I, 1913, after a marble of 1912) by Brancusi. Photograph courtesy of The Museum of Modern Art, New York.

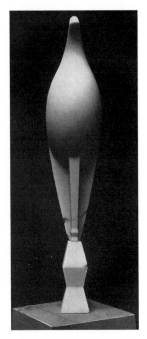

**FIGURE 3.16.** *Bird,* 1915, marble, by Brancusi. Photograph courtesy of George Braziller, Inc.

**FIGURE 3.17.** *Bird in Space, 1926,* polished bronze, by Brancusi. Photograph courtesy of George Braziller, Inc.

**FIGURE 3.18.** *Bird,* 1933-37, black marble, by Brancusi. Photograph courtesy of George Braziller, Inc.

expressions (from the book *Constantin Brancusi* by Carola Giedion-Weicker, pages 219- 20):

- It is not making things that is difficult, but putting ourselves in condition to make them.
- When we are no longer children, we are already dead.
- Create like a God. Command like a King. Work like a slave.
- All my life I have only sought the essence of flight. Flight! What bliss!
- I am no longer in this world, no longer attached to my person, I am far removed from myself, among essential things.

### Alexander Calder, 1898-1976

Alexander Calder, with his mechanical mobiles and stabiles, is probably the most recognized and innovative twentieth century sculptor. He is one artist that common adults and most children can recognize, understand, and enjoy. Calder came from a family that was heavily influenced by the arts. His great grandfather and father were sculptors, and his mother was a painter. Calder, called "Sandy" by family and friends, had his first studio by the age of 10. He appreciated engineering and earned a degree in Mechanical Engineering from Stevens Institute of Technology. From there, he studied at the Arts Student League in New York. To illustrate Calder's appreciation of engineering, he could not help but apply his engineering knowledge to the characters he devised for his famous miniature circus figures, his mobiles and stabiles (Figures 3.19, 3.20, 3.21, 3.22, 3.23, 3.24 and 3.25).

### Isamu Noguchi, 1904-1988

Another great American sculptor was Isamu Noguchi (Figure 3.26). Noguchi was a Japanese American who apprenticed in Paris under Constantin Brancusi. Later, he had studios in New York and Japan, his father's homeland. Noguchi and Alexander Calder were close

## Calder's Success

The following is a list of what I believe to be the key aspects to Alexander Calder's success:

1. He was not intimidated by the size requirements he established for his designs—minute or gigantic. His circus performers were miniature figures, while his gigantic urban sculptures provide a pleasant contrast to a background of minimal architecture.

2. Calder possessed a sense of humor that appealed to people of all ages.

3. He did not shy away from using new materials.

4. Calder, as a generalist, also became an outstanding graphic designer and draftsman.

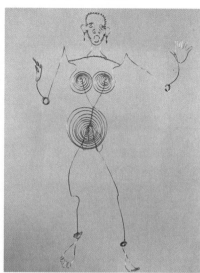

**FIGURE 3.20.** Alexander Calder standing outside of his studio with one of his mobiles, 1966. Photograph © 1999, Pedro E. Guerrero.

**FIGURE 3.21.** *Josephine Baker* by Alexander Calder. Iron-wire construction, made 1927-29. Photograph courtesy of the Museum of Modern Art, New York.

**FIGURE 3.19.** Alexander Calder in his Roxbury studio, c. 1960. He had his first workshop before he was ten years old. Photograph © 1999, Pedro E. Guerrero.

**FIGURE 3.22.** Calder's BMW 3.0 CSL, one of BMWs Art Car series. Produced in 1975, this creation was one of Calder's last works before his death. Photograph courtesy of BMW, Munich.

**FIGURE 3.23.** Alexander Calder's stabile, *La Grande Vitesse* (1969, painted steel plate), located at Vandenberg Center, Grand Rapids, Michigan. Photograph courtesy of City of Grand Rapids, William Cunningham, photographer.

**FIGURE 3.24.** A stabile outside of Calder's hilltop studio in Sache, early 1960s. Photograph © 1999, Pedro E. Guerrero.

**FIGURE 3.25.** Calder's *Red Lily Pads* on display at the Guggenheim Museum in New York in 1964. Photograph © 1999, Pedro E. Guerrero.

**FIGURE 3.26.** Isamu Noguchi (r) with Buckminster Fuller, c. 1970s. Photograph courtesy of the Isamu Noguchi Foundation, Inc., New York.

**FIGURE 3.27.** George Gershwin, 1929, bronze, by Isamu Noguchi. Photograph courtesy of the Isamu Noguchi Foundation, Inc., New York.

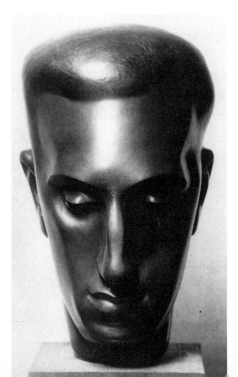

**FIGURE 3.28.** Isamu Noguchi's *Sunken Garden* for Chase Manhattan Bank Plaza, 1961. Photograph courtesy of the Isamu Noguchi Foundation, Inc., New York.

friends in the early days. In fact, Noguchi ran the Victrola for Calder's circus performances. Noguchi and Buckminster Fuller also became close friends in the late 1920s, sharing an apartment for quite some time. In the book *Isamu Noguchi: Essays and Conversations* (page 119), Noguchi describes his admiration of Buckminster Fuller:

> His [Fuller's] thinking which started out with much the American dream of material progress would seem inevitably to come to question the means by which this has come about. Bucky himself is without acquisitiveness excepting possibly with boats. Believing in man's essential rationality, Bucky remains the supreme optimist—there is a way out. This must be his great appeal to the young. He is a true believer, a prophet for our times. The ultimate machine is no machine—a little black box he calls it—no machine but the knowledge and control of the forces of nature that binds us all in mutual dependence.

Noguchi specialized in sculpture gardens and environments, designing over 20 gardens and plazas. He also did portrait sculpture,

particularly of his friends, such as Irving Berlin, Buckminster Fuller, Martha Graham, and George Gershwin (Figure 3.27). Also, he created abstract stone pieces, ballet sets for Martha Graham, and some furniture for Herman Miller and Knoll Furniture. In New York City, one can see may examples of Noguchi's work. His public sculptures include:

1. *News*
   Associated Press Building, Rockefeller Center
2. *Lobby Ceiling and Waterfall Wall*
   666 Fifth Avenue at 53rd Street
3. *Red Cube*
   Liberty Street between Broadway and Broad Street
4. *Sunken Garden* (Figure 3.28)
   Chase Manhattan Bank Plaza, William Street between Pine and Liberty Streets.

Perhaps Noguchi's greatest contribution was his ability to study a space and envision a series of shapes and forms which would be beautiful in their juxtaposed arrangement (Figures 3.29 and 3.30). The results established a feeling of contentment for the viewer, a needed contrast to today's high-speed living. Noguchi's work is also displayed at The Isamu Noguchi Garden Museum, located at 2-37 Vernon Boulevard, Long Island City, New York. Regarding his work on gardens, Noguchi says (from *Isamu Noguchi: Essays and Conversations,* page 64):

> I am not concerned here with monument or embellishment but with gardens, by which I mean that self-contained sculpturing of space with whatever medium, be it trees, water, rocks, wire, or broken-down automobiles. The totality of the experience so controlled adds up to more than the sum of its parts. It is this larger entity that I prefer to call a garden rather than "sculpture court," which would imply sculpture in a space, rather than the space which has itself become a sculpture.

**FIGURE 3.29.** Noguchi's *Black Sun,* 1969, located at Volunteer Park, Seattle, Washington. Made of black Brazilian granite nine feet in diameter. Photograph courtesy of Seattle Art Museum.

**FIGURE 3.30.** This is a plaster model of Noguchi's unrealized proposal for the *Tomb of John F. Kennedy,* 1964. Photograph courtesy of the Isamu Noguchi Foundation, Inc., New York.

It is quite interesting that four of the outstanding artists/designers/sculptors of the time, Leger, Calder, Noguchi, and Buckminster Fuller, while working in a different medium, were well acquainted with each other's philosophy and work. They all were sensitive to the fact that environments could be enhanced and the world improved by their designs. It almost seems as though they were responding to man's yearning for a safe, quiet place in which to retreat from the stresses of modern life and new forms to express modern living.

## Sculpture in the Late Twentieth Century

Sculpture in the latter part of the twentieth century has not been dramatic or particularly influential to industrial design, like the sculptors discussed above. There has been a growth in what is called environmental landscape design. Artists like Andy Goldsworthy of Great Britain and his subtle environmental adjustments have been visually and tactilely surprising and appealing. The work of others, such as the American landscape designer Nancy Holt and British designers Charles Jencks and his late wife, Maggie Keswick, are outstanding and their work is truly visually delightful.

A modern landscape sculpture design that most people are now familiar with is the Vietnam War Memorial (Figures 3.31 and 3.32) in Washington, D.C., which was designed by a talented Yale architectural student, Maya Ying Lin. This memorial has generated a great deal of praise and controversy. The row upon row of names carved in black granite captures the years of agony, paralysis, and indecision our government displayed trying to win an unwinable war. The seemingly endless names on the wall signify the hopelessness and sadness of this period. This memorial definitely expresses the futility of war.

Now that I have discussed sculpture and graphic design, what impact have these artists had on industrial design? There is much to be explored in seeking new forms which have evolved from more traditional expressions of art. Some of the art forms are pleasing and

**FIGURE 3.31** Looking toward the Lincoln Memorial.

**FIGURE 3.31 & 3.32.** Two views of the Vietnam War Memorial designed by then 20-year-old Yale architectural student Maya Ying Lin in 1982.

readily accepted into our lives. The shapes that Ray and Charles Eames and George Nelson used for their chairs are examples that comes to mind.

Efficient communication is paramount. Many viewers of an artist's exhibit do not wish to take the time to study an exhibition program for an explanation of what an artist had in mind when he or she constructed some piece of art. The viewer should be satisfied using his or her own imaginative powers and storehouse of experiences. Artists and sculptors try to dig deeper into information about their subjects to express their feelings. Clearly, in art, an idea can sometimes be best expressed in abstract ways rather than acting like a camera.

**FIGURE 3.32.** Looking toward the Washington Monument.

What visually excites designers and "would-be" designers in art and sculpture has now been discussed. The question is why? After seeing the work of others, what stimulates a person to want to create art, whether it be painting, sculpture, graphics, or industrial design? What happens in young people's lives to influence their creativity? How do we find and recognize such creative students and help them into the system? The next chapter looks at the different ways in which people learn and are stimulated to become creative individuals. It asks the questions, "Who are designers and why are they what they are?"

### CHAPTER FOUR

# CREATIVITY, INTELLIGENCES, AND "CRYSTALLIZING EXPERIENCES"

*One is never tired of painting,
because you have to set down,
not what you already knew,
but what you have just discovered.
There is a continual creation
out of nothing going on.*

William Hazlitt

# CREATIVITY (INVENTIVENESS)

There are assorted qualities which a person should possess to become a successful designer. One must be able to recognize design problems. Some designers can spend a lifetime on a problem and do nothing about it. Urban blight, crime, poor education, pollution, and unethical behavior are a few examples of problems which come to mind. As a designer goes through life, opportunities to develop better designs present themselves. A designer may say to himself, I can do better. Once a problem is recognized, the designer should explore the problem's cause. A successful designer must also possess the ability to listen to those most impacted by the problem, and those closely associated with the designer who has ideas and suggestions for the problem's solution. Once the problem has been defined, the creation of a solution begins.

Designers must possess five important qualities:
1. Designers must have a will to see the project through.
2. Designers need to appreciate the value of aesthetics. Why try to correct a problem if the solution is not beautiful? The solution must look better than what already exists.
3. Designers must have interpersonal talents which make them and their ideas attractive to the opposition as well as teammates.
4. Designers must have the courage and self-confidence to respond to the challenge and be daring in their solutions.
5. Lastly, designers must possess creativity. This one quality is probably the most important. It helps the designer envision a potential solution to the problem, and then assists at each step through the design process.

Creativity is the core of industrial design. What is creativity? Since everyone has been a child once, it is perhaps easiest to relate to the observations of childhood experiences in discussing creativity. Paul Torrance studied more than 15,000 children and concluded that creativity reaches its peak in a child's development at about age four and one-half. When a child enters kindergarten, creativity takes a dip and slowly declines until the age of eight. At nine years of age, children see their creativity drop sharply. Most experts agree that children are continually forced into a mold at this age to do what they are told.

## Stifling Creativity

Dr. Fredelle Maynard, in her book, *Guiding Your Child to a More Creative Life* (pages 7-8), observes:

An educator, prominent in creativity research, describes a visit to a kindergarten group making May baskets. All materials had been "prepared" in advance: pieces of paper just the right shape with dotted lines showing where to fold, strips for the handle and diamond-shaped pieces of contrasting color to decorate the finished product. Having explained exactly how the baskets were to be constructed, the teacher moved up and down the aisles, checking. Most children diligently followed instructions. One little sinner, however, had pasted his diamond decorations vertically, not horizontally as directed. Teacher pointed out the error. When the child insisted, "I want to do mine this way," she briskly peeled off his "mistake" and pasted on a horizontal diamond. He wasn't even allowed to leave a fourth side plain. Further checking revealed a still bolder heretic—a girl who, observing that other children's paper handles didn't stick properly, had chopped hers up and used the bits for ornamental touches. "Oh you've spoiled your basket!" the teacher moaned. "It's all messy and it doesn't have a handle."

… I remember a sixth-grader who came home in tears with her composition paper. The trouble? For the assignment, "Give three reasons why spring is your favorite season," she'd written a poem telling why she loved summer best of all. F—the teacher had printed. "Not what I asked for."

## Stimulating Creativity

Harvard Professor Howard Gardner wrote many books on the topic of intelligence, psychology, education, and the mind. What follows is a summary of Gardner's steps for the encouragement of creativity:

1. Young children learn best when they are given the freedom to create on their own without adult interference. They need to experience it by building or creating something with their own hands. One cannot simply tell a young child how to build a tower out of blocks. Children should be allowed the opportunity to assemble the tower as they see fit. This slowly turns into a learning experience.

2. If a child is presented with changes or new ideas, he is most readily able to accept them if they can be applied to his own artwork. In other words, do not ask a child to apply color to someone else's drawing. It will be more meaningful to the child if he or she is asked to apply color to his or her own artwork.

3. Teachers of art curricula, whether it be music, visual arts or fine arts, must know their subject matter and be able to "think" and "feel" in that particular artistic media. Teachers of design curricula must be able to "think" and "feel" design.

4. Artistic learning, or any learning for that matter, is best arranged around long-range projects which totally involve the children. This atmosphere allows for the interchange of ideas through discussion. For instance, if children are studying birds, it is most meaningful to them to construct a birdhouse in shop class, draw or paint pictures of birds in art class and explore the migration of birds in science class.

5. Artistry involves continuing exposure to various developmental levels, but not in the sense that there exists one set of problems at grade two, another at grade three, and another at grade four, etc. Any curriculum should build on previously learned concepts, but in an increasingly complicated and challenging way.

6. Evaluation of one's progress is essential to the arts. (Industrial design mock-ups and models must be made and tested for the validity of a concept.)

7. Art evaluation and criticism involves interpersonal sensitivity and respect for fellow human beings, particularly toward others on the "team" who are creative. (In industrial design, the designer must be tactful and sensitive in dealing with the work of engineers, and vice versa.)

8. Artistic taste is acquired, not taught. We all have a certain amount of artistic appreciation, but true artistic taste evolves over a considerable period of time. Appreciation for the arts is best acquired through contact with other individuals who value art. When faced with a design problem, it is surprising that unanimity can be achieved among fellow designers who respect one another. It is usually achieved following an intense debate regarding the pros and the cons and the summation of all the judgments made, leading up to acceptance of the final design.

9. Art (and design) education should be a cooperative effort, involving many people and their philosophies. During design evaluations the opinions offered by nondesigners are important. Their opinions, thoughts, and prejudices should be respected.

10. There is too much in art and design to master everything. Knowing a lot about a specific area such as human factors or materials and processes is more valuable than knowing a little about a lot.

Society is hard on creative thinking, particularly in children. Many researchers believe that schools are the problem.

Children soon learn in school to do what they are told and not "make trouble." So, if creativity is stifled, then what is it that is stifled? Creativity is the opposite of copying. It is something new and transformative. Dr. Maynard presents an interesting observation about children (page 10):

> Along with a special kind of perceiving goes a special capacity for absorption. If you've watched a three-year-old building a teetery block tower or trying to sink a cork, you know exactly what I mean. It's as if all the rest of the world had fallen away, so that there's no mother, no dinnertime, nothing left except the utterly fascinating NOW. Discovering a problem, immersing oneself in it, trying out possibilities, rejecting false starts, battering away until a solution emerges—all this is a fundamentally creative process that carries with it its own reward, a satisfaction variously described as "the Eureka feeling" or simply "Aha!"

To be creative, a person must possess the following characteristics:

1. Fluency (lots of ideas)
2. Flexibility (different kinds of ideas)
3. Redefinition (turning an idea upside down and sideways)
4. Elaboration (carrying the idea to extremes)

Indispensable to creativity is a willingness to take risks. Some children accept both risk and instructive failure. This is likewise true of industrial designers.

Is there a relationship between creativity and intelligence? A University of Minnesota study tried to answer this question (From *Guiding Your Child to a More Creative Life,* page 13):

> When the University of Minnesota tested elementary school children for both intelligence and originality, 70 percent

of the most creative children failed to distinguish themselves on standard intelligence tests. In other words, if you relied on intelligence tests alone, seven out of ten highly creative individuals would be missed.

This is very important information when thinking about solutions to the problems our world faces today. What about tomorrow? Psychologist Donald F. MacKinnon tested a group of highly creative architects and found their IQ scores ranging from very low to very high. The significance of MacKinnon's research is that a child with a mid-range IQ may be exceedingly creative. A stimulating and accepting environment can enhance creativity. On the other hand, a repressive one can destroy it.

---

### Phases in a Creative Person's Life

In *Multiple Intelligences,* Howard Gardner discusses the different phases in a creative person's life. Here is a summary of his findings:

1. **The Preschooler**
   During the first few years of life children develop theories and concepts of how the world works. They develop symbolic skills to reconcile what they do not understand. They experience interaction with the world in which they live. Children have "crystallizing" experiences that are path forming as well as benchmarks for the future. When crystallizing experiences happen, the individual undergoes a positive, memorable reaction toward the subject or the event.

2. **The School Age Child**
   Youngsters, on the whole, want to know the rules of operation and want to comply with the expectations of society. If there is a certain area that interests them (a domain), they seek to master the necessary skills to become experts in the field as rapidly as possible. This period in time is thought of as

*Phases in a Creative Person's Life (continued)*

the "apprentice period." Youngsters who seem willful, ambitious, and who have the ability to persevere while being criticized for their endeavors stand a strong chance of becoming creative adults.

3. **The Adolescent**

Between the ages of 15 and 25 the moment of truth arrives for individuals. Some adolescents discontinue their creativity altogether while others continue development of their talents. Obviously, not everyone will become successful. Individuals in this age group who apply themselves for at least a decade and experience some success in a field or domain have a strong chance of becoming an expert. More than likely, they can continue in this field into the foreseeable future.

4. **The Mature Practitioner**

By the age of 35, individuals usually have achieved their place as a satisfied master of their field, a dissatisfied master of their field, or have tried and failed. Characteristics that identify such people are ambition, self-confidence, and risk-taking and are often considered irrational but definitely different. On page 59 of his book *Multiple Intelligences,* Howard Gardner describes the personality of a creative individual:

> My own studies confirm that creative individuals, whatever their domain differences, have quite consistent personalities, and that they are typically demanding, self-centered individuals, with whom it is difficult to remain on good terms.
>
> ... Understanding creativity is difficult enough; to shed light on genius borders on the impossible. Let me simply propose that the genius is a creative individual who is able to arrive at insights that are novel, and yet strike a deeply responsive chord across the world's diverse cultures.

So how does a designer, like myself, use creativity to help solve design problems? First, the designer must understand the design problem and may possess a preconceived idea of how the problem might be solved. As the designer begins to assemble the design requirements and restrictions, the objective remains vivid in the mind. Self-confidence is usually high. Design restrictions, however, prevent the immediate completion of the design process.

By the time work begins, the design objective is so imbedded in the designer's mind that the designer can go almost anyplace, anytime, and still recall the design problem with all its detail. While I am sure that other designers solve problems differently, I have rested on a daybed trying to solve a problem and worked so hard at it that I have ultimately insisted upon billing the client for this time. Then, when I turned away from the problem and went for a walk or a swim, possible solutions came to mind with startling clarity and with little or no effort on my part. Psychologists have written extensively on the power and use of the subconscious mind to solve creative problems. Naturally, not all design problems are solved exactly like this, but some very complicated solutions have been conceived in this manner.

Other designers may solve design problems differently. What follows is the technique I use. At times, I have concentrated so intently on the problem that I have been able to turn away and later, a possible solution or solutions present themselves as images in my mind. This is how the subconscious mind works! I am then able to sketch a picture of the image in either perspective or orthographic projection. The problem is not yet completely solved! The design solution now takes on the characteristics of an unbaked cake or bread. The solution needs reshaping to properly adapt to the design. Tracing paper is now placed over the image just drawn and the reshaping process begins. Some designers, particularly new graduates, pride themselves on the potential designs as expressed in large quantities of conceptual sketches.

Two important points should be considered. First, the concept needs to be evaluated. While I may like and consider what I have done an ideal solution, others may seriously question the design's practicality. Over the years I have discovered that friendly, constructive criticism of the design by others is critical. Close friends and family members, while my strongest supporters, have become my best critics. Design does not evolve in a vacuum. Second, how does one create a suitable or memorable shape for the product? I have always believed that the brain is the recipient and warehouse of an unbelievable number of shapes and forms, both man-made and from nature. As one designs, his mind reviews familiar shapes until a suitable, unique, aesthetically pleasing shape is selected.

Two other aspects of the design process must be reviewed. The first is what we call "intuition." The dictionary suggests intuition is the ability to stop, study a design, and then pass judgment on the appropriateness of the materials and their structure for the design. For small products it is not necessary for one to analyze, through stress formulas, the size and type of material to be selected with the aid of an engineer or materials specialist. Yet again, when public safety is critical, experts thoroughly familiar with the stress, strain, and fatigue limits of materials need to be consulted. It is imperative that all correspondence and reports from such experts be preserved.

Here's the last part of the design process that must be discussed: "Is all of this really worth it?" The work can be a hassle on the body if the mind is disturbed, troubled or stressed. I have seen designer friends suffer heart attacks when wrestling with serious problems. Others have cultivated nervous disorders, such as shingles. I agonized with a duodenal ulcer which forced me to stop smoking and limit my intake of alcohol.

The flip side to this can be a great design that is useful and worthwhile, which makes everybody happy. Designing such products can be a joy and somehow very satisfying. Do other professionals such as architects or engineers talk about their work being fun? Designing can be fun! Why go through life doing something which you do not enjoy? One can drive a taxi or build a house and experience similar feelings. Usually people know when they have hit on a satisfying and fulfilling vocation.

This chapter shows that designers may be intelligent in their profession, but are inadequate when measured by the standard SAT tests and thus might be tagged as failures in other professions. To illustrate, if my class that enrolled in a college physics course is any indication, we would have failed out of college. We had to pass physics to earn our industrial design degrees. There were about 15 to 20 industrial design students, including me, tucked in with a large group of forestry students. Believe me when I say we were different. We looked different because of our clothes. We shaved and the foresters did not. They wore checked lumber shirts while we wore our tired World War II uniforms. They wore heavy ankle-high lumbermen's boots. We wore our combat boots, saddle shoes or gray bucks. They passed physics exams; we did not.

We could grasp the theory of physics, but the calculations used in solving problems were beyond us. Our professor tried his best to help, but with little luck. When it came time for final exams, the professor ushered the group of industrial design students into another exam room and told us to write an essay on how we believed physics could help in the field of industrial design. Needless to say, we sighed a collective air of relief. Our professor never received such wonderful essays as he did that late May examination day. We all got "Bs" and passed physics.

For many years I have thought about this experience. Why did we as a group find this one course so difficult when the forestry students seemed to have no trouble at all? I felt that we were as intelligent as the foresters but were missing something unique and important. After reading *The Unschooled Mind, How Children Think & How*

*Schools Should Teach* by Howard Gardner, I finally understood why physics was so hard for us. Our strength was in our other intelligences. We did not possess great skill in the logical-mathematical intelligence. I was surprised to find the author's daughter had suffered as well at the hand of physics and called her father for help and understanding. She told him that she never really understood physics. Gardner explains the difference between getting the correct answer on a test and really understanding the concept (*The Unschooled Mind,* page 6):

> ... In schools—including "good" schools—all over the world, we have come to accept certain performances as signals of knowledge or understanding. If you answer questions on a multiple-choice test in a certain way, or carry out a problem set in a specified manner, you will be credited with understanding. No one ever asks the further question "But do you really understand?" because that would violate an unwritten agreement: A certain kind of performance shall be accepted as adequate for this particular instructional context. The gap between what passes for understanding and genuine understanding seems great; it is noticed only sometimes, and even then, what to do about it remains far from clear.

## LEARNING STYLES

According to Gardner, there are three kinds of learners: intuitive learners, scholastic learners, and disciplinary experts:

**Intuitive learner**     A young child is an example of an intuitive learner. They are natural learners, i.e., all children learn to understand and use their language and/or symbolic gestures.

**Scholastic learner**     This is the traditional student. One who understands and responds in the way that is expected of him in school.

**Disciplinary expert**     Gardner describes the disciplinary expert in *The Unschooled Mind* (page 7) as, "an individual of any age who has mastered the concepts and skills of a discipline or domain and can apply such knowledge appropriately in new situations." These are the students who really understand physics or history and can apply it correctly.

In *The Unschooled Mind,* Gardner further discusses the three types of learners (page 10-1):

> It is my claim, however, that these three characters do not mesh smoothly with one another and that the resultant gaps among them pose tremendous educational problems, particularly because those gaps have not until now been widely appreciated.

> ... Why, one may ask should we care about erasing these gaps? And, in particular, why is it important that natural or scholastic understandings give way to disciplinary understandings? To my mind, the answer is simple: The understandings of the disciplines represent the most important cognitive achievements of human beings. It is necessary to come to know these understandings if we are to be fully human, to live in our time, to be able to understand it to the best of our abilities, and to build upon it.

The disciplinary expert can take a wide variety of information and rearrange and apply it to the problem at hand. Students who learn by "rote" may possess facts but have trouble applying the information to any useful purpose. Successful industrial designers are disciplinary experts and possess these qualities.

## MULTIPLE INTELLIGENCES

Everyone possesses a wide variety of intelligences. As a matter of fact, Professor Gardner, in his book *Multiple Intelligences,* has recognized seven different types of intelligences which people possess. Even disciplinary experts possess varying degrees of different intelligences. As readers study this list, they can see the optimum traits for a successful industrial designer. Gardner stresses that, except for abnormal individuals, the intelligences always work in concert. In other words, while one type of intelligence may be dominant, an individual usually possesses several types of intelligence. *It is interesting that most students must be assisted in their choice of careers.* Gardner warns, "An exclusive force on linguistic and logical skills in formal schooling can short-change individuals with skills in other intelligences." Here I have summarized the seven intelligences defined by Gardner:

1. **Musical Intelligence**

   People with a strong musical intelligence, like Bach and Mozart, find themselves biologically prepared to express music, whatever the media.

2. **Bodily-Kinesthetic Intelligence**

   This type of intelligence is best described by one who experiences fulfillment and learns best by working with one's body (hands). For example, designers may develop concepts with their brains, but they need to make a model with their hands to finish the design process. Other examples of kinesthetic intelligence would be athletes and dancers or mimes, who use their bodies to express an emotion. In *Multiple Intelligences,* Howard Gardner uses the following illustration about Babe Ruth as an example of bodily-kinesthetic intelligence (page 18):

   > Fifteen-year-old Babe Ruth played third base. During one game his team's pitcher was doing very poorly and Babe loudly criticized him from third base. Brother Mathias, the coach, called out, "Ruth, if you know so much about it, YOU pitch!" Babe was surprised and embarrassed because he had never pitched before, but Brother Mathias insisted. Ruth said

   later that at the very moment he took the pitcher's mound, he KNEW he was supposed to be a pitcher and that it was "natural" for him to strike people out. Indeed, he went on to become a great major league pitcher (and, of course, attained legendary status as a hitter)—Connor, 1982.

3. **Logical-Mathematical Intelligence**

   People who possess this type of intelligence as dominant are the same who perform well on SAT and IQ tests. These are the people who do well in traditional classrooms.

4. **Linguistic Intelligence**

   Linguistic intelligence is the ability to comprehend other people and to communicate effectively with them. All people possess this intelligence to some degree. Even when people are incapable of using the traditional method of communicating—through the spoken word—human beings are quite good at "inventing" their own means of communication, such as the way sign language is used in the hearing-impaired population.

5. **Spatial Intelligence**

   Spatial problem-solving is required for navigation and the use of maps. Chess players look for problem solutions from different angles. The artist, graphic or industrial designer, must possess this intelligence to envision a solution to a design problem. Before designers commit themselves to a concept on paper they must envision potential solutions in their own minds.

6. **Interpersonal Intelligence**

   Interpersonal intelligence allows one to understand and to work with others. Industrial designers must possess interpersonal intelligence. They must listen carefully as their clients or employers describe the design problem. Industrial designers must also be friendly and attentive to their clients if they want to keep them. (I would speculate that Pablo Picasso would have failed at industrial design because of his lack of this type of intelligence alone.) A high degree of interpersonal intelligence is essential for industrial designers to achieve success. They need to be salespeople. They need to sell their designs to their employers or clients.

## 7. **Intrapersonal Intelligence**

Intrapersonal intelligence is the ability for one to understand and work with oneself. An industrial designer must possess self-confidence, thus intrapersonal intelligence. Personal instability often negatively impacts the success and consistency of one's design work.

It should be remembered that all humans possess certain core abilities in each of these intelligences. Linguistic and logical skills form the core of most intelligence evaluations as we know them. The high school valedictorian is placed on a pedestal. Graduation exercises epitomize this fact.

What the profession, as well as modern industrial design schools need is a process for better and more comprehensive assessment of a potential designer's intelligences. People being tested must demonstrate their will and ability to solve problems. The testee should be able to recognize the use of different intelligences to solve problems. The test should rely on interviews and other types of problems rather than "paper and pencil" tests. Results would be reported as a profile rather than a traditional test score being the entire basis for one's academic standing. This approach was used by the Army Air Corps during World War II, when they supplemented the results of the Binet IQ test with a battery of psychological and physical tests. Psychomotor tests for kinesthetic ability were used to determine the flying potential of cadets. The results of such alternative tests should suggest options for the future. The Binet IQ test, which most of us have taken at one time or another, is only part of the total human intelligence quotient. There is much, much more to be considered. If design educators can accept Gardner's thinking, then additional material besides the SAT tests (linguistic and logical) is needed to evaluate a design school candidate. Successful designers demonstrate excellence in all of the intelligences but especially spatial intelligence, body-kinesthetic intelligence, interpersonal intelligence, and intrapersonal intelligence.

From reading Dr. Gardner and Dr. Maynard, I see that the message is clear. We somehow must find youngsters who possess strong creative tendencies, the will to produce, and the necessary intelligences, and guide them toward the design profession. Somehow these candidates need to become aware of their potential abilities and the field of industrial design. Most good design and art schools today use a personal interview and portfolio along with SAT scores to analyze a student's potential.

Here are some questions to ponder. Does America lead the world in design? Are we recognizing and attracting the brightest and best industrial design candidates? Are we doing it early enough? Are we redirecting those who might wish to be an industrial designer, but who may not have the right kind of intelligence? What do we have to do to acquire a position as a world leader in design?

With the arrival of China on the world industrial stage, does this mean we should consider looking for those candidates with high linguistic intelligence to master the Chinese language? Perhaps. Can Americans continue to get away with learning one language, English, as we move more and more into one global economy?

## CRYSTALLIZING EXPERIENCES

Somehow I made the decision to become an industrial designer in my middle teens. Are there other people who possess creative talent and

**FIGURE 4.1.** Dr. Guy G. Stevens, my father, carrying me from the barn to the house following one of his calls. I was about four years old at the time in 1928.

**FIGURE 4.2.** A steam traction machine. The action could command my attention for a considerable period of time. Seeing such machines left a lasting impression on me.

the desire to succeed as a creative designer but need guidance to convince themselves and their families that this is the appropriate profession for them to enter? Perhaps this discussion on crystallizing experiences will be helpful. Crystallizing experiences are described by Howard Gardner as critical moments when events, environments, people, and/or stimulus come together to help a person truly believe this is the field (domain) or profession that he is destined to serve. In *Multiple Intelligences,* Gardner describes these moments (page 29):

> In the case of very talented children, such discoveries often happen by themselves through spontaneous "crystallizing experiences." When such experiences occur, often in early childhood, an individual reacts overtly to some attractive quality or feature of a domain.

Since I have described what Gardner defines as "crystallizing experiences," I thought that it might be interesting to discuss some experiences I had as a child. Perhaps students and others interested in industrial design will see a parallel to some of their own experiences.

I, of course, am an industrial designer and have wanted to be one since my early high school years. Like many other designers, I came from small-town U.S.A. There was little or no knowledge about industrial design available to my high school guidance counselors, so I counseled myself. The only information I had on industrial design was from such books as Norman Bel Geddes' *Horizons,* and Walter Dorwin Teague's *Design This Day.* Occasionally, articles on design appeared in leading magazines such as *Fortune, Time,* and *Popular Mechanics.* I did not consciously go out and collect these books and magazines, but years later, when thinking back, these experiences come to mind as important and influential.

When I was a young child, my veterinarian father took me with him on his calls to local farms (Figure 4.1). He would tend to the sick animals and leave me in the car to watch the action in the barnyard. A visit during the harvesting season was better than watching a circus.

**FIGURE 4.3.** This is our first design. We got the idea to build a train from a book borrowed from the library. It generated great interest on the street. I am in the center, 1937.

Occasionally, a farmer would use a giant steam traction machine with its noise, fire, smoke, steam, and plenty of shiny moving parts (Figure 4.2). The action would keep me enthralled for hours. The excitement and mystery of mechanization was now a part of me. I wondered, "How were these mysterious machines made to work?" It was what I heard, saw and smelled. Steam traction engines, earth moving machines and railroad engines all captivated me. This was the age when our country moved its concentration from the battlefields of World War I to great architecture, civil engineering, and the surge of industry. Construction of the Empire State Building was started in 1929 and the Golden Gate bridge began in 1932.

As a preschooler, I vividly recall some of the mysteries that took place in my mother's sewing room. My grandmother, who studied as an artist, was an accomplished seamstress and she helped my mother make her dresses. I can still see the women huddled together over my mother's sewing table with Vogue patterns pinned out on chosen fabric being readied for cutting. The ladies debated and worked for hours scheming about the best placement of folds, fastenings and flairs. This was deadly serious to them, and I was captivated by their intense concentration. I wanted to know more about what occupied these women with such intensity.

My hometown, Groton, New York, was dominated by the Corona Division of the Smith-Corona Typewriter Company. My neighbors who worked in the engineering department at Corona seemed odd, at least in my eyes as a boy of six or seven years old. However, I was aware that they carried themselves with a deep commitment and concentration that separated them from other workers. This observation took place during the lunch hour or after work while the men's subconscious was still focused on work. They had self-confidence. Several walked by my house on their way from work and I was fascinated watching them. They were absolutely absorbed in deep thought and seemed to shut out the rest of the world. Other employees avoided them but deeply respected them.

When I was eight or nine my mother began taking me to the library on a regular basis. I explored all kinds of interesting books and magazines. One book I borrowed was about some children my age who took a wooden crate, barrel, and funnel and built a simulated train (Figure 4.3). I showed the book with its illustrations to my friends and before long we made our own train. We found a barrel for a boiler, funnel for a smoke stack, a real bell, a crate for a cab and covered the sides with burlap bags. It became a big hit on the street and our parents and even the mailman complimented us on our creativity. This was the beginning of the construction of all sorts of vehicles in our barn.

Later, I discovered *Fortune Magazine*. I recall one beautiful modern cover designed by Herbert Bayer, a former Bauhaus graphic design instructor. *House Beautiful* and *Popular Mechanics* became my favorites. *House Beautiful,* every so often, had an article on a new house designed by Frank Lloyd Wright which enthralled me because this was the wave of the future.

Recalling my elementary school days, I found that my third grade was pivotal. I hated school and was not particularly good at it. At the age of eight I could see little value in reading, writing, arithmetic, and especially spelling. When I should have been paying attention in class, I gazed at the pressed metal patterned ceilings in all the classrooms and was mesmerized by the design and assorted visual arrangements my imagination could make. I discovered I could visualize beautiful patterns, such as squares and groups of rectangles. It was easy to envision rows of them extending forever and eventually joining. I tried to interest others in my observation, but no one else shared my enthusiasm. This fascination particularly distressed my mother. She truly believed I was on my way to becoming a daydreamer and an academic failure. My grades and teacher's comments led me to believe I was different. I simply did not respond to the educational system which was a "one system fits all" approach. Fortunately, most of my teachers were patient with me.

I do not know how I got through fourth, fifth and sixth grades. Probably sheer fear of the teachers' wrath or a strong desire on my part to please. School was still difficult but I found joy and self-confidence in my art work. I got along well with my art teacher, but she was not particularly encouraging to me because I did not fit the mold of a good art student. Later, in high school, I explored the idea of becoming an artist, illustrator or cartoonist. This same art teacher went out of her way to impress upon me the hardships she had endured in art school. As I was considering architecture as a career option, she made certain that I understood I could never master it. It would be too hard for me, she said. Curiously, I was later accepted at The Harvard Graduate School of Design, Department of Architecture to study under the great Walter Gropius.

In 1936, when I was 12, my hometown began having "old home days." This became an annual event to help the community literally get out of the Great Depression doldrums. We had ball games, band concerts, flower shows, plays, dances, and even a soapbox derby. A great idea! The village officials asked my friends and me to enter the derby. Our garage developed a reputation. There were no rules regarding size or weight except we could not have an engine and we were expected to ride down Cortland Street hill, the tallest hill in town. The street was constructed of brick pavers. Every vehicle that drove on the street, whether it was a wagon, a car, or a truck, found itself almost rattling or vibrating to pieces as it bounced over these bricks. The idea of building a racer was great and four of us from our neighborhood formed a consortium. We were going to build two racers, but would split any prizes we won four ways. We scurried about the neighborhood looking for wheels, finding tricycle wheels, baby carriage wheels, scooter wheels, and cart wheels.

My friend Tucky Higgins and I built our racer from the wheels off his old cart. We used a loud speaker grill from an old Atwater-Kent radio to cover our racer's front end, simulating a radiator. Two other friends, Hugh Brooks and Malcolm Bethel, built the Bs Bullet which had ball bearings (Figure 4.4). The wheels came from a Flexible Flyer sled-like cart which Hugh's father had bought for his kids. The axle was narrow, but the racer could move and we sensed we had a winner! On the day of the race, people lined both sides of the street (Figure 4.5). When the race started, racers came screaming down the hill. Because of the roughness of the road, it seemed like racers spent more time in the air than on the pavement. Some carts seemed to simply disintegrate with wheels and axles going in one direction and drivers and their chassis in another. Thank goodness no one was hurt. True to form, the Bs Bullet streaked across the finish line, winning not only its heat, but eventually the entire race. The total prize was $5.00.

**FIGURE 4.4.** Our soapbox derby racer in action. Tucky Higgins is driving while I am pushing. In the background is Bs Bullet, with Malcolm Bethel driving and Hugh Brooks pushing, 1937. Bs Bullet won the race for a couple of years in a row. Later, Hugh, following a year or so at Yale, joined the Army and was killed in the Battle of the Bulge.

**FIGURE 4.5.** The day of the race with a motley collection of racers from all parts of the town. Bs Bullet is in the center background, waiting to race in the next heat, 1937. Photograph courtesy of the DeWitt Historical Society of Tompkins County, Ithaca, New York.

We were terribly proud and kept up our entries for years, improving wheels, brakes, seats, steering mechanisms, and yes, driver comfort. Parents watched the races but wisely stayed out of the barn. In 1937 I recall we were in the process of designing a seat for me since it was my turn to drive during the race. The design process was to use anything we could get our hands on that worked and that our folks did not want. We found an old orange crate with solid wooden ends and discovered one end was warped and curved in shape and formed an ideal seat back. This was great! The other end of the crate was a warped short "S" shape, which lent itself to a seat. This was the beginning of my introduction and application of "human factors." We put the chassis on saw horses, carefully balancing it so the weight was equal on all wheels and attached the seat at a comfortable angle. Placement of the steering wheel and brakes was easy from there. Little did I realize that 20 years later I would be specifying operator control placement and comfort in mining and construction machinery, and proving the design in our design laboratory with carefully constructed mock-ups of wood and steel.

My parents sent me to a YMCA camp during the summer months of my youth and I enjoyed being around the counselors. One time a counselor built a model airplane from balsa wood, demonstrating extreme patience and showing me how the model had very accurate section drawings in its plan which must be followed. He spent hours sanding the model to conform to the assorted sections. By the end of the summer, he had a beautiful model airplane. I learned the value of patience and discipline from watching this model evolve.

Does everyone in the creative arts experience "crystallizing" experiences and memorable events like these? Should students be tested, interviewed or queried, perhaps in early high school to explore their "crystallizing" experiences? Concurrently, should interviews and tests assist in determining one's standing in critical intelligences? Does a movement or an event or a collection of events really help us determine our occupational tendencies? If families and institutions could help students early enough, possibly careers, time, and resources could be better arranged to provide occupational satisfaction. Howard Gardner believes that each school system needs a counselor he calls an "assessment specialist." He describes the role of an assessment specialist in his book *Multiple Intelligences* (pages 72-4):

> The assessment specialist shares findings and recommendations with students, parents, teachers, and the occupant of a second role called the student-curriculum broker. Based on a current view of the student's intellectual profile, this broker recommends which courses the student should elect; and, in the event of a uniform curriculum, recommends how these materials are most likely to be mastered by the student.
>
> To the extent that there are electives, it is pertinent for students to know their own proclivities. This knowledge should not be used to dictate electives (in itself a contradiction in terms!). Rather, knowledge of one's own strengths can help one to choose courses that might be particularly congenial to one's learning style. In the case of a uniform or required curriculum, such information is equally important. For even if the courses themselves are mandated, there is no reason why they need to be taught in the same way at all.
>
> ... In my own view, nothing is more important in a student's educational career than the encountering of a discipline or craft that fits a particular blend of intelligences—a pursuit worthy of a student's effort for years or even a lifetime. Individuals of accomplishment often attribute enormous importance to "crystallizing experiences" where they first confronted a pursuit that fit their learning strengths and styles. All too often, these matches occurred completely by chance.
>
> The goal of the school-community broker is to increase the likelihood that students will discover a vocational or avocational role that matches their own profile of intelligences. To accomplish this goal, the broker assembles information about apprenticeships, mentorships, community organizations, and the like; each of these learning opportunities should exemplify a particular blend of intelligences ...
>
> ... [F]or those students with unusual intellectual configurations, the school-community broker can provide the, perhaps, life-changing opportunity to engage in an activity that matches a specific configuration of talents.

If the profession of industrial design truly seeks better practitioners, then it must use the best tools available to find them. Once students are ready for college, they need the best education possible. The next chapter looks at the industrial design college curriculum and career opportunities.

### CHAPTER FIVE

# INDUSTRIAL DESIGN CURRICULUM
## and
# CAREERS

*Perhaps the most valuable result of all education is the ability to make yourself do the thing you have to do, when it ought to be done, whether you like it or not.*

Thomas Henry Huxley

A young person considering industrial design as a career should at some point ask these questions: "Who is an industrial designer?"; "Could I become one?"; and "Do I have the necessary qualifications?" Anyone who possesses the following qualifications, regardless of gender, can possibly become a successful industrial designer:

- creativity—invention, taste (an interest in things which are beautiful), and talent (ability to make a picture and a model of a project),
- strong spatial, kinesthetic, and logical (ability to handle basic math and physics) intelligences,
- gifted in interpersonal and intrapersonal intelligences,
- strong linguistic intelligence (This will become more and more important as a student passes through college and into the world of design. One must be able to compose a simple, readable report in English. The grammar, punctuation, and spelling must be correct. Mastering a foreign language should be a must and will give a student a distinct advantage.),
- an understanding of basic ethical and civic responsibilities.

Each industrial designer, when given a design problem, goes about solving it with different, but acceptable techniques. First, designers must recognize the design problem and plan an approach to solve it. Second, adequate time must be allocated to visualize a potential solution. These processes use creativity. This chapter explores in detail the application of talent, creativity, and industrial design as illustrated in the education process. Designers must possess a degree of talent. Those sensitive to problem-solving are keenly aware of the thought and emotional process called talent. Designers must actively pursue exercising taste. Taste is essential if the designer is to develop an acceptable design solution.

Designers must also possess strong interpersonal skills, as the ability to work well with others is important when communicating designs. Designers must be reasonably contented with their solutions to design problems. How can they create enthusiasm in others unless they possess self-confidence? Designers must skillfully manage their time and possess the technical skills necessary to accomplish their designs, and then communicate them to others. Finally, they must possess a will to succeed and the personal drive to see the project through to completion.

If one is convinced that he or she possesses all of these qualities and has the desire and means to achieve an education and become an industrial designer, then perhaps industrial design is the correct profession for this person. Once the decision to become an industrial designer has been made, then the best place to acquire the necessary education needs to be determined. There are currently fifty-four colleges and universities throughout America offering an industrial design curriculum. Most modern industrial countries have design schools. In the United States, there are at least three different industrial-design degrees offered.

Some schools prepare designers for a specific industry that the school is closely affiliated with, for example, the motion picture or auto industry. The primary thrust of a school may be two-dimensional (graphic design) with little emphasis on human factors or model development. This is important for students to know. If they want to become proficient in the design of complex, man-machine type products, then a model lab is absolutely essential. Most schools offer generalist exposure to a variety of two-dimensional and three-dimensional problems. This approach is desirable. Schools recognize that some students have a specific talent or area in which they wish to specialize, such as exhibit, toy, consumer electronics, or automobile design. These students should be given their basic design disciplines and then given some freedom and encouragement to gravitate toward their desired field, and not be forced into a predetermined school mold where all students must always do the same projects. This is the

**FIGURE 5.1.** Professor Antonin Heythum, 1902-1954, had a strong theory of design. He believed that good design came from the appreciation of human factors. He was loved by his students, and like Gropius, believed that each student should aspire to his or her maximum ability. He felt teachers existed to help students achieve success. Photograph from late 1940s.

philosophy that Walter Gropius encouraged at the Bauhaus, and Antonin Heythum[1] employed when he was head of the Department of Industrial Design at Syracuse University (Figure 5.1). Both teachers wanted students to evolve into the best designers that they could become using their own unique abilities. Professor Richard Koontz, who worked in Raymond Loewy's office and served as a professor at Syracuse University alongside Professor Heythum while I was a student there, also shared this philosophy.

One of the major problems in design education is, how does one teach ethics? Unfortunately ethics are extremely difficult or impossible to teach as a classroom subject. It is learned by listening to discussions and observing the actions of others and watching how well they adhere to and carry out their responsibilities and objectives. A school should establish a code of ethics, similar to or the same as adapted by IDSA and insist that both the faculty and students adhere

to it (Appendix A). Would not observing this day-to-day behavior be the best teaching technique? Professionals in the field must follow an ethical code if they want to be accepted as fair and equitable by fellow professionals, clients, and employees. What better place to learn such behavior patterns than in school itself? This would mean that every faculty member and student should become a member of IDSA. Naturally, a school has its own rules for behavior and expected scholastic achievements, but a professional code of conduct should also be included.

Most industrial design programs teach ethics as part of their Professional Practice class, but I believe they should do more. Ethics must be the very first subject students are exposed to when they enter the industrial design program. Ethics must extend beyond IDSA's guidelines to include social and environmental responsibilities and public ethics. I believe that universities have the responsibility to instill a social consciousness in students at every level of their education.

## PROFESSIONAL AFFILIATION

Is there a student chapter of IDSA? How active is the group? How about HFES (Human Factors and Ergonomics Society) and other organizations? What responsibilities do they have on campus?

Becoming acquainted with practitioners can be invaluable. Helping to build a student chapter of a professional society brings one in contact with professionals and helps a student become aware of major design problems.

## CURRICULUM

On page 87 is a sample current curriculum for a Bachelor Degree in Industrial Design (B.I.D.).[2] This example is for a five-year program on

---

[1] Antonin Heythum, noted Czechoslovakian designer, architect, and educator, chaired the Industrial Design Department of Syracuse University from 1947 until 1953.

[2] This curriculum was provided by Associate Professor Ronald Beckman, Coordinator of the Industrial Design Department at Syracuse University.

**FIGURE 5.3.** Electric iron project, model, created while I was a senior at Syracuse University, 1948.

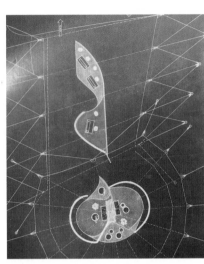

**FIGURE 5.2.** Electric light socket project, model, designed while I was a sophomore at Syracuse University, 1947.

**FIGURE 5.6.** Rendering of how design might look in production.

**FIGURE 5.7.** Outdoor exhibit project, plan view, 1950.

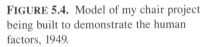

**FIGURE 5.4.** Model of my chair project being built to demonstrate the human factors, 1949.

**FIGURE 5.5.** Here I am sitting down on the job testing out the design.

**FIGURE 5.8.** Outdoor exhibit project, perspective drawing.

**FIGURE 5.9.** Outdoor exhibit project, side view.

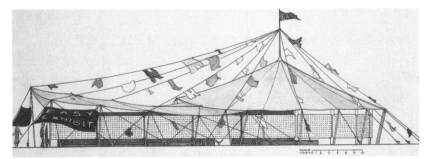

## Sample B.I.D. Curriculum

| FALL | SPRING |
|------|--------|
| **Freshman** | |
| History of Art I | History of Art II |
| Philosophy and Issues in Art I | Philosophy and Issues in Art II |
| Drawing I | Drawing II |
| 2-D Problem Solving | 2-D Problem Solving |
| 3-D Problem Solving | 3-D Problem Solving |
| English or Writing I | English or Writing II |
| **Sophomore** | |
| Principles of Industrial Design I | Principles of Industrial Design II |
| Principles of Industrial Form I | Principles of Industrial Form II |
| History of Modern Design | Academic Elective |
| Academic Elective | Academic Elective |
| Studio Elective | Studio Elective |
| **Junior** | |
| Industrial Design: Product Technics | Industrial Design: Product Technics |
| Production Processes: Metals | Production Processes: Plastics |
| Human Factors | Design Graphics: Principles |
| Academic Elective | Academic Elective |
| Studio Elective | Studio Elective |
| **Senior** | |
| Industrial Design: Product Development | Industrial Design: Product Systems |
| Design Graphics: Practicum | Industrial Design: Environmental Practicum |
| Computer Aided Design | Art History |
| Academic Elective | Academic Elective |
| Studio Elective | Studio Elective |
| **Fifth Year** | |
| Industrial Design: Product Practicum | Industrial Design: Advanced Problems |
| Industrial Design: Research | Industrial Design: Thesis |
| Industrial Design: Professional Practice | Industrial Design: Philosophy & Ethics |
| Academic Elective | Academic Elective |
| Studio Elective | Studio Elective |

the basis of a fall and spring semester. Naturally, this curriculum does not represent all industrial design programs, but this should give a general idea of what to expect.

Each of the courses earn three credit hours toward a Bachelor of Industrial Design, with a total of 156 credit hours required. The student must select academic electives (Humanities, Behavioral Sciences, Natural Sciences, and Management) totaling 24 credit hours, 9 credit hours of Art History electives—which includes engineering and architecture—and 24 credit hours of Studio electives. Attending a university as opposed to a design school has the advantage of offering students a good cross section of elective courses. For example, studio electives can be selected in visual and performing arts, fine arts, sculpture, photography, computer courses, etc. A wide variety of courses can expose a student to more opportunities within the design profession.

The industrial design curriculum has not changed very much since the late 1940s, except for adding obvious technological (computer-aided design) advances and the elimination of a couple of courses that did not relate directly to industrial design, such as a sociology and an advanced, impractical math course.

What types of industrial design problems are assigned in design school? Following a general introduction to design, a student can expect reasonably simple design problems at first. For example, I once was given the assignment of an electric light socket (Figure 5.2). The problem was to design a plastic light socket. I learned the problems of injection molding, product assembly, human factors, and safety, as well as aesthetics.

During my third year in college I was assigned an appliance, a chair, and an interior design (Figures 5.3, 5.4, 5.5 and 5.6). The fourth year's problems were even more complex. I recall working on an outdoor exhibit for a washing machine manufacturer (Figures 5.7, 5.8, and 5.9). I had to be concerned with the movement of people and

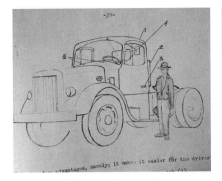

**FIGURE 5.10.** My college thesis project was a truck cab. This is a three-quarter side view of the truck-cab design with the operator standing beside the cab to suggest scale, 1950.

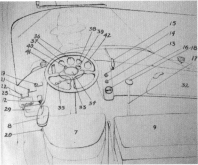

**FIGURE 5.11.** Operator's view of the control panel indicating placement of controls and dials for efficient operation.

making a visually enticing exhibit, structurally sound and easily executable. My final college project was a thesis on a truck cab interior design (Figures 5.10 and 5.11).

These above examples are typical student-design assignments. Would a graduate today have accomplished this same curriculum and become a better designer? It is doubtful, but he would be more efficient. What needs to change in the teaching process to make a better designer? As discussed in Chapter 2, there is a need for the modern student to become more sensitive to environmental problems, cultural values, civic and ethical challenges as well as placing more emphasis on linguistic and interpersonal skills plus adding exposure to team problem-solving and related disciplines. These added professional responsibilities demand more time. A four-year curriculum becomes inadequate. Industrial design is sometimes taught as a five-year program. In my opinion, if we are to maintain our leadership in world design, industrial design college programs must now be expanded into five years!

Once designers receive their education, how do they fit into our society and the workplace?

Getting the first job takes planning, patience, and motivation. Long before graduation, most students begin to think of where and/or for what industry they would like to work. Usually students' college work reflects their area of strongest interest. A good school allows this to show in the student's portfolio. For example, if a student feels destined to become a toy designer, that student's college projects should show talent in that area. Before students leave college they should be particularly knowledgeable in their area of interest. They should take advantage of cooperative or internship programs between industries of their choice and the school. Summer employment in the student's chosen field throughout college will also be helpful. Designers of the future may have to look outside their native country to find employment, or at least get started. This, of course, may necessitate learning another language and adjusting to a new culture.

Designers, like most of us, procrastinate and put off thinking about what they really want to do. Many feel that there is time in the future, so why think about career objectives at this time? However, before graduation is the critical time to consider one's professional objectives. Besides the specific field of interest, the different types of work institutions should be considered:

1. work in industry,
2. work for a consulting office,
3. become an entrepreneur,
4. do freelance work,
5. become an educator.

## INDUSTRY

Usually, the atmosphere in industry is more conservative than that of a consulting office. New ideas a staff designer wishes to promote are going to be slow to be adapted. However, the corporate world often provides more shelter for a new employee through its sheer size. The chance of a layoff is diminished as compared to a design consulting office, but with the downsizing trends of industry today, employees can still lose their job for no special reason.

The pros and cons of working in industry versus a consulting office should be considered by the student. The experience and exposure of working in industry are invaluable! Experts in manufacturing processes and materials are more readily available to a designer in industry. Thus, it is easier to get help when needed. It is much easier to see and learn how products are conceived, modeled, engineered, marketed, advertised, and finally fabricated in industry.

We live in a political world, and the political atmosphere seems to be much more intense in industry than in a consulting office. There is usually more time to play politics in industry. Political behavior fosters bad judgment and stifles creativity. Consulting offices have these problems, but to a lesser degree because they are smaller in size and the work is more frantic, leaving less time for politics.

## THE CONSULTING OFFICE

Many graduating designers seek employment at a consulting office. They often enter such employment at a disadvantage because they are expected to help industry, yet have never worked in industry. They believe that this is where the action in design is taking place and want to be associated with that action. Sometimes beginning designers want to learn how to manage a design office so they can eventually open their own office. There is nothing wrong with this approach as long as the new designer conducts himself or herself in an ethical fashion.

Working at a consulting office offers one the opportunity to work on varied projects. If designers work in industry, they may spend their entire career working on just one type of product. A consulting office usually works on different products for different clients. Thus, a designer can quickly develop a more diversified portfolio which suggests a more experienced designer and makes him more valuable.

Designers who work for consulting offices sometimes meet other designers with broad backgrounds. Meeting such diverse people stimulates the interchange of new techniques and skills. Naturally, this helps promote exciting design ideas.

Designers in consulting offices are likely to be paid less than their counterparts in industry. Because of a firm's small size it may not offer the job security and benefits that industry provides. In a consulting office one may unwillingly be denied access to the client's staff, such as marketing and engineering experts as well as management itself. The experience of starting one's design career in industry to gain experience and then moving to a consulting office has proven advantages.

## ENTREPRENEUR

Occasionally designers will become entrepreneurs immediately upon graduation and work for themselves. I had a friend, two years behind me in college, who wanted to be a toy designer. All of his training and efforts were toward this goal. Upon graduation, he became incorporated and built a small shop in the back of his apartment to design and construct prototypes of toys which he sold to manufacturers. He was an immediate success and was earning two to three times what the rest of us were making after graduation.

A few years ago I heard from a young graduate who became frustrated with the way bicycle racks attached to automobiles, so he started designing and manufacturing his own racks. First he made a rack for himself. Then his friends wanted a rack. People kept him so busy making racks that he soon found himself in business.

However, there are disadvantages to becoming an entrepreneur. Capital can be a problem unless a person has independent resources. It can take a long time to sell an idea to a manufacturer. Self-manufacturing a product may require skills and resources that an individual does not possess. There are no regular paychecks or benefits when a person works as an entrepreneur, and it takes one longer to acquire diverse experience than, for instance, working in industry or a consulting office.

## FREELANCE

Another option an industrial designer has is doing freelance work for industry or a consulting office. Sometimes a corporate industrial design department has a temporary situation—too much work for its staff to handle. In one case it may hire an outside design consulting office for help. In another case, it may choose to hire an individual person for a specific assignment or length of time.

In some instances, consultant offices hire freelance designers for the same reasons they are hired by industry. A freelance assignment could, conceivably, turn into a full-time job opportunity. The advantage of this type of work is that the designer becomes his or her own boss. However, there may still be strict deadlines to meet and the designer may work more hours than if employed by someone else. This type of work gives the young designer a wide variety of experience and can enhance one's portfolio. A disadvantage for the freelancer is that, as with the entrepreneur, there may be no regular paychecks or benefits. To be happy in this situation, a designer must be extremely self-motivated and confident to say nothing about being talented. Many designers, who have been laid off due to corporate downsizing, or have chosen early retirement, or simply retired from industry, do freelance work. They are usually financially secure and their experience is valuable.

## EDUCATION

Once in a while a few designers become so enthralled with the educational process that they want to become educators. This is an honorable goal but it is difficult because it means at least a year or more of additional education (acquiring a master's degree) accompanied by the high cost.

## SEARCHING FOR A JOB

Once student designers have decided in what field or area they want to acquire experience, they should focus their energy on trying to find that job with the right company. They should begin trying to sell themselves to prospective employers even if it is for summer employment.

Students should work closely with their thesis adviser and choose a topic which will help them become more familiar with the industry of their choice. Start looking for that first job the sophomore year in college and set a goal to earn that unique position by graduation. Take advantage of summer internships and cooperative programs. I have seen this lead to future employment. Be selective. Do not take just any job that comes along. A student should seek a company that does what he/she wants to do and then convince them of his/her value. If it is a dynamic company and the student has something unique to offer and can really help the company, more than likely it will try to find an opening.

My own long range objective was to work with transportation clients and specialize in the area of human factors. To achieve my goals, I envisioned myself working for a short time in industry and, with experience, moving on to a consulting office. In the next chapter I will describe my experience working for industry.

### CHAPTER SIX

# WORKING FOR INDUSTRY: CONVAIR

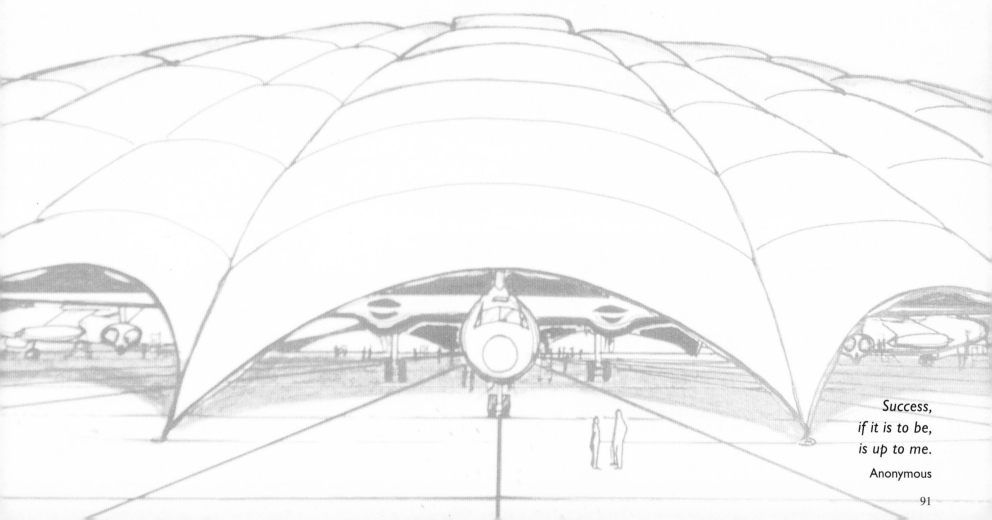

*Success,
if it is to be,
is up to me.*
Anonymous

## CONVAIR—MY FIRST JOB EXPERIENCE

Representatives from Convair, the military aircraft division of Consolidated-Vultee Aircraft Corporation, of Fort Worth, Texas visited Syracuse University while I was a fifth-year student. I saw a notice on the bulletin board that its recruiters were coming and I signed up for an interview. As I explored this company, I discovered that it met some of my criteria. It was involved in human factors, transportation, and national defense. The engineer interviewing me showed keen interest in my thesis, particularly my application of human factors to truck design. Following an excellent meeting, discussion of my résumé and careful portfolio presentation, we talked about my work objectives. I was offered a chance to join its engineering team as a "junior engineer" in its furnishing group. After some time and careful deliberation, I decided to accept the company's offer. I grabbed my degree, bought a Ford and drove to Fort Worth.

When I arrived in Texas in 1951, the Korean Conflict was still raging. The Cold War was in full swing. The *B-36*, the world's largest bomber, was coming off Convair's production line (Figure 6.1 and 6.2). I was 27 years old, armed with a good education and filled with enthusiasm and drive. Students, as they prepare for their first day of work, will find different circumstances.

On my first day at Convair I was introduced to an American defense industry (Figure 6.3). For security reasons I was fingerprinted and photographed. Chuck Stanley, my supervisor, was a veteran aircraft designer, having worked at both Fort Worth and the corporate headquarters in San Diego. He took me upstairs to the engineering department. For as far as I could see, one-quarter mile in each direction, there were men slumped over drawing boards or calculators—a thousand of them. Chuck asked me in a calm voice if I could make mechanical drawings. I immediately vowed to myself that I would never be one of these engineers and I implied that I could not. I bounded back with a sales pitch based on my expert perspective

**FIGURE 6.1.** The Convair *B-36*. Its maiden flight was in 1946; removed from service in 1959.

**FIGURE 6.2.** The *B-36*, three-view silhouette drawing, showing the magnitude of the aircraft as compared to the famous *B-24 Liberator* bomber used in World War II. The fuselage length of the *B-36* is 162 feet versus the *Liberator* fuselage which is 67 feet.

**FIGURE 6.3.** The *B-36* on the production line at Convair in Fort Worth, Texas, late 1940s.

drawing ability. This was a drawing technique that I doubted these engineers could do. I had used such illustrations many times in school to great success. I eventually used it at Convair to show engineers what their work would look like in the aircraft while it was still in the concept stage.

I also decided that I would try selling myself as an industrial design/human factors consultant to the engineers. My supervisors consented to this informal consultation approach for a trial period just to help get quality and human factors into the backlog of work. I used my perspective drawing skills with success while design consulting at Convair. I supplemented the drawings with cardboard mock-ups and, in some cases, plywood models, all to help the engineers visualize their designs. This technique saved critical time. When changes were necessary, we would talk about new approaches and compromises. I

learned patience, tact, and the value of friendship in work. I was beginning to develop a good design philosophy: do not redesign a product unless it can become a better product. A better product works better, costs less, is easier to control, handle, and looks better. If we cannot contribute with these features, it is best to leave the design alone. I also concluded that any new design must have qualities or features that no previous design or competitor possessed. Working closely with the engineers to think out the problem and trying different design solutions was paramount to me. However, an industrial designer should not try to outdo an engineer because this can destroy the professionalism between the two.

There is a distinct difference between design consulting, designing, and design directing. In this application of design service at Convair my function of design consulting was that of helping the engineers envision what they were designing and encouraging them to use human factors wherever possible. Regarding designing itself, I was given design assignments and was expected to produce them on time like everybody else. The process of design directing takes place when the designer tells others what he wants and sometimes how he wants it. I did not do design directing until I had my own firm and also when I was managing the Smith Corona Marchant (SCM) industrial-design department.

After weeks on the job, I finally received my security clearance. Convair's *B-36* was a major player in The Cold War and I must describe my introduction to the mighty plane. During the first night in my new room in Fort Worth I was awakened by the windows loudly rattling and then hearing the slow, deep rumble of aircraft engines. The sound and vibration intensified until even the bed quivered as this mammoth flying machine ever so slowly passed over the city, destined for the giant runway which Convair used. This sound was generated by six 19-foot diameter propellers beating the sky.

**FIGURE 6.4.** Convair's *YB-60* taking off on its maiden flight, April 1952.

**FIGURE 6.5.** The *YB-60*s control wheel (before), shown in relationship to the pilot's seat and aircraft gauges and controls, 1951.

**FIGURE 6.6.** The *YB-60*s control wheel (after), also used on the B-36.

The specification called for a bomber that could carry five tons of bombs to a target and then fly back, all at a total of 10,000 miles. Often flights lasted 35 hours or more of flying over or around the then Soviet Union. Fatigue hampered the crews on such long trips. What could be done to reduce fatigue, thus preserve efficiency? When I arrived at Convair a program called "crew comfort" had been implemented. It provided hammocks for sleeping, racks for luggage, enclosed, comfortable toilets, and a galley for cooking. The engineers and executives began to understand the efficiency provided by human factors.

Early in the 1950s Convair began to develop its replacement for the *B-36.* This aircraft was called the *YB-60* (Figure 6.4). The management of Convair came to us in the furnishings group. It wanted us to develop the best-looking interior and most comfortable crew compartment of any large bomber, within weight and altitude requirements. We focused on human factors. Personally, I wanted to demonstrate how the application of human factors could contribute to the crew's efficiency, thereby improving the aircraft's performance. Thus began the human factors department at Convair.

One of my first design challenges was to change the cockpit color. First, I felt that the traditional dark olive (green) drab used throughout aircraft interiors as an Air Force standard had to go. Company executives agreed. Crew members scan the bright sky at high altitude continually looking for hostile aircraft, and then return their gaze back into the dark crew compartment and study their black operator's control panels. This looking from intense light to dark areas caused eye fatigue. A neutral gray color interior seemed the best choice to relieve eye strain. After I left Convair I was informed that the color scheme, which I developed (two-tone gray), was adopted by the Air Force and became standard.

I was then asked to redesign a control wheel for the pilot and co-pilot (Figure 6.5). To understand exactly what was needed, I interviewed Convair's test pilots in the cockpit. They wanted a wheel that:

**FIGURE 6.7.** Serving tables which could rest against the wall, providing needed space for waitresses to rest the trays. The tables fit neatly between two circular tables and also could slide into a corner, 1952.

**FIGURE 6.8.** Several triangular serving tables put together to form a larger table for serving or dining.

1. did not hide gauge faces on the instrument panel from the pilot's view,
2. was slightly wider for better leverage when turning or banking, and
3. incorporated a thumb-operated, emergency rear-wheel control button, intercom button, and auto-pilot control, within the wheel housing.

These requirements were accomplished. This new wheel was eventually installed on all *B-36*s (Figure 6.6). We made the wheel of an aluminum casting, giving it a special finish to resist wear. Here was an example of an excellent relationship among the designer and the people who are going to use the product. The pilots cooperated extensively, making many helpful suggestions, and could not wait to use the design they helped create.

By now I had advanced to full engineering status. Occasionally, I was asked to do some interior design for the Fort Worth facility. For instance, a large conference room for the engineers and a series of serving tables for the waitresses in the corporate dining room were needed (Figures 6.7 and 6.8). I found a lot of pipe from discarded wing and fuselage work stands which made excellent table legs and the designs worked quite satisfactorily.

Every couple of months the engineering department would have a security review. The importance of security was impressed upon us. We were to keep quiet about the work we did and it was made clear that we would be publicly marched from the plant if we were ever caught aiding and abetting the enemy. Nobody wanted to be like Julius and Ethel Rosenberg who gave away American atomic secrets to the Soviets, and were caught, tried, and executed. I listened carefully, but could not believe that anything I was doing would give comfort and aid to the enemy. The security of the work done for employers or clients is imperative. Creative thinking is proprietary. Companies go to great length to secure competitor's designs.

Soon after one security review I received two letters. One was from my college roommate, Eric Caldor, asking me if I would give him a recommendation since he was about to be drafted into the Army and wanted to join a special Army intelligence unit. I promised

**FIGURE 6.9.** The Convair *Crusader,* America's first nuclear test aircraft, began development in mid-1951. Its first flight was September 17, 1955. The cockpit was shielded with an 18-inch thick wall of lead.

him the recommendation. The second letter was from Professor Heythum, my college professor from Syracuse University, asking me what I was doing. I replied in a note that most of the work that I did was classified and I could not talk about it. However, I did feel that I could discuss my work on color and eye fatigue. Little did I know that Professor Heythum would post my letter on the bulletin board for the whole school to see. Anyway, I didn't think much about this letter.

Following the *YB-60* exercise, another new project was announced. The Air Force wanted an atomic-powered aircraft which could stay almost indefinitely in the air with minimal refueling time. This project compared to the atomic powered *Nautilus,* a submarine which could hide in the ocean for considerable periods of time unde- tected. The first challenge was to develop an atomic reactor small enough to fit in a *B-36* type aircraft, and second, to eventually power

such an aircraft. Authorities also wanted to know what the impact of radiation would be on aircraft components as well as the crew. Convair began construction by modifying a *B-36,* calling the project the *Crusader* (Figure 6.9).

Convair assigned us the task of modifying the front crew compartment. To protect the crew from radiation, we started by surrounding the crew area with an 18-inch-thick lead wall. The wind- shield required 22-inch-thick leaded glass. I was challenged to provide suitable lighting for the crew. The crews' work panels, lighted by one light each, had the operators sitting side-by-side with a narrow aisle between them. To keep the light out of each other's eyes as operators turned to look at others behind or next to them, I developed very careful light shields to restrict the light to shine on the panels only. Such shields took peculiar shapes. Since it was possible for the shields to come in contact with crew members heads as they moved about the cabin, I made them from a semi-rigid rubber. These light shields did the job.

Years later, when the crew members finally flew the aircraft, they told reporters that the interior was so quiet because of the deep lead shielding surrounding the crew compartment that they could not hear the aircraft when its engines were running. Unfortunately, due to the intense radiation dosage, the crew piloted the aircraft only once and then retired. A second crew navigated the next test flight.

Then, the advanced engineering group invited me to work with them. Convair was concerned about suitable hanger facilities for the atomic-powered aircraft because the radiation would contaminate most materials used in modern building construction. I searched for a new and radical solution. After much effort, I proposed that Convair develop a "weightless" hangar which raised a few eyebrows (Figures 6.10, 6.11, 6.12, and 6.13).

Since helium is a gas that would be used in and about the reac- tors, my concept was that some of the gas could be diverted into

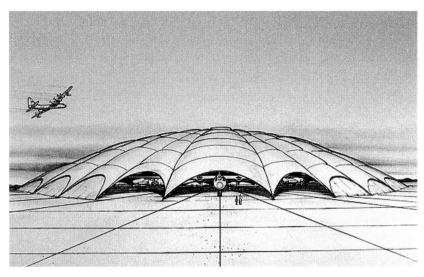

**FIGURE 6.10.** My design for a "weightless hangar," developed to house atomic-powered aircraft, 1952.

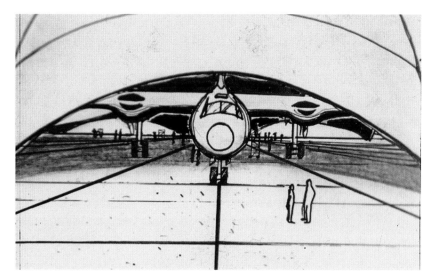

**FIGURE 6.12.** Showing the scale of an aircraft within the hangar.

**FIGURE 6.11.** Close-up image of weightless hangar.

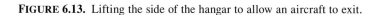

**FIGURE 6.13.** Lifting the side of the hangar to allow an aircraft to exit.

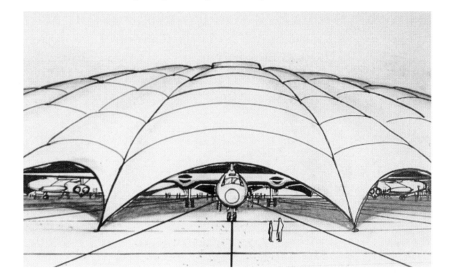

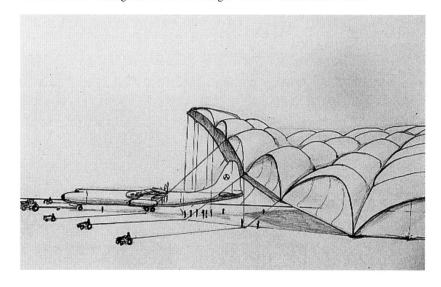

supporting a hangar structure. The structure would be a dome. The dome's roof was composed of a series of interlocking pillows filled with helium. Catenaries or internal walls inside each pillow helped maintain the pillows' elliptical shape. Around the bottom edges of the bottom row of pillows, tie-down cables dropped to the concrete apron and were anchored in place. Relaxing the cables on a portion of the dome would make the hangar lift, thus provide an opening suitable to allow an aircraft to be moved in and out. The aerodynamics group assured me that such a shape and design could work. This represented the largest and most dynamic project I have ever worked on.

About this time I made plans to leave Convair. My original plan was to stay there a year or so and then move. Though I liked Convair, the engineering staff, and the fabulous opportunities, I wanted different challenges. It would have been easy to stay there and stagnate as a couple of my friends did, but the time to try something new arrived.

One day I came home from work and saw an ominous-looking man sitting on my front porch. I figured that he had been eyeing my MG (I had recently sold the Ford) and wanted to buy it. When I reached the front porch he turned to me and introduced himself as a F.B.I. man. Immediately I remembered the letter I had written Professor Heythum and figured that at last they had caught up with me. I had visions of being handcuffed, taken downtown, blindfolded, interrogated for endless hours, and probably having my fingernails

pulled out. One cannot imagine how I regretted sending that letter to Professor Heythum, writing about color and planning to reduce the fatigue of aircraft crews. The F.B.I. agent asked if I knew Eric Caldor, who claimed to be my roommate back at Syracuse University. He said Caldor wanted to enter the Army Intelligence and had listed me as a reference. I indicated that I did know Eric and said that he was a person of honorable character. The agent thanked me and left.

One may wonder why I chose to join an industry when my career objective was to have my own design consulting firm. The advantages of the job at that point in time outweighed trying to open a consulting firm simply because I had no experience. What better place to gain this vital knowledge and develop the ability to consult? There were about 40 special engineers in our group and over 1,000 on staff at the Fort Worth facility. What greater work environment for product development could be arranged for a young designer? My job was to seek out and help implement industrial design with an emphasis on human factors for all aircraft interior design efforts. I had access to some of the most sophisticated materials and processes, design information, and the best aircraft designers in the world. Also, I believed my professional service to Convair contributed to the protection of America. This was very satisfying!

The next chapter discusses the pros and cons of working for oneself and my experience establishing a design consultancy.

### CHAPTER SEVEN

# WORKING FOR YOURSELF

*The exclusive worship
of the bitch-goddess Success
[is] our national disease.*

William James

In January 1954, with mixed feelings and a packed MG, I drove north from Texas. Leaving a good, challenging job and plenty of friends was sobering, but deep down inside I knew I was doing the right thing. I was tired. In fact I was wrung out and definitely needed a change. Marriage, home and a less stressful job, I believed, were the answer. My plan was to work on building a consulting office like the "big four." I knew I would need space, supportive clients and a good staff. This was enjoyable for me to think about, but I knew my goal would be really difficult to achieve. I had no one to turn to for advice. In fact, throughout my career, not having a good counselor has bothered me the most. The people who did advise me the best were my banker, a friendly plastics vendor, my lawyer, and my wife. Slowly a plan evolved and ultimately worked.

On my way to Boston I stopped at Syracuse University to see many friends and particularly the faculty. When I was visiting Syracuse University, the professors asked me to give a presentation on my work at Convair, deleting, of course, the work that was "secret." I recall stressing that when a recent graduate is faced with the choice of either working in industry or a consulting office, that industry was a better choice, particularly early in one's career. Several graduating students followed my advice. It seemed the opportunity to use new materials and processes and to meet and work with experts was greater in industry than in a consulting office.

My fiancee and I had worked out a careful plan for our future. First she was to finish college, having about a year and a half left at Radcliffe. I sought whatever kind of job I could find in the greater Boston area. Then, upon her graduation, I would go into business for myself. Once the firm was running and we were making money, we would buy a house and start a family. Later I would help her financially with advanced degrees, if that was what she wanted. After surveying the northeast, we agreed that upstate New York seemed like it was one of the ideal industrial areas in the country and reasonably

central to cities like Rochester, Buffalo, Utica, and Albany, as well as accessible to surrounding states like New Jersey, Pennsylvania, and Massachusetts. It was also close to our parents' homes and we were familiar with and loved the area regardless of the season. Perhaps the most important reason for my decision was the very diverse group of companies located there. To me, this seemed healthy. Some of the companies included the following: General Electric (the defense industry with radar and sonar); Carrier Corporation (heating and air conditioning); Crouse-Hinds (industrial electrical components); General Motors and New Process Gear (auto parts manufacturers); R.E. Dietz (emergency highway and vehicle lighting); as well as Eastman Kodak (photography and office equipment); and Xerox (xerographic machines) in nearby Rochester. Over the past 40 years, a few of these companies have been dissolved, moved away or simply stagnated. However, other interesting companies have sprung up to take their places. At the time of my move to upstate New York, these companies were leaders in their industries and looked ripe for help. Also, there was virtually no competition for me at that point in time. Today there are about 15 competitive design consulting firms in the upstate New York area.

In hindsight, Anne, my first wife, and I should have reconsidered the Boston area with its growing technology developing along Rt. 128 and its close proximity to M.I.T. and Harvard University. Anne liked Cambridge and we might have been happier there. In the long run, we discovered that the firm's location was not critical as transportation became more efficient in the northeast with super highways and efficient air travel. Anyway, we had a plan and decided to work it from central New York State.

Meanwhile, I found a job in Boston as a store planner/designer at Bernard-Soep Associates, a leading store planning firm in the area (Figure 7.1). There were only four of us, Bernie Soep, the owner, the secretary, myself, as the designer, and an assistant designer. The firm

**FIGURE 7.1.** Author working as a store planner at Bernard-Soep Associates in Boston, 1953.

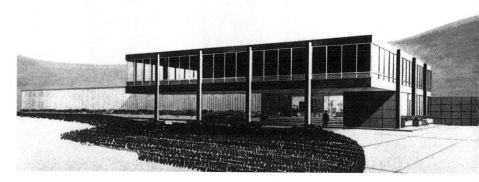

**FIGURE 7.2.** Author's concept sketch of the Colonial Provision building in Boston, 1953.

was the biggest one in New England offering this service at the time. Bernie, my boss, was patient with me, and we became good friends. Nowhere in my background had I been trained in merchandising, merchandise display and interior design and construction. I could make a store look like a poor man's "Mies Van Der Rohe" but the tourist shopper in New England wanted to see the "colonial-nautical" look (Figure 7.2). The Colonial Provisions project was an opportunity for me to design the facade of a new corporate headquarters for a meat-processing plant. I recall requesting architectural drawings of the building to better understand how it was constructed so that the exterior would relate to the interior structure. Unfortunately, the client did not provide this information to me. I ended up "working in the dark" even though this was probably the most significant work that I did while in New England.

Designing stores and their interiors was my responsibility. Today, I consider this experience essential to my design education, but I never sought to design stores again. I learned how to design interiors, including furniture and fixtures, efficiently. A store's interior is a place to stimulate the sale of merchandise just like an aircraft cockpit is an environment for the pilot to control efficient flight. Perhaps the most value I gained was learning how to prepare a site location, take an existing store, redesign it while making it possible to continue in business with ongoing reconstruction. The objective is to create an environment that encourages consumers to part with their money. In store design, you live in a fairytale land. Customers do not care about the genuineness of the design or for that matter the pure beauty of the interior. The sales atmosphere is like a stage setting and is a backdrop for product display. All that is needed is an appealing environment for product sales—period. This type of hard, cold design for the sale of merchandise was exactly what I needed, even though I hated it. This experience made me appreciate what it is like to own and operate a commercial establishment and see how important, yet insignificant, design can be in the total scheme of merchandising. One of the big opportunities I gained was learning how to manage a consulting firm.

My year and a half in Boston was coming to a close and I had redesigned a couple of department stores and a women's specialty shop in Hyannis. Regardless of how hard I worked at such projects, it was difficult for me to design anything of which I was particularly proud. My heart and soul were not into this type of work, and my mind was on moving to New York and opening my own firm.

While I was finishing up my work for Bernard Soep, my wife graduated and came to Syracuse on her own and found a good apartment for us in a quality neighborhood. This apartment had to double as an office, and I acquired approval from zoning officials. Actually, the dining-room table became part of the office! I called my firm "Philip Stevens Associates."

When one goes into business, the ever-present question is how to win design consulting work. This task has been a challenge for designers since the era of the "big four" when they tried to steal work from each other. This highly competitive effort lasted as long as they were in business. What follows are my comments on many items that relate to obtaining work. For me, soliciting business is the most annoying chore about being in business. This task may be somewhat easier today than when I first started. Manufacturers see the advantages of well-designed products and consumers demand human factors, aesthetic appeal, safety, and performance from the products they purchase and use. On the other hand, there are more practicing designers than ever before.

## INITIAL CONTACT

Designers should, very early on, develop a long list of potential clients in the field that they would like to work in and/or companies they know they would enjoy working with. Some design consulting firms hire a person as their marketing expert. I have done this once but it was not successful. However, sometimes marketing experts make a firm a success by getting just the right clients for them.

A marketer's first job is to visit the local library, chamber of commerce or business office, and gather names, addresses, phone numbers, and a detailed description of what these companies manufacture and sell. From this list, a master file of potential clients can be prepared and every contact with them should be recorded.

The first contact a design firm makes with a potential client is usually a query letter and brochure. Often nothing happens from this effort. Thus, a phone call is needed to follow up and ascertain that the marketer has the correct person to contact. From telephone conversations, the marketer can determine how much interest the potential client has in design service in general. The objective is to get an invitation to visit the potential client's facility and put on a slide presentation to show the complete capabilities of the consulting firm. Hopefully, after such a presentation, possible clients will let the marketer know about problems they experience and indicate whether they would like some design help. A good place for a design firm to start would be to build a file of about 100 or so potential clients.

Determine the status of interest for each potential client and a time for follow-up or contact again. Doing a good job for a client on the first design project opens up potential design work within other areas or divisions of the client's facilities. Referrals seem to be the best technique for building business. In the last chapter, I mentioned Brockway, Graflex, SCM, and Itek. All of these companies gave me additional work as soon as I successfully completed their initial design project.

I have found that it is best to present one's firm as a generalist design firm with some areas of expertise we could focus on. For example, I could talk at great length about typewriters and calculators. It is easy to adapt this experience to data processing equipment and small, laptop computers. Areas I felt comfortable presenting myself as an authority include product design, product planning, corporate identity, human factors, and packaging.

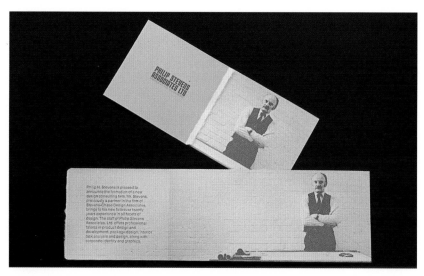

**FIGURE 7.3.** An introductory brochure for Philip Stevens Associates, developed in the 1970s.

## THE BROCHURE

My firm's brochure is wrapped in an attractive cover stock which functions as a folder holding assorted loose brochure pages (Figure 7.3). These pages are case studies of projects we have successfully completed. In the past we have had a letter campaign, similar to a direct mailing, which was sent out monthly or semi-monthly to prospective clients telling them about a recent project. We included a color photograph of the finished project and perhaps a "before" photograph as well. We followed up each letter with a phone call. From this effort, we were occasionally invited to make a presentation at a potential client's facility.

## THE PRESENTATION

When we prepared a presentation for a possible client, the objective is to discover their problem or problems before we meet with them. If we know what a company needs, we can modify our presentation to convince its staff we have worked on similar problems and can help. I call this a "rifle" approach versus a "shotgun," generalist approach which shows capabilities in a wide variety of areas. I once heard a quote; "To be a success in business, be daring, be first, be different."

I use a 35-mm slide projector to present my work. During a slide show references are made to the brochure. I notice people sometimes taking notes on the various brochure pages as I make my presentation. If potential clients like what they see during a presentation, and have design problems, they may ask for a proposal.

## PROPOSALS & CONTRACTS

Every new assignment warrants a proposal and a contract. A design proposal 1) states specifically what services the designer will provide, 2) who the service is being done for, 3) what the client can expect to receive (drawings, models, etc.), 4) when the client can expect each phase of the project to be complete, and 5) the cost and terms.

There are distinct similarities among all proposals. It is possible to take one good proposal and use it as a guide to compose other proposals. I have saved all of my past proposals in one book. It is now easy to prepare others by referring to the book for special clauses and ideas. See Appendix E for a sample proposal.

The problem in preparing a proposal is how does a designer know how much to charge a client for a particular service or job? I have found it absolutely necessary to build a collection of project histories. I use a bar graph format to record past projects, but any technique that is logical to the designer can be used. I keep track of total hours spent on all phases of a project, including consultation with the client, concept development, research, model work, etc., because sometimes each of these services is charged at a different rate. Designers are usually billed out at different hourly rates depending upon the service they are providing and their level of skill.

For example, a senior designer is charged out at a higher hourly rate than a junior designer, draftsman, or research assistant. Project histories are invaluable when trying to determine what to charge for a new project. I can always find a project something like the one that needs estimating. It is important that all data be kept in "hours worked" and not "dollars charged." This enables anyone to look at a project completed 10 years ago and calculate what it would cost in today's dollars.

I also have a contract book which contains all of my design contracts. It also provides us with ideas and language we can use again and again. For a sample design contract, see Appendix F. Often when corporate lawyers review our proposals and contracts, they feel compelled to prepare their own contract, and this is acceptable. The Industrial Designer's Society of America has sample design contracts and proposals one can purchase at a nominal fee.

## ESTIMATING & PROJECTION

In operating a design consulting firm, it helps if the owner is a good foreteller. Besides being ethical and paying one's bills on time, there are two areas where one must be very careful. First, design firms must know how to estimate their upcoming expenses and income. Often business is slow but all financial obligations must still be met! I adopted a technique used by many families in the depression time when facing a financial crisis such as paying medical bills and still affording new shoes for their children. A process that I call "projection" is in order. First, compile a list of all anticipated expenses for the next month or two. This list should include all debt payments as well as taxes, insurance, payroll including anticipated raises, marketing costs, travel, utilities, maintenance, and incidental expenses such as meals for clients, Christmas cards, etc. From this list, one can arrive at the amount of money necessary to meet expenses.

In order to properly estimate expenses, careful records must be kept. Go through the monthly expenses from the previous year and the year before to develop a reasonable idea of anticipated expenses. Then estimate the anticipated income for the same period of time. Approximate the number of billable hours in a period of time (say a month) and multiply by the hourly rate for design service. If income does not exceed expenses, determine how to cut expenses or increase income. This could conceivably be done by increasing billable hours (becoming more productive). This simple process has helped me over many financial crises and debates.

## BEGINNING WORK

I am sometimes asked to relate what it is like to win a client, and also what it is like to lose one, and why. Winning a contract can be sweet, particularly if the designer has been competing against a formidable competitor. Once a designer wins any contract, the objective is to move quickly to start delivering just as delineated in the proposal. Then meet the goal by finishing on time and within budget.

Once in a great while, something will go wrong and the client will dismiss a designer and his firm. Designers should be courageous and gallant in any defeat, and above all, should be professional. Both the designer's staff and the ex-client's staff will be watching carefully. Professionals should always demonstrate their resilience.

## TIME BOOKS

All designers carefully log all work on a project in a time book. I have always used a time book similar to an appointment book, showing a full week on one page and 15-minute intervals recorded. Use the time book to prepare bills during and at the end of a project. Note the start time and finish time for a particular task, record the client's name and project, and describe the type of service provided. Keep time books indefinitely for future reference.

## WORKBOOKS AND DIARIES

Designers need to protect their ideas. A designer's creative effort should produce ideas as solutions to design problems. How do industrial designers protect their ideas, particularly if the ideas are considered original property? Designers are obligated to record their ideas, usually in a workbook or a diary. This should be in the form of an easy to read descriptive or narrative along with accompanying sketches or drawings that are dated and witnessed if possible. The purpose of this workbook is so that if at some point in the future a design is contested as not being an original idea, the workbook can be submitted as evidence to the contrary.

In my firm, when a new project begins, a "project workbook" is started. This book lists the client and the name of everyone involved in the design process, important notes, facts, the project specification as prepared by the client and all preliminary sketches, ideas, meetings, phone numbers, questions, critical conversations, etc. Later, when the industrial design specification is prepared by the designer, this plan should be included in the workbook as well. I strongly recommend that if the work being done for a client is significant, the designer should explain the work to another person and have him or her witness the work by signing on that page(s) of the workbook.

Another important area of record keeping and documentation is photography. For years I had a standing order that as work progressed on a project, it was photographed by me or the project designer. For instance, all rough mock-ups and models would be photographed even though they may not ultimately be shown to the client. Not all work is significant to the end design, but one has to bill for the time and materials spent on the client's behalf and be able to verify the work. Photographs help justify the billing. Who knows, there may come a point in time when a discarded idea becomes valuable and can be developed into a workable design.

My firm has collected thousands of slides over the years. These slides have served many purposes. First, in brochure development they illustrate the birth of ideas. Second, slides are sometimes used to establish and verify proprietary rights, and lastly, they are useful in public relations efforts. We carefully log each slide by client or manufacturer, project, date, and service rendered. Two slides each were always ordered. Duplicate slides go into a fireproof file at another location.

### CASE STUDY NO. I: SMITH-CORONA

While I was in Texas, I kept in close contact with family, friends and design developments at Smith-Corona in my hometown of Groton, New York. The Corona division was still growing and making money. It had recently introduced a small, compact, portable electric typewriter, the first of its kind in the world. Sales went through the roof. Other projects, such as products for Sears & Roebuck, became difficult to process since the electric typewriter demanded the bulk of engineering time.

Smith-Corona and Sears & Roebuck had an interesting business agreement in that Smith-Corona would not let Sears sell the popular Corona designs with the Sears name on them. Sears did carry the Corona in its catalog; however, Sears wanted its own typewriter and needed a less costly machine to be competitive. To keep from losing Sears' business, Smith-Corona gave Sears a special model typewriter with the Sears name on it. The machine was the same in quality, but minus a couple special features and Corona made it look different so that the customer would be less apt to confuse the two. The problem was how to significantly change the appearance of the machine since it would be coming off the same production line and selling on the same shelf or counter.

To accomplish this, Smith-Corona's management decided to redo the ribbon spool cover, one of the largest and most visible parts on the typewriter. Changing this part was an ideal solution since it was one of the last parts added to the machine on the assembly line. My responsibility involved redesigning the cover. Approaching this design assignment demanded a real test of my philosophy. For instance, little could be done to make it more efficient and little could be done to enhance the cost. There were few human factors involved. But, the shape could be aesthetically improved and I developed a shape that blended with the surrounding jacketing parts. Having no design laboratory or tools, I went out and bought a jeweler's saw and some blades, solder and soldering iron, and sheet brass. I did have clay, so I could sculp the design right on the machine by using the hinges and sides from the existing cover system. The brass and solder provided the foundation for the clay. I developed an aesthetically-pleasing shape by blending with the front and sides of the machine. It looked simpler and seemed to fit with the base. Smith-Corona liked the new design so much that it wanted to keep it and give the original Smith-Corona design to Sears. Ultimately, Sears' executives received the new design and were happy. Smith-Corona acquired a good solution to its difficult Sears' development program. I successfully accomplished a difficult design assignment and gained a happy client. ∎

While my apartment made a good office, I sensed I needed a real office now, even though clients were not coming to my facilities (Figure 7.4). I knew I would eventually need some sort of a design laboratory. I started to look for space within the neighborhood. I found room available in an old mansion that had recently been bought and converted to offices (Figure 7.5). The solarium adjoining a beautiful library became my office. I used the basement as a design laboratory. A design laboratory is basically a big room in which I would eventually have a beautiful work bench, table saw, band saw, production floor sander, drill press, circular saw, power sander, power drills, etc. with buckets of clamps and hardware, with lots of lighting. I had a friend who helped me slowly collect the needed equipment. This laboratory was exactly what the room says it is: an environment for testing and trying assorted three-dimensional, full-scale mock-ups and building full-scale models of designs to demonstrate to clients. Years

**FIGURE 7.4.** Author's first office located on DeWitt Street in Syracuse, New York, 1954.

**FIGURE 7.5.** Author's Oak Street (Syracuse) office, 1955.

later we added a mock-up room which housed an over-the-highway truck, a dental laboratory and electric, narrow-isle lift trucks. However, I had to share my office space with two psychologists. They needed an office on weekends to hold psychological testing and perform personal evaluations. My landlord insisted on this arrangement which worked out well since we all had comfortable facilities and paid reasonable rent.

## CASE STUDY NO. 2: CAMILLUS CUTLERY

My second big job was for Camillus Cutlery Company, a world leader in the manufacture of jackknives and kitchen cutlery, located in Camillus, New York, a suburb of Syracuse. Camillus is an old mill town and had experienced many ups and downs since the first grist mill was established in 1806. The company still operates in Camillus and has been a major manufacturer of jackknives in America.

I called Camillus Cutlery and spoke with its general manager, Dean Wallace, explaining who I was, what I had done and what I could do for them. I was only aware of the jackknives that the company manufactured but the general manager had other ideas for expansion. The company sold an inexpensive, low-quality, plastic-handled, paring knife which was mass produced with little or no quality in design. Wallace wanted a better designed paring knife, something new and

**FIGURE 7.6.** My collection of kitchen tools used for research, study, and design development. Our spatula design is fourth from the left. Our carving knife is eleventh from the left, and our paring knife is third from the right.

different. Here, at last, was an opportunity to develop a new product from scratch that would be all my design. There might also be an opportunity to develop something unique.

To better understand the importance of tools and cutlery used in food preparation, I needed to know what designers in other countries had done in kitchen cutlery design. I immediately started my research and soon it was apparent that there was little unique information offered here in the United States. Slowly I began a collection of paring knives (Figure 7.6). I went to Syracuse University's and then to Cornell University's Home Economics Departments to interview their staffs and study international periodicals on culinary arts and equipment. I found that the Scandinavians had done some research to better understand cutting and paring efficiency. I had to have these foreign bulletins translated into English. This research was helpful in establishing the design criteria for my paring knife. It was difficult to believe, considering the emphasis being placed on kitchen efficiency at this time, that no one outside of Thomas Lamb, an American industrial design consultant to Everware, had questioned the contemporary design of paring knives. What was on the market was ugly and lacked human factors. The knives were usually made of two pieces of wood riveted together with the tang (metal blade) sandwiched in between.

After surveying the whole field, collecting assorted paring knives and watching people use them, I gradually was able to identify the appealing features of each knife. A new design began to emerge in my mind which

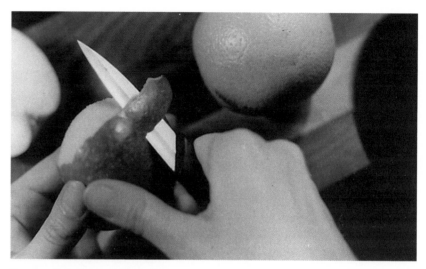

**FIGURE 7.7.** Our paring knife design in use. Notice how the handle extends over the blade slightly for better cutting leverage.

I felt had unique features. One interesting idea was to bring the handle toward the point about 1/4" up over the top of the blade so that as one pares a vegetable, the forefinger rests on this part of the handle rather than on top of the narrow blade which can become uncomfortable over time. This design gave the user extra leverage when cutting. I took the tang, the metal blade and anchor shaft, from an existing product and then built up a handle of plastic to the exact shape and form desired. Models were tested against competitive designs and redesigned where necessary. Once I had completed a model I returned to the university professors who had been so helpful to me and asked for an evaluation of my design. I never knew if they were just being nice or they did not wish to show ignorance on such a basic subject, but they raved about the design. I felt that I was on the right track (Figure 7.7 and 7.8).

Once I was confident my design was the best it could be, I showed it to Dean. Camillus Cutlery liked the design so much that it asked me to design a companion utility and carving knife. This led me to design a serving fork, mixing spoon and spatula for them (Figure 7.9 and 7.10).

**FIGURE 7.8.** Our paring knife, final design.

**FIGURE 7.9.** The complete product line—from right to left—carving knife, utility knife, paring knife, fork, spatula, and mixing spoon.

**FIGURE 7.10.** Our spatula design is on the left. Notice how the curve of the blade matches the inside radius of the frying pan to ease the removal of food.

Regrettably, the president of the company decided he wanted development resources spent on jackknives, not kitchen tools. So, this great product line was shelved. This was the beginning of my indoctrination into industrial politics. ∎

---

**What did I learn from this experience?**

1. Before starting any project, be sure everyone on the client's staff is aware of it and supports the effort.

2. Do not hesitate to do thorough research. In fact, research is a necessity in any product development program.

3. Do build models and test them against competitive products.

---

## A NEW PARTNERSHIP

Around this time I received a call from David O. Chase. He had been one of the students to whom I had lectured when I stopped at Syracuse University during my drive from Texas to Boston. Chase worked for Worthington Pump as an engineer and did well. Now he wanted to become an entrepreneur and returned to the Syracuse area to seek out opportunities.

Apparently Chase had contacted the Syracuse University's industrial design department members and they gave him my phone number. I recalled talking to him when I gave my lecture while stopping at the university on my way to Boston from Fort Worth in 1953. I assumed that he was looking to purchase a business. He asked me many questions about what it was like working as a design consultant, and within reason, I answered his questions. I am sure I told him I worked for Smith-Corona and Camillus Cutlery while he described his work at Worthington Pump in New Jersey.

My wife and I talked at length about asking David if he might wish to join me in forming a design consulting firm. We agreed that the two of us could do the job better than one could, but were we compatible? It had not yet occurred to me that two people with similar backgrounds, tastes and skills might be weaker than if we had different talents, thus complementing one another's abilities. I did, however, decide to query my fellow office friends, the psychologists, about how I could determine our compatibility. I asked them if they could test our personality traits, evaluate them and advise us on whether we should work together. There was a lot about Chase I did not know and the psychologists felt they could help, so I approached him with the offer of forming a partnership. He was interested and agreed to taking the test for compatibility. At that time people were, and perhaps still are, sensitive about psychological screening and evaluation or even talking about psychology or psychotherapy.

Following our completion of a battery of visual and verbal tests, the psychologists gave us the results. First they hedged their bets regarding our potential compatibility. Chase and I were similar in many respects thus there might be fewer areas of conflict. On the down side, however, having similar traits might mean we would be less apt to discuss and reconcile unresolved differences, which, over time, could erupt and hurt the relationship. We both were aware of our weaknesses and it was refreshing to openly talk about the other person's problems. We talked about how we might handle disagreements. Later on I felt that we would need an in-depth discussion immediately following a "blow-up" about how, why and what was needed to avoid future clashes. Later I discovered that I became very sensitive to the possibility of disagreements between us and went to considerable effort to change and avoid what I felt were irritating causes. I spent considerable energy, which should have been spent on work, trying or giving the appearance of being reasonable. My partner may well have been doing the same thing but I was not particularly aware of it. Anyway, we worked together for 15 years and produced many quality designs.

## Setting Up Our New Business

We went ahead and decided to call ourselves "Stevens-Chase Design Associates," developing a new logo and stationery. We had a list of real items that had to be resolved before we could do business:

1. We had to have a "buy and sell" agreement in case one of us wanted out of the relationship. This involved a lawyer.
2. A logo and mark had to be designed and agreed upon. Then we had to register the firm's new name with the state to be sure that no one else had the same name.
3. We had to be sure we had adequate drawing room space.
4. My model laboratory needed enlarging and new tools added.
5. We had a sign made for our business.
6. We previewed and established an office leasing agreement to include:
   a. aspects of parking for ourselves, employees, and potential clients
   b. adequate restroom facilities
   c. lunch room and coffee area
   d. insurance
7. Taxes (federal, state and FICA), worker's compensation, disability, etc. and health insurance needed to be established.
8. Ownership of tools and furniture I had brought to the firm needed to be identified.
9. We opened a bank account.
10. We hired a secretary, bookkeeper, and chose an accountant.

I am sure there were other considerations not listed here.

Next we built a portfolio representing our past work. Chase, employed previously at Worthington Pump as an engineer, had done some interesting work. Our combined portfolio looked good but we soon discovered that while it looked nice, potential clients want more:

1. They wanted us to provide them with some sort of brochure to show others on their staffs what we have done and are capable of doing.
2. A brochure helps to open the door for the consideration of our services even if we cannot get through the door ourselves.

3. A slide show was needed so that we could present to a group what we were capable of doing. This involves taking progress slides as well as photographs of finished projects.

In order to find clients, we used the New York State Industrial Directory as well as the telephone book. We separated the list into geographic regions and each of us picked an area of the state and focused on contacting the industries in that region. First we placed a telephone call and followed up with an introductory letter. If possible, we visited the potential client and gave him a presentation of our work along with a discussion on the value of industrial design. Eventually work came our way, but it sometimes takes two years or longer to cultivate a new client.

## CASE STUDY NO. 3. BROCKWAY MOTOR TRUCKS

One of our first projects together involved Brockway Motor Trucks in Cortland, New York. The design staff there remembered me and had helped me when I wrote my thesis back in 1950 while a student at Syracuse University. Brockway Motor Trucks started as a carriage manufacturer in Homer, New York in 1851. In 1912, the company began to manufacture over-the-highway trucks, or tractor trailers that they are commonly referred as today. By 1917, it was established and helped in World War I. All branches of the government, from the Army to the Post Office bought Brockway trucks. Following the war, Brockway resumed manufacturing civilian trucks and its sales spread to some 65 countries throughout the world.

In 1956, Brockway joined forces with Mack Trucks, Inc. and in 1958 the famous "Husky" line was introduced (Figure 7.11). Many of these vehicles are still on the road today. As truck development became more complex and cost more critical, it was more efficient to move key Brockway employees and production to Mack Trucks' facility in Allentown, Pennsylvania. Eventually Mack closed the Brockway plant— Cortland County lost a great manufacturer and Stevens-Chase lost a good client.

Brockway's president called me in one day and announced that since Mack Trucks had bought Brockway and Mack had a bull dog for a hood ornament, Brockway wanted a special ornament as well. But, Brockway wanted to have a husky dog. I wish that the company had asked us to propose an idea rather than just telling us what to design. Anyway, we did what

FIGURE 7.11. "Husky" hood ornament as used on a Brockway truck, 1955.

they asked for and it did work out. Even today, many years after Brockway was fully absorbed into Mack, their trucks drive the roads and proudly display our radiator hood ornament. After getting the assignment we contacted Syracuse University for a sculptor and we retained him to help us. This was wise since neither Chase nor I considered this our area of expertise. Our final design was a big success, which pleased Brockway. We liked the name Brockway and wanted to redo its logo, but management would not hear of changing its script to block letters which, in our view, best typified or characterized the company. ∎

## CASE STUDY NO. 4: R.E. DIETZ

The R.E. Dietz account was interesting in that the company made lanterns in the last century and wanted to aggressively seek the auto "after market." Dietz struggled to be efficient and modern as a manufacturing facility. The engineering staffers were not particularly innovative or ambitious which made them difficult to work with. Management wanted us to design a 360-degree revolving warning light for emergency vehicles. There was also a cost objective. I had talked with the chief engineer off and on for about a year and he finally consented to try our services.

At Stevens-Chase Design we divided the problem into two parts. Chase felt more comfortable with the mechanism and worked on the motor,

**FIGURE 7.12.** A working prototype of the R.E. Dietz revolving light, 1956.

We were terribly disappointed and frustrated since we had put all this effort and spent so much of the client's money to make the design the best. The client who retained us was also frustrated when he compared our original model to the final design. A design he thought would be great was now compromised by careless product engineers and could not be corrected without great tooling costs. Little did I realize that this experience would be repeated again and again throughout my career. Clients can enhance the relationship and the design service by encouraging their engineering

**FIGURE 7.13.** R.E. Dietz revolving light on a rescue vehicle.

drive train, and light brackets. I focused on the appearance of the exterior. Clients then often referred to this as the style.

I designed several dummy plaster housings hoping to find the best shape for the light. We then put them on cars and ultimately chose the best size and form. Models showed the relationship between the lens and metal housing which usually attached to a vehicle's roof (Figure 7.12). Dietz helped us determine the best manufacturing technique since most components would be made in its facility.

Everything went well until the first parts came into the plant and we began to assemble the product. The large, clear red plastic lens cover, the largest part, finally arrived and adapted to the top of a deep drawn sheet metal base. It looked great except the upper corner radius joining the lens dome or top to the sides had never been incorporated as we designed it, even after giving the client both a model and drawings (Figure 7.13). The two slopes intersected at a sharp angle rather than a gentle radius. We surmised that the client's engineers did not want to take the time to follow our drawings and model. We feared such problems, which is why we insisted upon making a model to show everybody what the design should be like.

staff to work together with the industrial designer. Successful products depend on both engineering and industrial design. The two should be interwoven. To help our clients we build full-scale models of our designs and there are two reasons for this. One is to prove the concept, manufacturability, and the allotment of space for internal components. The other is to show the client exactly what the design looks like from all angles long before expensive production tooling is constructed. This way, if changes are required, they can be made prior to tooling at little cost.

What else can be done to avoid such problems? We have tried writing it into our contracts that the designer will visit the client to review preproduction samples before the final commitment to tooling is made. This has never proved particularly effective for us since the client simply forgets to call us or does not wish to take the time when judgment should be made on component acceptability. The problem for industrial designers is that they may spend a year or two developing a design and in the end a mistake by the client hurts the design. This ulti-mately hurts the designer through no fault of his own. The product, nevertheless, may be in great demand and a marketing success and the fault may only be recognized by those trained and experienced in indus-trial design. Designers always look for the success of this design to propel them into the next design assignment, whether it be for a new client or for the same one. The next client may be very sophisticated in industrial design taste and reject our proposal to do his work because our former work does not appear quite right and he wants designers who do it right.

When I have tried to discuss this problem with clients, they claim that they have bought the design service and have every right to change and modify the design as they see fit. We understand this. Some clients, in my opinion, fail to consider that our future depends upon how faithful they and their staffs are to the design. The design is us! Most sensitive clients call us and discuss any problem that may necessitate changes, giving us an opportunity to execute such changes to insure that the integrity of the design is maintained.

As time passed we kept following the sales progress of the R.E. Dietz revolving light. It was doing well and we wanted to do more develop-ment work for the company. We found Dietz receptive to product planning ideas from us. We heard that a competitive company had developed an electronic siren. Chase and I then pitched the idea of a combined light/siren for Dietz to manufacture and we all agreed to design a simple combined product. Police garage mechanics hate to take the time to install a siren and a light separately so the idea of one product with one installation would appeal to them. Dietz awarded us a development contract to do the complete job, and we did it successfully.

Our research necessitated that we visit New York City, Boston, and Syracuse to talk to police and fire chiefs to determine exactly what they needed. While we were in New York City, an aircraft crashed into a school, and I had an unusual opportunity to see and hear all types of emergency vehicles. The Boston fire department pointed out the need for variable sound systems. In other words, one sound for police, another for fire protection vehicles and still another sound for ambu-

**FIGURE 7.14.** Fiberglass model of R.E. Dietz light/siren, 1960.  **FIGURE 7.15.** R.E. Dietz light/siren on a vehicle.

lances. The New York City police wanted the sound to be low frequency so that officers at an intersection can determine the direc-tion an emergency vehicle is traveling. We built a fiberglass model and went into a field behind our new office and designed the sound with the help of an electronic engineer (Figures 7.14 and 7.15). This product was a success. ∎

By this time, 1957, we outgrew our Oak Street office and needed larger quarters. We had hired one employee and needed yet another. A friend of ours who had done some machine model work for us suggested we consider an old shop he owned next to his house in Split Rock, a suburb of Syracuse. The building was perfect for us so we bought it and moved in (Figure 7.16). At last, we made money and even set some aside. Up until this time we were not drawing a salary. All the money earned went back into the business to expand. Thank goodness we had saved money and could pay cash for this building without the burden of carrying a mortgage. We converted the garage in this building into our design laboratory which worked, but was crowded. The rest of the building provided excellent storage space,

**FIGURE 7.16.** Stevens-Chase Design Associates' Split Rock Office building in Camillus, New York, 1958.

**FIGURE 7.17.** Chicago Pneumatic model #707 three-quarter-inch impact wrench used in the production of air conditioning equipment, 1958.

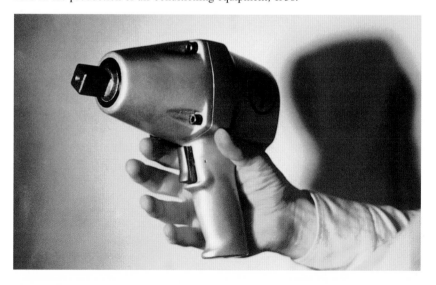

designer cubicles, a small conference room, efficient secretarial and reception area, and adequate space for the normal utilities.

## CASE STUDY NO. 5: CHICAGO-PNEUMATIC TOOL COMPANY

In 1956 we followed up on a call we had made to Chicago Pneumatic Tool Company. Its facilities were in Frankfort, New York, just outside of Utica. The company originated in Chicago and moved east prior to the war. Chicago Pneumatic manufactured pneumatic hand tools, and it wanted us to look at its 3/4" impact wrench. This tool is a production-line, pneumatic-powered wrench used in the assembly of semi-heavy products.

Prior to issuing us a contract, people at Chicago Pneumatic were continually asking about how much power tool experience we had. This was a proper inquiry by the client. I recall going to great lengths to put the client at ease regarding our experience. While I had designed a flight control wheel and paring knife, they were not pneumatic-powered tools. We simply had no power tool experience. Chicago Pneumatic finally relented and awarded us the contract. We were anxious to please the company and went "all out" on this assignment.

First we studied how the power wrench was used. The client arranged for us to see the product in operation at nearby Carrier Corporation where it was used for the assembly of parts on the production line. We studied production line workers and interviewed them and discovered that because of the heavy weight of the product, hand and arm muscles became readily fatigued. Next we simulated using the product in our design laboratory by using lead weights in a mock-up. Considering the product's weight, we wanted to design a more comfortable and less fatiguing wrench. We also wanted to make the product useable with one hand, thus enabling the operator to start a nut with one hand while holding the tool in the other.

We designed a sculptured shape under the motor called the saddle (Figure 7.17). The area between the thumb and the forefinger of the hand supported the tool. The finger bones of the hand are now in sheer. We wanted the tool to sit on the hand with minimum gripping. Gripping causes unnecessary hand fatigue. As the tool tilts forward

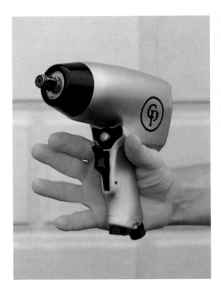

**FIGURE 7.18.** Chicago Pneumatic model #734 impact wrench. Notice the shelf which allows the product to sit on the hand. We discovered this was a good feature when we designed the model #707. This became the most popular and most copied wrench of its capacity in the world. This photograph shows our appearance model being held in the hand, demonstrating the value of the shelf under the motor, 1959.

**FIGURE 7.19.** The Chicago Pneumatic model #734 impact wrench (l) compared with a competitive pneumatic Ingersoll-Rand wrench (r) of the same capacity. We designed the Ingersoll-Rand wrench many years after working for Chicago Pneumatic. The Ingersoll-Rand wrench, however, did not possess the one-handed, reversing feature.

during work, the center of gravity moves forward and the tool falls away from the back of the saddle to rest on top of the third or fourth finger under the trigger. With the underside of the trigger avoiding contact, this avoids pinching. We built a lip, or pad, forward from the handle for the third or fourth finger to rest on. Considerable force was needed to activate the trigger, so we made it an optional feature for one or two finger operation. To prove our concept we built an appearance model loaded with lead to simulate the weight. Our model verified our theories. As far as we know, this is one of the first applications of human factors in the design of a tool like this. The tool succeeded in sales when compared with the previous design.

Following this project, Chicago Pneumatic asked us to take a look at a new impact wrench used in automobile service stations. It was unique in that the direction of the rotation of the wrench could be changed by the hand holding the wrench. This permitted one-handed operation and made it possible for the operator to hold his work with the opposite hand, particularly when working on the underside of a vehicle. For instance, replacing a muffler was usually an awkward task, but this wrench made the job easier for the service technician. This wrench contributed to efficient work and became the most popular wrench of its capacity in the world and was often imitated (Figures 7.18 and 7.19). ∎

## CASE STUDY NO. 6:  SCM

Then Smith-Corona (SCM) called us back to work for them. Our design service and the success of the Sears typewriter assignment in 1954 led to the redesign of Smith-Corona's large electric machine, the 3E model (Figure 7.20). This machine was just short of a disaster. It worked, but was not heavy enough to take the pounding of electric action. In fact, it was a manual with a motor in it. The IBM electric, Smith-Corona's strongest competitor, appeared to be a rugged machine from the frame to the carriage. This Smith-Corona project of trying to patch up its electric office machine went on and off for a couple of years. It seemed that the more IBM ate into SCM's sales, the more concerned the Smith division became. We found ourselves needing a

**FIGURE 7.20.** SCM model 3E (before design) typewriter, front view, 1958.

**FIGURE 7.21.** SCM model #400 typewriter, clay model of proposed design, 1961.

**FIGURE 7.26.** SCM model #400 typewriter, 3/4 view with machine in operation.

**FIGURE 7.27.** SCM model #400 typewriter with mechanism exposed. Notice that the housing fits snugly around the mechanism allowing for a compact product.

**FIGURE 7.22** SCM model #400 typewriter, side view, with ribbon spool cover elevated, 1960.

**FIGURE 7.23.** SCM model #400 typewriter, side view.

clear definition of the problem and a carefully delineated plan of action if we were to ever get the product out. Finally, in about 1960, SCM recognized that it must start over with a new design. When the new machine called the 400 was introduced, the "tab" system was poorly engineered and the product just did not function properly (Figures 7.21, 7.22, 7.23, 7.24, 7.25, 7.26 and 7.27). The product was loaded with features which it did not really need and entered the market terribly late. The problem can be blamed on the sales department, but more so on engineering. It seemed that every time a competitive machine entered the market with a unique feature, the sales department demanded that engineering add it to the Smith-Corona product. The result was deviations from the original agreed upon specification and further delay in the product's introduction. Engineering should have said "no" and insisted that the product be designed correctly before sending it to the market.

**FIGURE 7.24.** SCM model #400 typewriter, front view.

**FIGURE 7.25.** SCM model #400 typewriter, rear view.

However, our work on the model #400 was considered outstanding, one of our best designs. In fact, it was selected as part of the permanent exhibit at the Hanover Fair in West Germany in 1965. Upon reflection, regardless of how great a design is, if it does not work mechanically, it is worthless. IBM's introduction of the "Selectric" typewriter sealed the fate of Smith-Corona's new office machine. Here is another situation where, like the Convair *YB-60,* a company ignored new technology

**FIGURE 7.28.** SCM "Sterling" typewriter with its case.

which is really important and introduced a new machine which is technically out of date. Smith-Corona should have insisted immediately that all new products be as electronic as possible, as early as electronic technology seemed feasible. Hindsight is easy, however.

In 1958 we were challenged with redesigning Smith-Corona's standard portable typewriter, the Sterling (Figure 7.28). We had just six months time to do our industrial design work. We had to come up with a replacement for the most successful portable typewriter in history, from a sales and probably an engineering point of view. This was the same machine I had worked on to make a new ribbon-spool cover for Sears & Roebuck.

The company had many competitors but no one was strong. The corporation as a whole was facing a financial crunch. In order to carry the company into the future, it needed to increase its market share. While the product worked well, it needed industrial design help and we were given free rein. The new typewriter was named the "Galaxie." Without writing a specification we decided that for human factors and appearance sake the machine should be lower and more rubber should come in contact with the desk to prevent the machine from creeping and allowing pencils to roll under the machine as it was used, which was a real annoyance. The ribbon-spool cover must expose the whole ribbon system for easy, less cumbersome changing. This was a big annoyance with users. The machine had to function faster. We eventually

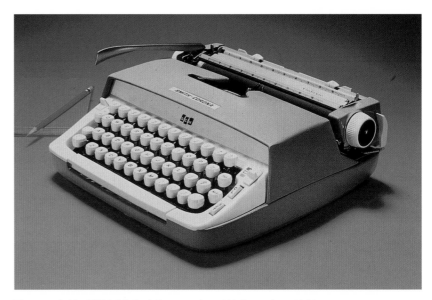

**FIGURE 7.29.** SCM "Galaxie" typewriter, 3/4 front view, 1961

achieved this by bringing the carriage return lever closer to the home keys so the operator took less time to activate the return of the carriage, thus avoiding a mechanical redesign (Figures 7.29, 7.30, 7.31 and 7.32). A more modern look was an absolute must. To reach our due date, we had to work literally day and night (Figure 7.33). There were no progress review meetings, yet we kept the client informed of what we were doing, since our new building was convenient for its engineers to occasionally look over our shoulders.

By now we had two designers working with us. The work was terribly intense, in fact, we used to call our long work sessions "all night, all frantic." I recall on the day of some final presentations the paint on some of the model parts still being wet when we put them in the car to go to the presentation. A typewriter is so complex with so many moving parts, such as the type bar which strikes the paper, key button levers which are activated by the fingers, carriage moving back and forth, rotating carriage return lever, rotating and ratcheting platens with paper moving out of the machine as well as a sliding ribbon-spool

**FIGURE 7.30.** SCM "Galaxie" typewriter with ribbon spool cover slid forward. This feature provides easy access to the ribbon system.

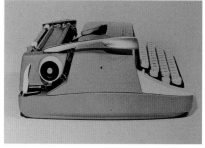

**FIGURE 7.31.** SCM "Galaxie" typewriter, side view. This machine possessed many human factor features and was very popular with the market. The typewriter was in production for thirty years with no significant changes!

**FIGURE 7.32.** SCM "Galaxie" typewriter with its carrying case and carton which we also designed.

**FIGURE 7.33.** Our "Galaxie" design team at work, from left to right: Roger Schindler, Philip Stevens, David Chase, and Brian Stewart.

cover, that the design could only be accomplished by designing over a working mechanism. Thus we were assured at all times of maintaining adequate clearances between parts. The fact that we knew in advance that the machine worked properly saved us considerable time, particularly in product and production engineering and planning.

Our employees were exhausted when we finished and presented this new portable typewriter model. Smith-Corona executives knew that if they could get this machine into production, they had a winner.

Everyone was excited. It was a success and hundreds of jobs were secure for a few years. Basically this product, with only minor changes, stayed in production from 1961 when it was first introduced until 1983. To my knowledge, this is the longest production run of a typewriter without a model change. Smith-Corona acquired and maintained its market share.

I am sure that by now to my partner and our employees I appeared as a design perfectionist seeking a result, which at times is just shy of being impossible. I knew deep down that if we were to do well as a design firm, we had to function as a team and work and rework our designs to achieve the best. A successful project would make our firm. This reworking process is caused by uncertainty of recognizing the right design solution when it appears. Not all ideas pan out. Experimentation with different ideas and concepts and working with three dimensional mock-ups and models is the only way to recognize and know what is best, at least it was with this problem. Change often is hard on others, particularly employees who are creative but after solving a design problem sometimes become lazy or inflexible and present a single design solution, sincerely believing that this is the only solution. They then often claim their good ideas are trashed by an insensitive boss when something better comes along. Little do they appreciate the fact that the boss's final decision is based on years of experience and first-hand knowledge of the client's needs. Furthermore, it was our name that was on the door, not theirs. The future of the client's company and the jobs of its employees depended upon the success of our designs. It was paramount that we produce the best designs that we possible could. ∎

## CASE STUDY NO. 7: GRAFLEX

Soon after this, we received a call from a company called Graflex, located in Rochester, New York. It was known for its professional press cameras and also 16mm motion picture projectors used in schools. Graflex manufactured a vinyl-covered plywood housing for its projectors (Figure 7.34). Most 16mm projectors go to schools as part of the audio-visual equipment. These projectors, often carried by students, are

**FIGURE 7.34.** Graflex 16mm projector housing, before redesign. Notice the plywood case with vinyl fabric cover. The housing scuffed and tore easily.

**FIGURE 7.35.** Graflex 16mm projector housing, clay model, 1961.

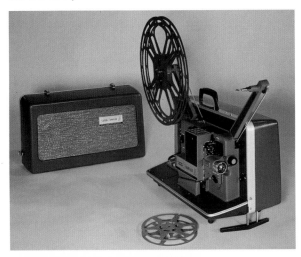

**FIGURE 7.36.** Our new design for Graflex's 16mm projector housing with solid fiberglass housing.

**FIGURE 7.37.** Philip Stevens (l) and David Chase (r) with new Graflex projector housing. We were feeling great, knowing our design had saved this company.

heavy and cumbersome. It was very easy for a student when carrying it to brush up against the hallway walls and tear the projector's vinyl-fabric cover, thus leaving an ugly, shoddy looking product. Our assignment was to come up with a jacketing system which would not be hurt by the everyday scuffing that the product might experience. We were given an extremely tight schedule, which was frustrating. We built a clay model to determine the best shape; then we sought out plastic-case vendors (Figure 7.35). One company made a fibrous-glass polyester case. The feature of this material is that it could be scratched but when wetted, the scratch disappears. The moisture removes the scratched off plastic. This solved the problem (Figures 7.36 and 7.37)! The president of the company sought me out one day and told me we had saved his company. They could now continue to offer 16mm motion picture projectors. ∎

## CASE STUDY NO. 8: ITEK CORPORATION

Another client, ITEK Corporation of Rochester, New York, had bought the old Photostat Company. It wanted us to help design an 18" x 24" microfilm reader/printer. We built a cardboard human factors mock-up to study the light pattern about the mechanism and determine the best viewing angle for both a standing and sitting operator (Figures 7.38, 7.39, 7.40 and 7.41). The objective was to make the machine as inviting and easy to use as possible. This was our specification, not the client's. The engineers were easy to work with, however, and were very proud of their

**FIGURE 7.38.** Itek Corporation 1824 reader/printer, cardboard-human-factors mock-up, 1960.

**FIGURE 7.39.** A designer studying and determining the best arrangement of controls for Itek's 1824 reader/printer.

**FIGURE 7.40.** David Chase (c) and Philip Stevens (l) with Roderick Bunyea (r) discussing control arrangement.

**FIGURE 7.41.** Designers testing viewing angle for the Itek 1824 reader/printer. The angle had to be acceptable for sitting as well as standing operators.

**FIGURE 7.42.** A production Itek 1824 reader/printer on display at the Robertson Center Gallery in Binghamton, New York.

work. They liked us and we were able to work well together. The design fell together nicely.

We relished the finished design so much that together with the ITEK engineers, we submitted it to the Master Design Award Contest as offered by *Product Engineering,* a McGraw-Hill magazine (Figure 7.42). Fortunately, we were selected along with about eight other design/-engineering projects as the best in the country, putting us on the map as a design consulting firm. The next year, 1963, David Chase and I were invited to judge the Master Design Award selection for McGraw-Hill which was a great honor. ∎

Thus far I have discussed the stories of clients that I brought to the firm. Chase was usually with me when we started a new project. We both believed this was important and helped eliminate misunderstandings. When we did typewriters or projects that needed everyone's participation, we would break off a part of the project and he would work for me. The reverse was also true when Chase needed help with clients he brought to the firm. I detected that he enjoyed being included in my projects, but preferred to work on his by himself or with one of the other designers exclusively. This was acceptable to me as long as he was happy. We lived in each other's pockets so to speak.

## CASE STUDY NO. 9: DESIGN DIRECTING

Smith-Corona's top executives felt they understood how industrial design worked and were aware of the work and time that was required to develop complex products like typewriters. While they didn't have trouble with our billing, they were very sensitive to the time and manpower it took to get a good design. Good designs require experimentation and that takes time. I am sure it was also annoying to them to see us working successfully for other clients. Smith-Corona finally announced that it wanted us to set up an industrial design department like our office inside its facility. By this time Smith-Corona had merged with a company called Marchant which was a leader in mechanical calculators. SCM wanted us to staff its design department, specify the

**FIGURE 7.43.** The SCM "Electra 12" typewriter, 3/4 front view. This typewriter had a twelve-inch carriage and was designed for office applications, 1961.

**FIGURE 7.44.** The SCM model #200 typewriter, side view. The model #200 was a compact version of the "Electra 12" designed for personal use. The model #200 was actually created first. Once developed, SCM discovered it had a new market to penetrate, thus added a twelve-inch carriage which could accommodate a piece of paper up to eleven-and-one-half-inch wide.

**FIGURE 7.45.** SCM "Electra 12", rear view. Robert Metzner was the project designer.

equipment and direct the design. We sensed that the days of Stevens-Chase doing all the design work were coming to an end. Yet we were working still on a photocopy machine and two electronic office automatic typewriter systems (not to be confused with an electronic typewriter like the "Selectric") and we were starting a telecommunications send/receive system. All this work kept us busy into 1966. We discussed this and it seemed more efficient for Chase to take over this project since the client was in California and it would be costly for both of us to go there. I was also busy with other work.

We ran ads in the *New York Times, Industrial Design Magazine* and local papers to look for staff for the new department. We held interviews and explained to the prospective employees that we would be giving

them a lot of latitude with design, but we were the directors and did have ideas about how the product line should look. We laid out the area in the plant we wanted for the department, and SCM gave us the approval to equip the area. This was fun since we could purchase expensive equipment that we would be hesitant about buying for ourselves. We hired a model lab manager who was experienced and helped each designer make models of his designs. Usually we had expected the designers in our facility to make their own models. We ultimately hired five designers, a model maker, and a secretary for the department.

One good thing came of our design directing experience, that is, SCM took the popular electric portable typewriter and modified it into a small office typewriter by incorporating a wider carriage to take 8-1/2" x 11" paper sideways. It was named the "Electra 12" (Figures 7.43, 7.44 and 7.45). The typewriter was a hit, particularly with small businesses. We encouraged the company's engineers to join us in submitting the design in the 1962 Master Design Award contest. We won a prize again. This helped SCM and Stevens-Chase Design Associates immensely. It verified that we knew what we were doing in the design of business machine products. The Corona Division's engineers were excited and happy. The Corona Division engineering executives, without college educations, at last, were getting professional recognition for their abilities.

Chase and I held regular staff meetings with the new department and appointed the most experienced designer as manager. We functioned as the directors of design, outlining the design objectives, but the manager was responsible for seeing that the work got done on time and kept us informed of any problems. We hoped to avoid all the corporate politics that accompanies any new department.

One day SCM's management approached me and asked if I would come and run the department. They left Chase out of this plan. I thought hard about the invitation. Did I really want to spend the rest of my life designing business machines? I had already been involved with seven typewriters. The challenge of designing new machines was fading fast. I decided it would not be fair to my partner or myself to accept the position regardless of the salary. It would mean I would spend much time doing Sears work, keeping records and playing corporate politics, all of which bored me greatly. I was particularly concerned about access to corporate management. Whoever ran the department could be easily overruled by engineering and forgotten or fired. Any corporate executive could decide to manage the design himself. For me this was a step down.

We ultimately recommended that SCM hire its own director, but we would continue to do the design directing until it found someone it was happy with. Concurrently, a couple of men sensing the situation, started challenging our authority. We were prepared to dismiss these men, but SCM overruled us. We discovered we had responsibility, but no authority. Our fears were justified; this was an intolerable situation. We encouraged SCM to hire a director in a hurry, and it finally did choose one. ∎

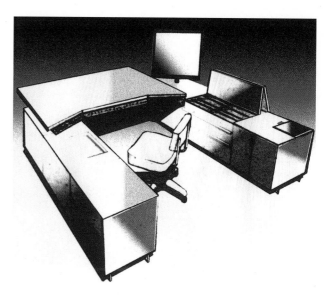

**FIGURE 7.46.**
Sketch of a typical workstation from our Integration Research proposal to SCM, 1964.

CASE STUDY NO. 10: ## SCM GRAPHICS AND CORPORATE IDENTITY

During this time SCM was merging with and acquiring diverse companies. While SCM felt that merging and acquiring was the only way it could survive this turbulent time, it realized early on that it could get into trouble if it did not plan carefully. SCM hired an ex-military telecommunications specialist named Richard LaVino for advice on its product planning.

SCM had many diverse divisions and nothing was being done to bring them together to build and generate new products to meet future needs which could never have been accomplished without the mergers and acquisitions. I approached Richard LaVino, the new corporate product planner, and there was no denying that there was a problem. We began what was called "Integration Research," i.e., the idea of how to integrate all these different companies to work together by creating a new efficient office product system or work station (Figure 7.46). He was receptive and we worked with him for a year or more on this problem.

We observed secretaries involved in generating original documents with calculations which needed to be duplicated, easily modified, circu-

lated by teleprinter, and filed, perhaps on microfilm. Obviously, at that time we did not have fax machines, personal computers, laser printers, or sophisticated photocopiers which enlarge, reduce, or copy in color. We felt that SCM should develop a modular system so that an office work station could be created using components selected to satisfy certain needs. Today it is incomprehensible to understand why this system could not have been developed at that time because the technology was known. All that was needed was corporate executives with foresight and a willingness to take a risk along with an imaginative marketing and sales force. In the end, nothing evolved from this work. SCM's lack of foresight, enthusiasm, and ambition left us totally bewildered.

The "typewritten message was on the wall." We took the past events at SCM seriously and tried to find replacement clients. Regardless of how nice the company officials were to us, we were going to be slowly phased out by this client. Corporate executives felt that to control their destiny they needed to control industrial design; it was too important to let outsiders like us dictate the policy of how their products were to be designed. They forgot that they originally called us in when they could not properly design themselves. Now they pinned their hopes on their new director. The cost of operating this depart-

**FIGURE 7.48.** A few of the many products we designed for SCM, from lower left clockwise: corporate identity guide, the famous "Galaxie" typewriter, office model #400 typewriter, light weight "Skywriter" typewriter, packaging for an adding machine, office calculator, portable electric typewriter, annual reports, and photocopy machine (center). Photograph taken in 1962.

ment was a serious consideration. It seemed like SCM cared little about cost as long as it acquired control and could play once again with the appearance of its products as it liked. We casually pointed out we could continue to provide them service at a fraction of what we projected it would eventually cost them. They did not want to hear this, and our predictions came true.

We designed great graphics, custom corporate and division signatures, a new logo called the tri-bar and packaging for SCM (Figure 7.47).

**FIGURE 7.47.** Typewriter packaging we developed for SCM, © 1960. Brian Stewart was project designer

We also prepared a corporate identity system along with an identity manual. This manual illustrated how signs should appear on buildings, the new logo would appear on trucks, and how the various division logos would appear with the corporate logo. As mentioned before, we still were finishing up a couple of products for SCM. Our attitude was that we would continue to provide good service because it is going to stop, and we wanted the executives as a good reference (Figure 7.48). ▮

## CASE STUDY NO. 11:  A MISTAKE

Then, we made a costly mistake. During the past couple of years SCM converted from making sheet-metal stampings and formed parts to injection-molded plastic parts. Injection molding is a process where a shot of plastic pellets or raw plastic is melted and pushed into a mold under great pressure. The mold cools rapidly, while the parts harden and then the completed part pops out at great savings over sheet-metal parts.

Chase and I thought this was a great business to get into which might augment our consulting work, particularly when the design business was slack. Not surprisingly, we discovered our business to be cyclical based upon the economy. We talked with experts and they warned us of the potential for failure and why. They spoke about the hidden costs of machines such as plastic drying ovens, a grinder which breaks up defective parts so that they may be recycled, the occasional need for extra employees, constant bookkeeping to say nothing about sales help and an operator/manager and multishift work periods. Nonetheless, we jumped in.

First we discovered our technical advisor took another job while his wife sued him for divorce. Our marketing man, who assured us of all kinds of jobs, backed out since we did not have experience in this type of work. The problems built up in a hurry and Chase and I were hanging on. All of a sudden we felt the cold wind of reality and found ourselves standing alone beside an assortment of nonrunning expensive equipment. What work we did have became a problem between us. This probably discouraged Chase, since he was president, when looking to me for practical help. I would gladly do the physically mundane work, but I kept thinking about how much more valuable I was as a consultant and that this venture was a misuse of our time and talents. I am sure this lack of enthusiasm was apparent. It simply was not me. It was obvious that customers would be giving us work, but in turn expected us to give them free design service. This I found repugnant, and I became discouraged with myself and our venture into plastic production. After much soul searching, we both concluded we had better get out of this business because it did not compliment our design service as we had hoped. I am sure this was hard on my partner. ∎

## A NEW OFFICE

At this time, we rapidly outgrew the Split Rock office. We had 10 employees and needed larger quarters (Figure 7.49). We had begun to work on bigger products like lift trucks, over-the-highway trucks, dental operatories, and eventually on an aircraft fuselage. All this necessitated a larger mock-up and model area. We had a full-time model maker and simply needed more space. Now that Diatech, our plastic injection molding facility was no longer in operation, we had a vacant building, ideal for a new office, located in Skaneateles, New York, about 20 miles west of Syracuse and 10 miles away from our Split Rock office. Skaneateles is a medium-sized town bordering on one of the beautiful Finger Lakes in central New York. The building was also on Rt. 20 which is a major east-west highway from Boston to Chicago. The community appealed to designers and prospective employees, an ideal place for a design office. Chase's family was from Skaneateles, and he knew many important residents. In fact, he had built a house on the lake, while I continued to commute from Syracuse.

We moved our designers and model facilities to Skaneateles and remodeled the building for a design office, a presentation and conference room, a model development laboratory and a large mock-up

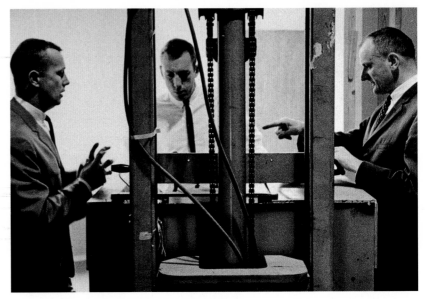

**FIGURE 7.49.** David Chase (l) and Philip Stevens (r) reviewing a Raymond materials handling truck with project designer Alan Brownlie, c. 1962.

area. The building was a modern, prefabricated steel structure built on a concrete slab originally used for farm machinery sales. Unfortunately, when the sun came out, the building creaked and groaned from expansion and contraction. The employees called it "the tin can." We kept the bookkeeping and secretarial services in Split Rock and commuted the 10 miles back and forth each day. We eventually put the Split Rock office up for sale and sold it within a couple of weeks for twice what we had paid for it. Then everybody was located in Skaneateles.

Chase and I had wanted to build our own office building from scratch. We even bought some beautiful land about three miles away, but the slowness of our business and the end of SCM as a client led us to believe we should stay where we were.

## LOSS OF A CLIENT

Just as one wins clients, one can occasionally lose a client. Thinking back over many of the clients I have accumulated over the years, it has been a wonderful experience winning their trust and conversely, sad and disturbing when the relationship comes to an end. The termination of a consultant/client relationship can evolve from a seemingly insignificant comment or gesture. To maintain a client through all kinds of adversity demands a great deal of tact, empathy, and patience. Some of the reasons I have lost clients are as follows:

1. **Insensitivity on my part to a client's needs**

   Many times there is a general lack of communication between the client and designer. The client sometimes cannot effectively communicate its needs and/or the designer does not interpret the client's needs correctly.

2. **Misunderstandings between the client and designer**

   Again, this results from a lack of communication. To illustrate, I once had a client ask if we ever adjust our billing. I answered "yes"—meaning that many designs we tried just did not work out and so we did not charge for all of the time spent on the problem. The client, I later presumed, interpreted this to mean that we had overcharged on this project.

3. **Your main contact person within the client's facility can change jobs**

   Some of my clients' engineers and designers have moved to another division or another company. Their replacements have not always liked my style of work, or they sometimes have design consultants with whom they are already working. When this happens, it is difficult to salvage a relationship with such a client. While the loss of one client is significant, it should not devastate a consulting practice. My partner and I began to cultivate potential clients in upstate New York even

before our contract with SCM expired. After losing SCM as a client we went on to provide successful design service for many companies. Some clients that we worked for included: Scott Aviation; Eveready division of Union Carbide; Raymond Corporation; Ritter Company; Castle Company; and Piper Aircraft.

## THE END OF A PARTNERSHIP

In the latter part of 1969, after we had been partners for about 15 years, Chase announced that he wanted to work alone, thus dissolving our partnership. Obviously we had different views of how to best provide our clients service and manage our professional lives. He believed that the firm was a business to make money and that was that! I believed much the same, but I also felt that, like the medical or legal profession, in design there is also a need to give back to society through community service. I believe at that time Chase was generating more income, but I felt strongly that we should also address professional responsibilities. I felt that breaking up the partnership was not in everyone's best interest—the clients, our employees, the firm, including ourselves and the profession, but so be it! I moved out, thus ending years of excellent industrial design service. While the firm of Stevens-Chase Design Associates ceased to exist, we both continued to provide the best service possible to our clients. Regrettably, the psychologists who interviewed us for compatibility prior to our partnership could not have had a crystal ball telling how we would evolve.

Now, looking back over my design career, it was almost half over. I recall asking myself where have I been, where am I now, and where do I want to go? I was 46 years old and had two wonderful children (Figure 7.50). We had common interests, including hiking and skiing. I had joined the National Ski Patrol System, teaching mountaineering which was very satisfying to me. My options were to either

**FIGURE 7.50.** The author, Philip H. Stevens, at 46 years of age, 1970.

go to work for someone else or continue working for myself. I decided on the latter, which necessitated the creation a new company.

## SETTING UP A NEW COMPANY

Most people think it is unduly complicated to open a design office. Designers have many choices in their professional careers. First, they can stay where they are and someday everyone will move away, die, or they discover their business has dissolved. This leaves the following three options:

- **Establish a Sole Proprietorship**
  The New York State Governor's Office of Regulatory Reform defines a sole proprietorship as follows: "A sole proprietorship is the simplest form of business structure. It may be suited to the start up of a one person business. It is more flexible than either the partnership or the corporation. However, all business responsibilities are those of the single owner. This includes unlimited financial liability incurred by the business."

- **Establish a Partnership**
  "A partnership is the relationship between two or more persons or companies that carry on a trade or business together," says the New York State Governor's Office of Regulatory Reform. Partners include their share of the partnership income on their

state and federal personal income tax returns. The income generated from a partnership is considered business income rather than wages or salaries. In selecting a partner, one should also look beyond his or her own profession to related fields. For instance, two individual designers with similar talents do not necessarily make a successful partnership. It might be better, for example, to take on a marketing person or an engineer as a partner. This way a partner's skills and talents can complement your skills rather than compete with them.

- **Establish a Corporation**
  Establishing a corporation usually requires an attorney to help prepare the necessary documentation, which varies from state to state. The New York State Governor's Office of Regulatory Reform defines a corporation as: "...[a]n entity separate and distinct from the individual(s) who own and manage the business. A corporation is authorized to sell, buy, and inherit property in its own name and is legally endowed with rights, powers and duties in the conduct of lawful activities. Business corporations are operated for profit and are authorized to raise capital by selling shares of interest in the corporation. A corporation's debts and obligations are distinctly its own."

The responsibilities of business owners are extensive. If they choose to start their own design office, they must follow the government's rules explicitly. If, for example, a design office provides a service and has been compensated, they will not be able to cash the check unless they have deposited the correct business documents with the bank. If a designer chooses to have employees, payroll withholdings must be made and the proper reporting must be made to the government. One also must provide his employees with unemployment, social security, disability, and worker's compensation insurance.

It is imperative that one acquire the necessary information to operate the business strictly by the rules. An excellent source of information and assistance is any local office of the U.S. Small Business Administration. Some communities also have separate development centers which provide assistance to upstart businesses. They can provide assistance, guidance, and in some cases, low-interest loans or grants to new businesses. They can discuss the advantages and disadvantages of each type of business entity. If a design firm expects to grow and have employees or associates, it can elect either a partnership or corporation. If it is concerned about liability exposure, it may elect to form a corporation. I have formed all three types of businesses, at one time or another in my career, and have felt most comfortable with the corporate structure.

I set up my new office across the road from where the old Stevens-Chase Design Associates office had been in Skaneateles, one of the best buildings available in town (Figure 7.51). It had nice lines, some called the roof style a pagoda, and the walls were constructed of brick. Built in 1900, it originally served as a trolley car power-converting station. Since a designer must project a good image, how one dresses, what car one drives, where one lives and one's office building must all portray good taste. What client would entrust a designer with poor taste to make his product look great? I did not have to do much to make the building function as an office. Over the years, the community and I looked upon the building as a landmark. I put in railroad tracks and ties in the front lawn to simulate the original rails plus a flower bed, much like the original operators had done. It could easily have been identified in the official landmark registry, but I wanted the freedom to make changes if necessary which might be contrary to the rules of "landmark status." I received many compliments on the appearance of the property. I eventually bought the building and put in a new furnace, heavy insulation, storm windows, removed the white paint from the exterior and repointed the bricks, then added a new roof. All the effort in updating and repair paid off when it came time to sell the building in 1995. Today it is still func-

**FIGURE 7.51.** Philip Stevens Associates' office building in Skaneateles, New York, an old trolley power station, 1974.

tioning as a comfortable office building. Perhaps the best feature is that everything is on one level. This was great for constructing large mock-ups and models—no stairs to deal with. My style of work continued as always.

I changed the structure of the firm to a corporation because my lawyer felt this was better than a proprietorship for liability reasons. Using a trusted lawyer has proven most satisfactory throughout my entire career. He became a most trusted confidant and friend.

I then asked some highly trusted friends who were successful in their own businesses to become my board of directors. I had great hopes that the members would advise me in areas of public relations and corporate management in which I felt uncertain. To be honest, these men tried to be helpful but they just could not appreciate the problems of a small, professional consulting office. Since they were not paid directors, rather advisors only, it was inappropriate to expect much. My lawyer and I soon discovered we could make the best decisions regarding the firm's business.

Work was more difficult since I had to guide my new small staff alone. Not everyone moved with me from the old firm. I had to check the books, pay bills, design and seek new business. I asked myself where am I going, and how am I going to get there? I had a good view of myself and I knew that making money was important, but was not everything. I do believe that as professionals we need to, or better yet, we have a responsibility to design the best products possible. Design can bring a more comfortable, efficient, and safer life, particularly to those who use our products. This seemed to be a healthy philosophy and the thread that ran through my work. Thus, why not continue doing what I had been doing? I was content with my professional conduct and I had many friends and would continue this course of offering the best service possible.

As Philip Stevens Associates, Ltd. started up, I needed to be involved in the business end of the firm. I found counting money annoying, but necessary. I needed help with the details. Subconsciously I found myself confiding more and more in my secretary and accountant. I found that a good secretary can become my second ego and a confidant. However, before I found the right person for the office, I had hired, fired, or simply parted on mutual terms with at least three such people. At first I hired for experience. I wanted an attractive, "take charge" type of person, someone with references who was competent in secretarial and bookkeeping skills, young in personality, quick mentally, gracious around clients, focused on work, motivated, and appealing as a person. Does such a person exist? I had shared in the partnership, two such people who fit the bill.

A real professional soon joined us who could do everything. I found the office running like clockwork. Shortly thereafter, she wanted to get married and have children. Subsequently, she introduced me to a legal secretary friend, and I hired her and she proved equally efficient. She attended a community college for accounting and was even better at bookkeeping. I had her doing projections, which is using past financial data to anticipate future expenses.

At last, this experience helped provide just what I needed to give me the objectivity to make good business decisions. To illustrate, there came a time when our rented office building was sold to a new owner. After much talk, my secretary and I agreed that some day soon he would demand that I buy the building or move out because he needed the ready cash. We projected our needs and started pinching and saving every penny we could get our hands on. Sure enough, the shark showed his teeth one Christmas and threatened to sell the building in 30 days if I did not buy immediately. I bought, but I bought on good terms. I was proud of myself.

Another illustration happened about 10 years later when I rented an apartment and hated it. My secretary at the time had previously worked in a bank. She piled up all the money I had and showed me how I could easily buy just the house I wanted and needed. I am eternally grateful to her since I did just that. However, a secretary or office manager on salary is much different than a partner. While both try hard to give good advice when counsel is needed, a secretary suffers little from bad advice since she does not have the responsibility of owning the firm. On the other hand, she does not share in the rewards either. A secretary gives an entirely different opinion from mine. Another difference is the competition factor one feels subconsciously with a partner. One consciously tries not to threaten the other partner and tries to be magnanimous whenever possible to sustain harmony in the face of discord. These feelings sometimes compromise good judgment.

Over the years I have hired many designers as employees. Most have proven interesting and enjoyable to know. When it came time to leave, most left the firm on their own, usually for less interesting but better paying jobs. Only three that I know of left to go into business for themselves. My observation is that the ideal designer has design abilities and is looking for a stimulating environment with the opportunity to exercise his skills, talents, and creativeness. On the surface, employers discover ideal designers through their portfolios. We also see their communication skills in their portfolios. Résumés obviously help indicate where they have been and what they have been doing. Subconsciously on my part, I look for their design talent and their life philosophy. This shows up in how they present themselves in their interview (dress, mannerism, etc.), and the extracurricular activities listed on their résumé. Some designers simply wanted a job, and usually were not hired. I do place considerable emphasis on a person's loyalty. Over time this is most important as they are entrusted with more and more responsibility. I also look at their ability to follow directions, creativity, efficiency, motivation, social skills along with a sense of professional management including ethical behavior toward all people inside and outside the firm. Most potential employees have serious reservations about becoming involved in professional associations like IDSA and avoid such responsibilities. They also avoid considerations of opening their own firm. Most designers came to me because they were aware of my work and thought well of it.

Over time I have become aware of the importance of always saying the same thing to each new employee. To illustrate, every year I am confused trying to recall if we always close down Columbus Day or Veteran's Day. To be consistent I prepared an office policy manual which carefully answered as many questions we could remember employees asking. The real value is that each employee knows that every other employee is conducting himself or herself by the same rules so there is no opportunity for confusion or privilege. However, from time to time we would open the manual for discussion, but I always had the last word. See Appendix B for a complete description of what is contained in an "Office Policy Manual" and a sample "Employee Agreement" in Appendix C.

Designers need to consider using public-relations efforts in publicizing their business. PR is a professional's way of advertising. It is done more discreetly than advertising, however. Early on in my business career I had several meetings with a friend of mine who was a public-relations consultant to several large companies in Rochester, New York. He felt that writing articles for professional magazines was one excellent means of establishing my name as a design expert. If a reputable trade publication carried my article, then I must be an expert worth listening to. Did writing these articles help? Yes and no. Yes, my colleagues saw my articles and were interested. Not many, if any, clients ever saw the material. Only after purchasing reprints of the articles and sending them to my clients did it pay off. No specific article ever brought the firm a new client, however.

Building an effective brochure for any consulting firm is serious business. It demands careful planning and design. I did my own planning, designing, and writing. I found a simple brochure which discusses the design problems I have managed and the results of my service to be most effective. This approach introduced me to the client and illustrated the benefits of my service. I have developed about 15 or 20 case histories on past projects. I chose projects which I felt would be relevant to most interested potential clients. They cover consumer products, graphics, semi-engineering projects, product planning, industrial products, etc. These pages are on an 8-1/2" x 11" format and can be mixed and matched as needed. I stuck to a consistent format over the years, and it has been successful for me.

A comprehensive slide show is also a must. A slide presentation shows potential clients about our capabilities—much the same way potential employees show their portfolio. This helped me say and illustrate in more detail what a brochure cannot. A slide presentation gives designers the opportunity to focus on what they have done in the past, what the client needs, and how others have benefited from their service.

When we completed our work for Brockway Motor Trucks, I had little new work coming in and had to let the project designer go. This was very unfortunate, but once in a great while necessary. The designer was new to the professional world and felt I owed him more than his severance and vacation pay and photographs of projects he had worked on which were not under contract. The Brockway contract, with its nondisclosure clause, was still in effect for a year at least after the completion of our work, and he knew this. This employee violated this contract and stole all of the slides we had taken to document our progress on the project. When I discovered this I pointed out to him the seriousness of his theft, but he chose to ignore me. Later, after reason failed, I had my lawyer call him and that produced the desired result. I suspect he had duplicates made and may have continued to show them to others to get work for himself. What hurt even more was that he went to Brockway, my client, and tried to solicit work for himself. Brockway called me about the incident. This designer "shot himself in the foot" so to speak. How could I ever give him a good reference? He ended up working as an employee of a local company.

CASE STUDY NO. 12: **KENNEDY VALVE MANUFACTURING COMPANY, INC.**

Kennedy Valve Manufacturing Company, Inc. in Elmira, New York, a division of ITT Grinnell Corporation, asked us to help with a new fire hydrant. This was a fun project. The design criteria was to make a hydrant that was shorter, more compact thus less weight, and having a more appealing shape than its standard hydrant (Figures 7.52 and 7.53). First a clay model was constructed which led to a solid plastic model. The internal mechanics of the hydrant dictated the product's form. This hydrant was selected by *Industrial Design Magazine* as an outstanding design in 1970.

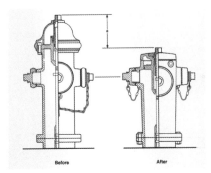

**FIGURE 7.52.** Kennedy Valve hydrant, before-and-after sketch.

**FIGURE 7.53.** Kennedy Valve hydrant design, 1971.

I have described in this chapter three types of business structures, a sole proprietorship, a partnership and a corporation. The question is, which is best for most people considering going into business for themselves? The advantage of working alone in a sole proprietorship is the joy and deep satisfaction in developing a product that a client can manufacture, sell, and derive profit. Much of the same satisfaction can be derived from a partnership. Having a partner (or partners) one trusts to try ideas on is great. A partnership provides this overview of performance. The mutual support is much appreciated, while continual criticism is divisive. See Appendix D for a list of considerations for establishing a design consulting office.

In the next chapter I will discuss how a designer can conduct life as a professional.

### CHAPTER EIGHT

# PROFESSIONAL LIFE

*Give the world the best
that you have to give,
and the best
will come back to you.*

Madeline Bridges

131

## DESIGN CONTESTS

Several design contests are announced each year and IDSA sponsors at least one of them. If a designer is cited as a winner, this award can be a springboard for much favorable publicity for both the designer and the client (Figures 8.1 and 8.2). If a winning design was a collaborative effort, the morale of both the designer's and the client's staff is enhanced. This opens the door for more work.

Participating in such contests can require large amounts of time. When we entered the Master Design Award Contest, for example, offered by *Product Engineering* (a McGraw-Hill publication), it was quite time consuming. However, the effort was well worth it. As winners we judged the next year's contest. This provided us with positive public relations exposure and experience.

*Industrial Design Magazine* also asked me to be on its annual editorial evaluation staff. My expertise was product safety.

## PROFESSIONAL ORGANIZATIONS

My friend Richard Hollerith, FIDSA, served as president of the Industrial Designers Society of America in 1977-1978. He became a member of the President's Committee on the Handicapped. This group of diverse specialists tried to develop a better relationship between the nonhandicapped and the handicapped. The committee is probably best known for its work toward providing barrier free designs or wheelchair accessibility to public facilities. Many designers admire the time and energy Hollerith put into this professional effort. He certainly set a high standard which many should seriously consider achieving.

I formed a safety committee within IDSA to establish goals for the society. I carefully recruited a few good designers to work with me, and we began to develop our statement as well as contacts in Washington, D.C. To the best of my knowledge, IDSA was the first and only professional society to take a strong stand supporting product safety.

**FIGURE 8.1.** Master Design Award received for the work done on Itek Corporation's model 1824 reader/printer, 1962.

**FIGURE 8.2.** We submitted SCM's model 200 typewriter to McGraw-Hill for consideration for a Master Design Award. The design was judged a winner. Here we are, left to right: Charles Kennedy, design manager for office typewriters, SCM Corporation; David Chase, partner, Stevens-Chase Design Associates; Joseph Barkdall, chief engineer for portable typewriters, SCM Corporation; Philip Stevens, partner, Stevens-Chase Design Associates; Edwin Mosher, Vice President of Engineering, SCM Corporation; Aaron Zeamer, design manager for portable typewriters, SCM Corporation; and E.J. Tangerman, editor *Product Engineering* magazine making the presentation.

In 1971, representing IDSA I testified about the need for product safety before Senator Gaylord Nelson's Commerce Committee. The engineering professions failed to participate. Together with my then-congressman, Jim Hanley (D) from central New York, and IDSA's lawyer, Charles Mandelstam, I went to Capital Hill, where Senator Frank Moss (D), chairman presided. What follows is an excerpt from the transcript of my testimony:

## Statement of Hon. James M. Hanley, U.S. Representative from New York

**Mr. Hanley.** Mr. Chairman, I am most grateful for your accommodation this morning, and I would be remiss if I did not commend you and your committee for having initiated these hearings on this most important legislation.

Certainly the ultimate of it all will produce better consumer products and hopefully assure the safety aspects of it. As we review the history of the issue, I think it is an activity that is long overdue.

**Senator Moss.** Thank you, Congressman Hanley. We appreciate your cooperation and help in this field very much.

**Mr. Hanley.** Thank you, Mr. Chairman. With that, it is a great pleasure to introduce one whom I regard as having very special expertise in the field of industrial design, and he is recognized nationally by that fraternity for this expertise.

He is chairman of the Safety Committee of the Industrial Designers Society of America, and along with him is Mr. Charles Mandelstam, who is counsel for the society.

So with that, it is a pleasure to introduce to you and committee Mr. Philip H. Stevens and his associate, Mr. Mandelstam.

**Senator Moss.** Welcome, gentlemen. We appreciate having you before the committee and look forward to your testimony.

Thank you very much, Congressman Hanley.

## Statement of Philip H. Stevens, Chairman, Safety Committee, Industrial Designers Society of America, New York, NY.; Accompanied by Charles Mandelstam, General Counsel

**Mr. Stevens.** Mr. Chairman and committee members, I am Philip Stevens, safety committee chairman of the Industrial Designers Society of America (IDSA). Beside me is Charles Mandelstam, the counsel for our society. Before commenting on the legislation before this committee, I would like to take a few moments to describe IDSA, in order to give this committee some context in which it may evaluate our position. This statement represents the consensus of our Safety Committee, and has the approval and endorsement of the President and Vice President of the society.

The society is a nonprofit professional organization established for the purpose of maintaining high standards of professional competence and integrity in the field of industrial design. Since it is national in scope and is the only such organization of designers in the United States, it serves as spokesman for the industrial design profession of our country.

IDSA includes both independent design consultants and staff designers of corporations. The basic requirement for membership is that candidates must have carried major responsibility in mass-market design projects which involved the integration of aesthetics, technology, and human factors. Such projects include product and product system design, packaging, corporate graphics, exhibits, space planning, and environmental design. We have designers in most of the major industries of the United States, working closely both with other technical specialists and with administrative decision makers.

Participation in the area of safety by our society goes back many years. In 1967 this interest culminated in the formation of the Society's Safety Committee. Since that time substantial efforts have been made to intensify concern for safety factors among both practicing and student designers. We have concentrated on such approaches as:

1. Encouraging design schools to become more involved in teaching safety and human factors.

2. Contributing to public awareness of problems of safety, and encouraging members of our society to involve themselves in safety oriented activities, locally and nationally.

3. Promoting awareness of safety problems by designers, and developing concrete applications helpful in responsible practice: the Society's membership has ratified a statement of its principles on safety. In addition, the Safety Committee is currently developing a detailed safety manual for use by anyone engaged in product development.

4. Working with other professional societies in the area of safety. I was invited before you today to represent the society and express its position on Safety Bill S.983 and S.1797, and I proceed now with some comments and our general conclusion regarding these bills.

Considering the issue abstractly, the Society's Safety Committee favors S.983. Aspects of special interest in this bill are commented on below. However, if practical considerations as to ease and economy of implementation (or more strictly political concerns) are seen by Congress to favor S.1797, we would find the latter bill acceptable and support it. Though less than ideal, it incorporates several of the important features of S.983.

As for S.983, we noted especially the following sections:

Sec. 3. The concept of a commission created to minimize political influence is probably the most outstanding feature of this bill. The idea of spreading the responsibility over a group of commissioners concerned with safety seems wiser than confining it to a department already burdened with many diverse responsibilities.

Sec. 4. We feel that the public needs an independent advocate in the specific area of consumer safety. This is one way to counter the lethargic and impersonal aspects of bureaucratic structures, and to make the government more responsive to the problems of the people.

Sec. 5. An independent Injury Information Clearinghouse at the Federal level is essential to a fair and thorough evaluation of possibly hazardous products, and of great value to an intelligent approach to designing new and safer products (see also comments on Sec. 11, below). As various kinds of national information systems increase, this should not be as expensive as it might first appear; in any event, the social and human benefits would more than justify it. Publication of data on accidents in the Federal Register should help to develop public support for the Commission and its objectives. We have one reservation concerning this section, however, in 5(c), 2 and in 5(g), the activities and purposes of the Commission should be more explicitly limited to the area of SAFETY in design.

Sec. 6. We commend the emphasis on developing priorities for action, from a periodic review of data.

Sec. 11. The design of new products to meet consumer needs and interests is a serious and complex responsibility. Development by the Commission, as proposed, of safety standards and of evaluation procedures for new products could make an important contribution to this enterprise.

Sec. 14. We strongly endorse the idea that the Commission be empowered to ban hazardous consumer products. While such action may be contrary to the interests of certain companies at times, the benefits to the public make us wholeheartedly favor this aspect of the legislation. In fact, the possibility of such action being taken against industry should improve the climate for the design and manufacture of safer products. A company aware that its products could be banned after manufacture will be more receptive the society believes, to the utilization of good design and a safety-conscious approach right from the start. Industrial designers have sometimes objected to a manufacturer's proposal about a product for reasons of safety, only to be met with resistance on the grounds that a change would be too costly. This legislation would make such situations less common.

Sec. 15. We approve the concept of an advisory council, drawing on persons of varied backgrounds, to assist and consult to the Commission. We see some advantage in extending the number on such a council from 15 to 20, with the additional members contributing further technical expertise (design, engineering, human factors psychology, etcetera) in aspects of product safety.

Sec.19(a). The idea that this Commission hold hearings concerning the safety of consumer products is very sound. The hearings of the National Commission on Products Safety attracted nationwide interest and certainly brought home the idea that the government is concerned about the welfare and safety of its citizens. We strongly endorse this feature of the bill. We recognize, as I stated above, that not all of these features are wholly unique to S.983, and that the other bill before you, S.1797, might be preferred if judged easier to implement and administer. Passage of either bill could greatly improve the welfare of the consumer users of our products.

**FIGURE 8.3.** Certificate of Fellowship awarded to me by IDSA in 1975. This is the highest recognition IDSA awards its members.

Mr. Chairman, the Industrial Designers Society of America appreciates this opportunity to present its views on this legislation. Mr. Mandelstam and I will be pleased to answer any questions you may have.

Following this presentation I spoke at many industrial design schools and IDSA chapter functions. I also testified before a Presidential Commission on the topic of fire safety. Not long after this presentation I was granted a fellowship by IDSA (Figure 8.3). According to IDSA,

"Fellow membership in the Society may be conferred by two-thirds majority vote of the Board of Directors upon members in good standing who have earned the special respect and affection of the membership through distinguished service to the Society and to the profession as a whole." This is the highest recognition a designer can receive from his fellow designers.

## PROFESSIONAL LIFE

Designers yearn for a thoroughly professional life, free from everyday hassles. They are not much different from other people. Designers want to work in an orderly world and appreciate order and consideration in their dealings with others. Most people looking at designers have little idea about the abundance of ethical problems that come about in a designer's life. I have known many designers and engineers who have developed ulcers worrying about work and the reaction of clients to a designer's service. I have also known three designers who died of heart attacks from simple overwork or worry.

It is appropriate to once again call attention to IDSA's *Code of Ethics and Articles of Ethical Practice* (Appendix A). Article III addresses the issue of competing fairly with our fellow industrial designers. I have always interpreted this to mean, stay clear of other industrial designers' clients and do not solicit them for yourself. A potential client will get strange ideas about industrial design and lose respect for someone who makes contemptuous statements about and belittles the work of their fellow designers.

Questions continually arise about contracts, deadlines, fee payments, statement of work progress, delays, etc. The designer not only faces ethical problems with his clients, but also his staff. Is work getting done on time? Is it correct? Can one charge what it is worth? What has been spent on the work up to now? How do I manage that difficult employee?

## LAW AND DESIGN

I have been in court twice regarding the law and design. In both cases it involved product liability for clients. The first case involved defending a client from the widow of a miner who claimed that a piece of my client's equipment (not designed by me) contributed to the death of her husband. The lawsuit claimed that the equipment was faultily designed. The miner abandoned the controls and climbed onto his equipment to help others disconnect a power take-off unit. The equipment slid down an incline, pinning the operator between the equipment and the roof of the mine, killing him. My job was to find out how the accident happened and then defend my client (the manufacturer), the equipment, and the design. We won the case.

Later a friend used a power saw and cut off three of his fingers on one hand. He asked me to help him prove the faulty design of the power saw. I pointed out to the jury that the injured party made the type of cut that any craftsman might make and the manufacturer should have warned the user of the power saw's hazard. There should have been clearly visible warning labels and illustrations on the product. The manufacturer claimed that the product could not support such a warning label. I showed them how it could be done and within three months after the trial, the manufacturer had added a warning label to its product just as I had suggested. Needless to say, I received no credit or compensation for helping the manufacturer in this fashion. Ultimately we lost the case and I even lost some friends who felt that I did not do enough to help the injured person. Perhaps they were correct.

Besides worrying about product liability, a designer must be careful not to plagiarize the work of others. Once I started an important design assignment for a client who was anxious to catch up on market share and I was told to "copy the competitor's design" if necessary by the chief engineer. I refused to do it and came up with a great design anyway, for which I received a patent.

The lesson is, *never, ever* consider copying a competitor's design, even if the client tells you to do so. It is never acceptable. Talk to a lawyer and he will say the same thing! The objective is to design a better product than the competition. It is acceptable to study competitive designs for product research and comparison, but do not copy!

## PROFESSIONAL SERVICE

I have talked about testifying before lawmakers concerned with product safety and helping to establish the Consumer Product Safety Commission in Washington. IDSA has been active in other areas, such as design for the aging and for the handicapped. I have one friend who was a member of the President's Commission for the Handicapped for many years. He was able, through design, to improve the world in which handicapped people live and move about. By lecturing to IDSA chapters and schools on these subjects, designers become sensitive to the design needs of others.

Designers should be encouraged to participate in such efforts as community service. In my own community I have seen the impact of working to establish zoning laws and helping in their enforcement within the town of Skaneateles and the city of Syracuse. I have designed a logo for my town and a calendar for a local art gallery. Years later I designed a war memorial for my World War II military organization at Fort Drum, New York. In the late 1980s the National Association of the 10th Mountain Division expressed an interest in constructing a war memorial at Fort Drum. The memorial would be erected on its parade ground. At that time the facility went through major reconstruction and looked more like a modern college campus than an infantry division's home base. I took an active interest in this project since I lived in New York and knew both active Army soldiers and veterans, and was interested in art and monuments. Having experienced combat during World War II in mountains, I believed I could make a worthwhile contribution.

In the case of soldiers in training, like the soldiers at Fort Drum, it is imperative to establish and maintain traditions. I decided the design must be a participating monument like the Vietnam War Memorial and not a static one like a statue. However, I knew the commanding general wanted a statue. Since the monument was to be about us, I suggested constructing a mountain. The theme was named "Climb to Glory" in either peace or war.

To begin my design, I went to Fort Drum to see the environment. There are no mountains in or about Fort Drum. The environment is dead flat! Anyway, my memorial design simulated a mountain shape in a triangular mound, which would appear at one end of a parade ground. The mound was long at its base, about 200 plus feet, narrow in width, about 50 feet at its widest point, and about 10 feet to 15 feet high with gently tapered sides. The top center of the mound was notched out and a wooden bridge would connect the two mounds. Steps from the parade ground would ascend up each long leg of the mound to the bridge, then after crossing the bridge, descend the other side back to the parade ground. Each step or riser would be one step up while the tread would consist of two steps forward. Each tread would have carved into it the name of a famous battle or peace keeping mission or engagement that the division had participated in. There would be plenty of blank steps for future missions or engagements to be inscribed. The idea is that during a parade certain troops could be honored before the whole division and invited to make "the climb to glory." On dedication day we veterans would initiate the process by marching first and the existing (new) division would literally march in our footsteps following us. The bridge symbolized a tie between the veterans and the new soldiers (Figure 8.4).

I achieved four important design objectives in this design:

1. A distinctive form, reminiscent of a mountain was to be used and it should be pleasant, easy to remember and recognize.

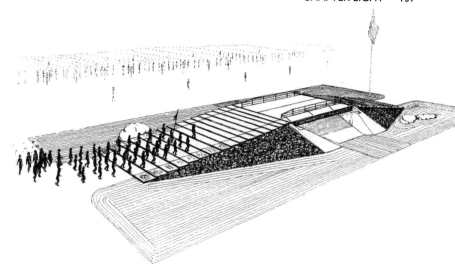

**FIGURE 8.4.** Proposed 10th Mountain Division participatory monument for Fort Drum, New York, 1982.

2. I wanted a pleasant, rhythmic effect seen as the men marched up and down the steps (one up and two across).
3. The bridge was constructed so that it would amplify the sound of the men's marching feet.
4. I wanted the height such that whoever was at the pinnacle or on the bridge could be seen by everyone on the parade ground.

Ultimately, the commanding general decided to construct a statue, bypassing our memorial committee which indicated it favored my approach.

I believe designers can and should get involved with design students at their local university or college. This can be done by lecturing, reviewing students' portfolios, giving them work if possible, or sponsoring a design contest and awarding a prize.

For some time, other semiretired industrial designers and I have wanted to help students in industrial design. We sponsored a design contest at Syracuse University and among ourselves defined the criteria. We did not wish to burden the school or faculty with any special requirements, rules, or ideas. We felt that there are usually plenty of awards or prizes for graduating seniors, so we suggested that our contest be open to lower classmen. We wanted the fun of picking the design assignment and awarding the student the prize. Our evaluation of the submissions would be the same as if this were a real design project. We wanted the problem given at the end of one school year and be due at the beginning of the next school year so that the participants could work on the project over the summer.

The first year we tried this approach we had five participants and all of the designs were satisfactory. The assignment was to design a prefabricated bathroom for upscale homes. The prize was $1,500.00 to the winning entry.

The design challenge for the second year was called "Incarceration Management." The assignment was to design a device like an electronic cuff or jail cell for first-time, nonviolent offenders. We chose this assignment in recognition of the problem that first-time offenders have when being associated with hardened criminals. We had three good responses. The students and faculty had an opportunity to pick next year's design problem. The coordinator of the design department was continually informed about the progress and contributes ideas and time to the evaluation of the entries. This is the type of project an industrial designer can initiate if he or she has a reasonable relationship with a nearby design school. This program continues to gain more interest and involvement each year.

## PLANS FOR RETIREMENT

What about a designer's retirement? Retirement, like deciding on what type of work one wants to do, choosing which college or university to attend, and acquiring a first job, requires careful thought and planning. Why retire? If one is in good health and enjoys his work, nothing says one must retire. However, fatigue does begin to set in. Doing routine chores becomes harder and takes more time as one ages. It does make sense to pass on some management responsibilities to others. This might include clients, works in progress, employees, facilities, investments, or contracts. Initial plans should be made for this event long ahead of time. As owner of a firm, one must establish his own objectives. For example, is it feasible to sell the firm to the employees? Do they want the firm?

One should know what the value of his or her firm is. Talk to potential buyers. Find someone who wants it, work out an agreement, then contact a good attorney to establish a smooth transition. Once a plan is in order, there will be a lot of discontent. Clients may become uneasy. Good employees may become worried and seek other employment. A thoughtful firm owner will have purchased a life insurance policy. In the event of an unexpected death, such resources can help others to properly dispose of the firm. In the case of a partnership, there should be a buy-out plan.

Many considerations a designer needs to make concerning retirement are the same concerns anyone else in any profession must make before retiring. Simple questions need to be asked, like where to live. Emphasis must be placed on financial security. One should know exactly what social security benefits he or she is entitled to. Also, know the value of one's 401K, military pension, and any other retirement plan one has available. All of these things need to be considered long before retirement.

In Chapter 9, I talk about what makes a good client. Case studies are discussed about many designs for two such clients, Ingersoll-Rand and SCM.

### CHAPTER NINE

# MORE CASE STUDIES

**Organizing for the production of good design.
What works and what does not work?**

*Any new venture
goes through the following stages:
enthusiasm, complication, disillusionment,
search for the guilty,
punishment of the innocent,
and decoration of
those who did nothing.*

Unknown

This chapter and the next are presented to help corporate executives who wish to make their organizations into strong, design-oriented companies. Many companies have tried this. Some, like Herman Miller and Steelcase, in the office furniture field, and Corning Glass, and Braun, in domestic products, have successfully portrayed themselves as being driven by "good design." Rubbermaid is one of the best examples of a design-driven company. It introduces one or more new products every day of the year!

I have worked for some well-managed clients and some not so well-managed clients. I have selected a couple of my clients to talk about their successes and attitudes and use of industrial design to develop successful products. Not all of the illustrations selected have been great commercial successes, but in many cases these designs have made it possible for the client to capture the lion's share of the market and maintain it. I will also discuss some products that "missed their mark" and have failed, thus impacting the client's market, jobs, industrial, and/or world position.

## WHAT IS A GOOD CLIENT?

One may appropriately ask, "What is a good client?" I do not know of an exact definition for a "good client." However, this is my list, and it should help:

1. Good clients have an idea of what kind of design they want and why.
2. Good clients appreciate and have a feel for "good design."
3. Good clients realize it takes time, patience, money, and thought to make a great design.
4. Good clients possess the courage to give the designer a chance to do his best.

Can we learn from the successes and mistakes of others? The intention of this chapter is to look at what others have done to foster good product-design development. And yes, since we can also learn from the mistakes of others, a few examples will be revealed as well. It is rare that a company sets up a design center or department that can consistently generate great products. American automobile manufacturers tried very hard but suffered through difficult times throughout the 1960s and 1970s. IBM has been successful in developing new and wanted products.

## CASE STUDY NO. 13:  SCM CORPORATION

The SCM Corporation was financially strong and had a good, healthy product-development program for both portable typewriters and office machines when I first started working for them. In Chapter 7, I talk about the client's perceived need for building and directing an industrial design department within SCM itself. The problems we experienced are also discussed.

The atmosphere existed within SCM for good designs to come about. Most of the designers working on their products believed in project research (interviewing users, sales personnel, and people on the assembly line) and took the time and effort to do it prior to leaping into a design effort. Engineers worked cooperatively with us, and we all reported to the vice president of engineering. Problems did occasionally come about, but it was up to everyone to negotiate a satisfactory solution.

The technique of building mock-ups and models over mechanisms proved invaluable. Most of our meetings and critiques took place in the model laboratory where we could see the complete product-development problem immediately. Even when we held development meetings at our office, we usually spent most of the time studying models and speculating about how mechanisms could be modified to accommodate the jacketing system or vice versa. What follows is an interesting story about product development and product introduction.

**FIGURE 9.1.** Working prototype of the SCM photocopier that we designed, 1959.

## Success With Industrial Design

SCM decided at a product planning meeting that it was time to develop and introduce photocopiers to its product line. The product planning team felt that photocopiers were an ideal companion to its typewriters. Our assignment was to design a photocopier housing. We developed a full-scale appearance model and presented the housing to corporate officials, who were truly excited about what they had seen. They decided to have us upgrade the model into a working prototype (Figure 9.1). SCM wanted to impress its board of directors by running a sheet of paper through the photocopier mechanism with our model housing on it right in the boardroom! I recall not being too enthusiastic about the idea. However, this was what the client wanted, and it seemed feasible.

We completed our model, but it did not have the engineered mechanism in it. The day for the presentation arrived, and we brought our finished model into the boardroom during lunch just as the engineers delivered the mechanism. We fit the prototype housing over the engineering mechanism, and when the board of directors came back from

their lunch, they wanted to see the copier work. One original document was fed into the machine and out came a duplicate. Everybody applauded and SCM had a new division to add to the corporation! This is an example of a most unusual use of industrial design. Forever after, our models worked perfectly, or else I would not allow them to be shown as a prototype.

One of the best products we designed for SCM was the SCM #311 teleprinter. This product was done at long distance because the client, SCM's Kleinschmidt division, was located in Deerfield, Illinois. The redesigned Kleinschmidt 311 teleprinter replaced a product which had been in its product line for many years. It sent and received telegraphic communications—very similar to communicating through telegraphic hand sets.

Since this product would be used mounted on top of and into a stand similar to a typing stand, we immediately decided to bury any noisy assemblies within the stand itself. To achieve the best human factors we set the keyboard and printer housing into a well cut-out of the top surface. This enhanced the relationship between the operator's hands and the pitch or angle of the keyboard. The keyboard was separate from the printer, similar to a computer monitor and keyboard, allowing the operator the flexibility to move the keyboard to the most comfortable and efficient typing position (Figures 9.2, 9.3, 9.4 and 9.5). The added box on the back was intended to meet special Air Force communications requirements. This communications product was used in all

**FIGURE 9.2.** Rod Bunyea, project designer, working on a clay model of the Kleinschmidt 311 teleprinter, 1968.

**FIGURE 9.3.** Kleinschmidt 311 teleprinter, side view of finished appearance model.

**FIGURE 9.4.** Receive unit sitting on a desk top.

**FIGURE 9.5.** Send/receive unit mounted inside its stand. We tried to minimize the noise of the machine by putting the mechanism inside its stand.

**FIGURE 9.6.** SCM "Skywriter" typewriter with injection molded housing. This typewriter was developed by SCM for a British company. This product was developed within the design department at SCM while under Stevens-Chase direction, 1967. Project designer, Robert Metzner.

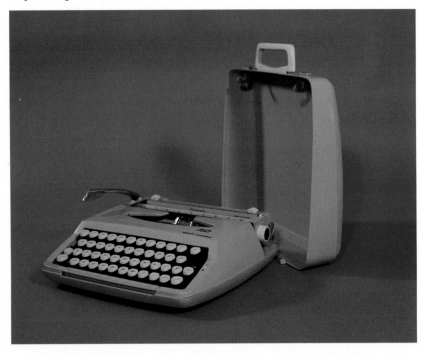

branches of the United States military as well as the State Department and the executive branch offices. This product was well received and did everything expected of it.

About this same time, a small laptop typewriter called the "Skywriter" was completed (Figure 9.6). This machine was designed by SCM's in-house design team under our direction to have a plastic jacketing system and to be manufactured in Great Britain. This product was successful as well. ∎

## Good Ideas and Designers

In Chapter 7, I mentioned a SCM project called "integration research" (Figure 7.46). This was a secret project intended to help product planning. For too long we believed products should be combined if possible. For example, if at one typing station a memo or a report could be prepared, typed, mathematically calculated, duplicated, collated, and faxed, it would save considerable work and cost. Regrettably, we, the designers, and SCM's product planning department were the only people enthusiastic about this project. Gradually this approach began to fade away. Today, the word processor or computer does much of the work we wanted this product to do. It is interesting to note that this idea came from industrial designers, not marketing or engineering people!

CASE STUDY NO. 14: **THE INGERSOLL-RAND STORY**

Another interesting company I provided extensive service to was Ingersoll-Rand. Before I go into detail about my relationship with 18 different divisions, I need to review Ingersoll-Rand's unusual history. The company has recently celebrated its 125th year in business! It all started with Simon Ingersoll of Connecticut. At this time, the typewriter (1873), submarine (1875), telephone (1876), torpedo (1869), and air compressor (1872) were all in development. Ingersoll himself invented many apparatuses. One such invention was for the shipbuilding industry. It was a wooden plug and wedge cutting machine

**FIGURE 9.7.** Simon Ingersoll's pneumatic-powered, tripod-mounted rock drill. Photograph courtesy of Ingersoll-Rand.

which replaced work that had previously been done by hand. He also invented a friction clutch, a gate latch, a spring scale, a gun and a projectile for throwing life lines.

At the urging of John D. Minor, his acquaintance, Simon Ingersoll in 1871 developed his most famous product, a rock drill. This drill was placed in front of a rock face, attached to a tripod and equipped with leg weights to hold it steady (Figure 9.7). The drill itself was mounted on a guide which could be fed forward by a crank and screw. Because of its mount, it could drill at almost any angle. This is important since competitive drills could not tilt. Ingersoll secured a patent for his invention on March 7, 1871.

Ingersoll significantly improved the power drive from steam to air. The development of the air compressor launched a major industry. Ingersoll-Rand today manufactures all sorts of air compressors, a wide variety of drills, hand tools, and hoists—all air driven.

At this time in America's growth and western expansion there was a tremendous need for a mechanical rock drill. Large American civil engineering developments such as the Niagara Power Development, New Croton Aqueduct, New York Subway, and the Panama Canal were under construction. The Ingersoll drill met this need.

However, there is an interesting story about Simon Ingersoll's drill breaking down during a demonstration and it was taken to Sergeant & Cullingworth, a nearby shop, for repairs. There, Henry C. Sergeant, another inventor, took it upon himself to modify Ingersoll's design to prevent further breakdowns. When Simon Ingersoll found out about this, he was enraged. After all, it was his invention and his product! This created the beginning of "bad blood" between the two men. Since the men could not work together amicably, Sergeant convinced his partner, a Spaniard named Jose Francisco de Navarro, to purchase Simon Ingersoll's patents. Ingersoll Rock Drill Company was born with Henry Sergeant as its first president.

Around 1884, Sergeant severed his ties with the Ingersoll Rock Drill Company and went west to take part in silver mining. When he returned east in 1885, he organized the Sergeant Drill Company, essentially competing with his old company. Eventually, the Sergeant Drill Company and Ingersoll Rock Drill Company merged, forming the Ingersoll-Sergeant Drill Company.

The Rand brothers, Albert, Addison, and Jasper Rand, manufactured gun powder. Drilling and gun powder go hand in hand in blasting rock. The process of drilling holes by hand was time consuming, costly, and dangerous for the workers. Holes dug by hand were naturally tapered and inefficient when blasting because the blast funneled out or back. Holes dug by a mechanical drill produced a consistent hole diameter. Mechanical drills made rock blasting safer and more efficient. The Rands became interested in mechanical drills simply to increase the sale of their blasting powder and the Rand Drill Company was formed about 1871.

Concurrently, John B. Waring developed a circulating, water-cooling process for air compressors. As a result, the Rands became interested in compressors. Compressors, of course, run drills. In 1872 the Rand & Waring Drill & Compressor Company was incorporated and a patent was issued to Waring for his cooling process. The Rand Drill Company replaced the Rand & Waring Drill & Compressor Company in 1879.

In 1905 the Ingersoll-Sergeant Drill company and the Rand Drill Company combined to form Ingersoll-Rand. A few years later, Ingersoll-Rand bought patents and began making jackhammer drills in Phillipsburg, New Jersey. Jackhammers and many other products are powered by compressed air.

Today, Ingersoll-Rand has expanded into nine major product groups offering a wide range of product, such as air compressors, architectural hardware, bearings, golf carts, off-highway drive trains, construction and mining products, pumps, skid-steer front end loaders, air systems, filters, and materials handling systems. Before my service to Ingersoll-Rand was over, I would work for at least 15 different product divisions.

## Industrial Design Service to the Corporation

When I started my service in 1973 for the Rock Drill Division at Phillipsburg, I was advised by President William L. Wearly to contact engineers working on rock drill equipment as well as the stationary compressors. The Rock Drill engineers had developed two functional prototype tools. One was a jackhammer and the other a pavement breaker (Figure 9.8). Ingersoll-Rand wanted the appearances of its products enhanced. After reviewing Ingersoll-Rand's history, I believed that its attitude toward design would be "no nonsense." This was true. The work I did had to be secondary to the engineering. Some human factors would be required. From our designs on paper we made a model to prove the concepts and they were well accepted.

The air compressor, called "Centac 10," was about seven feet square and five to six feet tall. The client and I discussed and debated to determine what was best for a front and back for the product and decided on an efficient orientation. Finally we suggested an arrangement of covers, controls, and a paint scheme. We then built an accurate scale model and our contributions were graciously accepted.

The successful completion of these first projects made it possible for me to visit Ingersoll-Rand's North Carolina Portable Compressor Division in 1974. First a little background on this product is necessary.

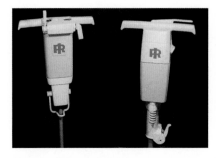

**FIGURE 9.8.** Finished appearance models of pavement breaker (r) and jackhammer (l).

**FIGURE 9.9.** Ingersoll-Rand's portable compressor before redesign. Photograph courtesy of Ingersoll-Rand.

The use and placement of a portable compressor is important. For example, it meant that power sources could be close to work sites. Using steam to operate rock drills as a power source meant the possibility of fire inside mines. This was dangerous considering the frequent presence of explosive methane gas. Air compressors replaced steam around 1872 and were made portable. The air compressor was powered by either motors or gas engines.

## An Air Compressor

I made two good friends when I visited this portable compressor facility. One was Ernie Hinck, the chief engineer, and the other was Frank Della Cave, the division manager. Hinck introduced me to the portable that I was to redesign (Figure 9.9). It was a small 75 CFM (cubic feet of air per minute) portable compressor, probably a gyro-flo (a rotary vane compressor) that had originally been developed at Painted Post, New York. This product had been in its line since about 1950. The design objectives were to reduce cost and enhance its appearance. The product would be manufactured in this country as well as in Europe and Asia. Some complicated parts would most likely be sent there from the United States for assembly. Larger products might evolve and the objective of using as many common parts as possible would be appreciated. We were given all the internal information and requested to provide adequate space for it, including the pavement breaker and air hoses. The engineers had planned to incorporate a screw or cycloidal-shaped design as the new air compressor.

Ingersoll-Rand called it the Spiro-Flo. Such a compressor, regardless of its drive, gas engine, or electric motor (for stationary models), was more efficient than the Gyro-Flo. We felt that if we could develop a good-looking, yet efficient housing design, we would have a winner.

## A Specification and a Plan

I recall having extended conversations with Ingersoll-Rand's engineering staff members to see what their ideas were. After I returned to my office, we drew up a wide variety of concepts and eventually presented them to Ingersoll-Rand. Together with the client, we arrived at a sensible, conservative design.

First we decided what the tooling cost should be for the most complex parts, the end caps. To justify this cost, we wanted to get the maximum number of parts off the tools, thus we designed two identical end caps per product. We also planned that the end caps be stackable to conserve space since some were to be shipped overseas and assembled there. We calculated that the number of units or compressors Ingersoll-Rand would sell would put it at a cost advantage over its competition, thus justifying the added end cap tooling cost. Next, this product, when assembled, had to look aesthetically pleasing regardless of the assortment of product lengths, and appear unique and distinctive. We did not want the product's appearance to be duplicated by Ingersoll-Rand's competition.

The sheet metal parts between the end caps would be made in this country and overseas. There was no expensive, complicated tooling involved to make these parts. We discovered that a local vendor possessed a large enough break form press to produce the variety of panels needed. Thus our specification was met (Figure 9.10).

We proceeded to make a design and coordinate it with the client, and with approval, we constructed a careful, partial scale model (Figures 9.11 and 9.12). Ingersoll-Rand was able to build a full-scale prototype in

FIGURE 9.10. Orthographic illustration of our new portable compressor design for Ingersoll-Rand, 1974.

FIGURE 9.11. Scale model with cover of the new portable compressor design. The model was constructed at the request of Ingersoll-Rand to illustrate the placement of all engine and compressor components.

FIGURE 9.12. Scale model without housing cover. Paul Pfuhl, project designer.

the time it took us to build our scale model. All parts worked and fit together, thus proving the design.

Following our presentation of the finished scale model, Frank Della Cave wanted to have the model shipped to corporate headquarters in New Jersey. As he ran out the door to catch an airplane, he asked his secretary to box it up and send it to him. She apparently did just that, but forgot to put in any packing material. When Frank opened the box,

**FIGURE 9.13.** Finished portable compressor design with graphics. This is model 175. Photograph courtesy of Ingersoll-Rand.

**FIGURE 9.14.** Model 100 portable compressor in use with a pavement breaker. Photograph courtesy of Ingersoll-Rand.

**FIGURE 9.15.** Here is a large portable compressor at a construction site. Photograph courtesy of Ingersoll-Rand.

there was what seemed like a thousand pieces of the model looking at him!

This compressor went on to become the best-selling, best-looking portable compressor in the world (Figures 9.13, 9.14 and 9.15). It is our understanding that five different length compressor models are enclosed within this single housing system. The system has been in use since 1974.

## Wankle Engine

Later that same year I was asked by Ingersoll-Rand to work on an engine. America uses more energy per capita than any other country on earth. Here in the eastern United States we are dependent upon electricity from Canada and atomic powered plants as well as natural gas to meet our energy demands. Gas gets here from southern states by being pushed through pipelines. The compressors that push the gas are giant in size as compared with portable and the typical industrial compressor. Such compressors utilize large diesel engines and turbo drivers for power. Ingersoll-Rand manufactured or offered such engines with the giant compressors.

In the early 1970s the "Wankle" engine used in the Mazda automobile looked like it might have promise if it were enlarged and was used to drive these giant gas compressors. The obvious advantages were fewer parts, less weight, less complexity, low vibration, variable load, less cost than the traditional diesel engine, and the attractive benefit of modular component systems for easy maintenance. This rotary engine was the largest to be developed in the world. The company claimed it was combining the best characteristics of the conventional piston engine with the advantages of a gas turbine driver. Such an engine would be ideal for pumps and all other industrial drive equipment. The engine came in 500 horsepower and 1,000 horsepower models.

## External Events Kill a Design

We reviewed the engine and developed an industrial design. Unfortunately, about the same time this engine was introduced, the energy crisis of the mid-1970s began. This dampened petroleum fueled engine sales of all kinds. Concurrently it was discovered that the seals between the parts enclosing the combustion chamber were failing. Within a short time the product was dropped. Our service involved softening up the form of the design as much as possible. To show how the design would work we built a scale model (Figure 9.16).

## Coal Mining Equipment

During the energy crisis the country began to show interest in alternative fuels. Perhaps it would be necessary to rely more on coal. The demand for coal and coal-mining machinery was growing rapidly.

In 1974 I visited the Lee-Norse Company, an acquired division of Ingersoll-Rand, founded in 1936. By 1960 coal-mining machinery went into a slump but even so, Ingersoll-Rand acquired Lee-Norse in 1964. Then the business became very profitable indeed.

When I arrived at Charleroi, Pennsylvania I was met by a most interesting engineering manager, Clyde Holvenstot. He felt my human factors background might be helpful and thought there may be a place for it in the design of their continuous miners. A continuous miner is about 9 to 10 feet wide and 34 feet long. It has a rotating cutter head, extending across the front and attached to two arms or booms. The head has carbide type picks which rotate, biting or chipping the coal off the face. This cutter head, when placed against the coal face or vertical wall, sweeps up and down cutting the coal free. The falling coal lands onto a tray under the cutter head, then is moved by the miner's conveyor to the rear and deposited into a shuttle car which removes the coal from the mine. The operator's cab is about 5 feet long, 2-1/2 feet wide and about 20 feet back from the front of the machine. Most cabs have adjustable height overhead guards. The guard protects the operator in case of a rock roof fall.

Around this same time I discovered that the Mine Safety and Health Administration (MSHA) showed interest in human factors. A continuous miner, used in underground coal mines breaks the coal free from its seam face. It, therefore, must be a low height product. While some high quality coal seams are only 2 inches plus thick, there

**FIGURE 9.16.** Our scale industrial design model of the Wankle engine, 1974.

are some high quality coal mines having seams of 18 inches thick, according to the Pittsburgh Research Center (Bureau of Mines). In one low coal mine that I visited, the seam was 30 inches high. My guide and I got around on an electrified personnel car and went into the mine about one half mile. I was more comfortable on my back. We traveled very slowly but I expected at any moment to be sandwiched against the roof having my helmet ground off along with my face. We traveled at about one to two miles per hour, but it seemed like 20 or 30 miles per hour. Low coal mining is not for those who are claustrophobic.

After seeing my slide presentation and hearing my approach to the design with emphasis on human factors, Holvenstot asked me to prepare a cost estimate for the redesign of the operator's compartment of a continuous miner. This product was complex! It was easily as complicated as any over the highway truck but would only move at approximately 70 feet per minute and was electric powered.

Safety in coal mining is absolutely imperative. The operating team is constantly guarding against methane explosions or fires. I have heard a tale of a cutter head striking a rock layer above the seam and creating sparks which ignited methane gas emitted from newly mined coal, starting an explosion and fire. The fire spread along the path of the coal, along the conveyer belt, through the continuous miner, right up to the shuttle car collecting the mined coal. The government insists that methane monitors be installed on the miner to help identify the presence of this explosive methane gas. As a precaution, water is continually sprayed onto the face of the coal and newly mined coal to inhibit sparks from igniting the escaping gas. There also are fire extinguishing systems built into the equipment.

## Research

To start the design I visited a mine and experienced first hand what it was like to see a continuous miner in action. Many people I talked to told me they would never go into a coal mine. The utterly dark, quiet, and mysterious environment would put them over the edge. I looked upon it as a job, but going into a super low-seamed mine of 30 inches or below does demand self control. I returned to Pennsylvania and was issued coveralls, boots, an emergency breather life support system, miner's lamp, and a hard hat. I went down and into a mine with a roof of about five feet high. It was painful since I, as a six foot man, continually crouched and rarely stood up straight. The floor was covered with about three inches of wet coal muck or mud—not a pleasant place to kneel or sit. My escort had lost all his front teeth in a mining accident years earlier when his electric car ran into another one on the track in the dark. His mouth was so badly injured he could not speak. Located in a remote part of the mine, it took hours before he was found and received medical attention. I tell this story to stress the unexpected hazards that sometimes must be taken into consideration when conducting research for a mining design assignment.

We went to observe a team in action. The operators had been choreographed in their precise actions. First the continuous miner crawls

FIGURE 9.17. Our human factors mock-up of the operator's seat for Ingersoll-Rand's LN-800 continuous miner, 1976-77.

FIGURE 9.18. Human factors mock-up of the LN-800 operator's compartment showing seat and controls.

forward to the face, then it cuts the coal and backs out of the way. A roof bolter advances into the newly mined area screwing bolts up and into the roof to strengthen it. Later, another vehicle called a coal scoop cleans up the area and the process is repeated.

With the knowledge I gained at this and other mines I studied the function and procedures for operating the continuous miner. Prioritizing the controls and the development of a seat which would be comfortable for all users, both men and women, from the fifth percentile up to the ninety-fifth percentile were the design objectives. To prove the design, I continually had men and women of all sizes sit at the controls in my office and verify the ease of reach, throw, and entering and exiting the cab in the worst (lowest) roof conditions (Figures 9.17, 9.18, 9.19, 9.20, and 9.21). Once I had finished a full-scale model it was trucked to the client. Clyde was most pleased with the design. Safety was critical. Notice that I covered a series of motor switches with "on/off" paddles. These paddles had holes in them. Thus, to start one of the many motors on the miner, the operator must consciously stick his finger into the hole to activate the switch. If for any reason an emer-

**FIGURE 9.19.** Demonstrating the adjustable canopy for the LN-800. This is the high position with a ninety-fifth-percentile operator.

**FIGURE 9.20.** LN-800 adjustable canopy in the low position with a ninety-fifth-percentile operator.

**FIGURE 9.21.** LN-800 operator's cab showing the adjustability of the seat using a fifteenth-percentile male operator.

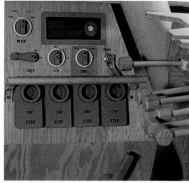

**FIGURE 9.22.** Human factors mock-up of the LN-800 controls.

**FIGURE 9.23.** Human factors mock-up of the hydraulic levers that control the assorted functions. The hydraulic bank rotates up and down, adapting to the size of the operator.

**FIGURE 9.24.** LN-800 continuous miner, actual unit. Photograph courtesy of Ingersoll-Rand.

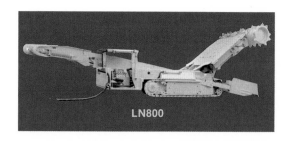

gency necessitates that the miner be shut down, his hand would be automatically at the "off" portion of the switch, the paddle. By ganging switches and paddles together, the whole machine could shut down very quickly (Figure 9.22). I also designed each of the hydraulic levers in front of the operator with a shape which suggested the lever's function (Figure 9.23). For example, the cutter head lever is round with simulated teeth. This helps the operator orient himself to his vehicle in any emergency dark situation. It was amusing when the client informed me that considering the abuse such machines get, the levers are apt to be broken and another control handle would have to be substituted which might not match the function, thus leading to confusion and perhaps an accident.

Over the course of several years we designed three different cabs for three different continuous miners. Since the overhead guard for the cab is the highest part of the miner in the design of the LN-800, our last component of this project was to design a seat and overhead guard which would go up and down. This allowed the miner to be used in a greater number of mines with varying seam heights. By offering this adjustable feature, the company needed fewer products in its line and less inventory (Figures 9.24, 9.25 and 9.26). Later, we designed other cabs with even lower height requirements.

## Human Factors

Did human factors and all this design effort help Ingersoll-Rand in the sale of its coal mining equipment? It is very difficult to know. I never heard of a sale being lost because a product lacked human factors. Yet I never heard of a sale being accomplished because of our design work.

**FIGURE 9.25.** LN-800 continuous miner on display at a show. Photograph courtesy of Ingersoll-Rand.

**FIGURE 9.26.** Actual operator's cab for the LN-800, displaying adjustable seat and hydraulic valve bank.

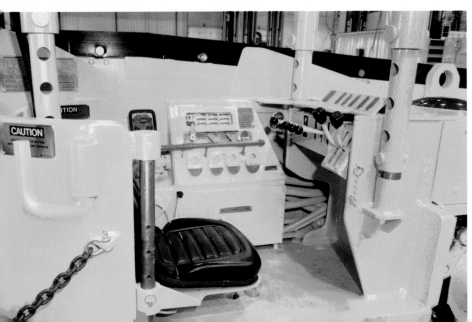

Did the sales personnel push it? I doubt it. The sales person was probably grateful to tell the mine operator how many tons of coal he could expect to mine per shift with this equipment versus his competitors for the same price. The mine operator did not work as a member of the mining shift team so he cared little about efficiencies and comfort offered the machine operator. Telling him that a comfortable operator with efficient control arrangements reduces team fatigue may have helped. A rested, efficient team mines more coal. I do not think the sales person thoroughly understood, or cared, and I doubt if a mine owner understood or cared much about human factors. Just show me more coal per shift! It should be noted that in today's market place, manufacturers are becoming more and more concerned about human factors, safety, and product design.

I never heard whether continuous miner operators insisted on operating a piece of equipment with good human factors. I do take my hat off to the enlightened management of Ingersoll-Rand who wanted our service. They believed that human factors and good appearance were more positive features that help the sales of all Ingersoll-Rand equipment. My objective was to have as much consistency across Ingersoll-Rand's product lines showing the corporation's consideration and desire for good design and human factors. It says the corporation cares about its customers and equipment operators.

## Roof Bolter

I was also asked to look at the cab of a roof bolter. A roof bolter enters a newly mined area after the continuous miner exits (Figure 9.27). The bolter then extends arms or jacks to support the roof while the men start drilling holes and inserting bolts with giant washers which are screwed up tightly into the underside of the roof. The pattern of these bolts help make the rock itself act as a truss or a beam thus making the roof strong enough to prevent a cave in. The government has strict laws which specify how this operation is to be performed. The system is much safer and takes up less head room than the old timber columns and buttress system. The bolting equipment takes up a great deal of space and offers little room for an operator's cab. We worked with a space of approximately 2 feet wide, 5 feet long

FIGURE 9.27. A roof bolter in a mine. Photograph courtesy of Ingersoll-Rand.

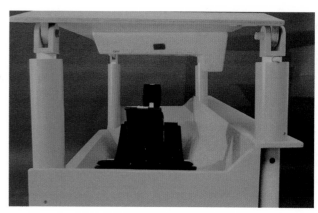

**FIGURE 9.28.**
Our swing-seat design for Ingersoll-Rand's roof bolter, c. 1976.

and about 30 inches high. When a low coal operator was in his cab he could only look forward between his tucked up legs. With the unit moving, his head would be very unsafe outside the cab since it could rub and/or be crushed against the side of the mine. The problem becomes more complicated, since what goes in, has to back out and the operator cannot turn his head around and drive backwards like backing out of a garage. Thus, when entering and leaving the mine, the operator must reverse direction within the cab.

### Empathy with Marketing Problems

To accomplish a satisfactory design solution to this problem we first designed an adjustable overhead guard that would support a roof fall (Figure 9.28). The adjustment feature offered the greatest height possible. Then we designed a reclining single seat system comprised of the seat, two seat backs on either side of the seat and narrow head rests above each seat back. The seat system was symmetrical. To take into consideration different size operators and heights of the overhead guard, we formed the seat system on a "S" curve with the seat at the bottom and each head rest at the top ends. The seat system was clamped between six inverted casters. The two casters at the center

held the "S" curve down while pressing the seat against the four bottom casters. This permitted the "S" curve to rotate up or down and be detented at a variety of heights. Thus, by folding the back rest over the seat and sitting on the seat, the operator could enter the cab, sit at a comfortable preselected height, straddle the spine of the seat system and head rest, and he could look between his legs and see where he was traveling. Controls were mounted on the bulkhead adjoining the center of the bolter or on the underside of the overhead guard. Rubber cushions covered the seats. Again, we built a full-scale working model and presented it to the client (Figures 9.29, 9.30, 9.31 and 9.32). Later the client built the seat design into a working proto-type (Figure 9.33).

### More Work Underground

Around this time I was asked by the Ingersoll-Rand research facility at Princeton, New Jersey to take a look at its plans to engineer a pick miner control system for the South African government. This was prior to the time the United States banned the sale of products to South Africa because of its apartheid policies.

**FIGURE 9.29.** Our working model of the swing seat with a ninety-five-plus-percentile male operator. Seat is in the mid position.

**FIGURE 9.30.** Swing-seat working model with a five-plus-percentile male operator with seat in mid-position.

**FIGURE 9.32.** Double exposure showing swing-seat working model with fifteen-percentile male operator, illustrating how the swing seat works.

**FIGURE 9.33.** Swing-seat production unit.

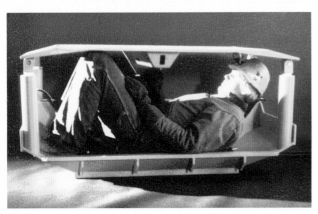

**FIGURE 9.31.** Swing-seat working model with a ninety-five-plus-percentile male operator with seat in the low position.

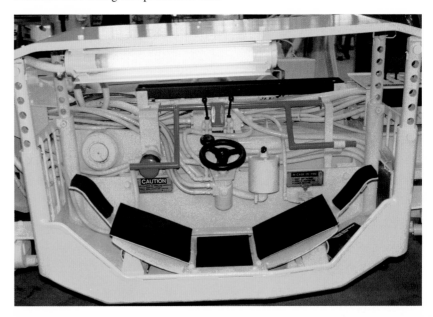

**FIGURE 9.34.** An Ingersoll-Rand engineer demonstrating the slope of a gold mine interior, 1975. A pick miner must adapt to this slope.

First I need to describe a typical gold mine, which is different from coal mines. Johannesburg sits on one of the world's largest deposits of gold. It is estimated that two-thirds of the world's gold comes from this area. To help picture this, think of a glass of water with Johannesburg at the top and center of the glass and the gold mines scattered about the perimeter of the glass approximately 300 miles, then mine shafts going down the side of the glass for over 2 miles (Figure 9.34). Around 100,000 men are employed in this industry. Most of them come from rural areas and are not particularly educated. I have never been in a gold mine, but it is a memorable experience according to "National Geographic Magazine." A January 1974 article describes travel down into the mine. Miners board an elevator that can hold about 120 men and feel the temperature rise as it descends. As a matter of fact, at the bottom of the mine the temperature can be as high as 105 degrees Fahrenheit. There is moisture in the air which increases the humidity and feeling of heat within the mine. Water is continually being sprayed on the mined rock at the face to keep the dust down. The working face is only high enough for a person to sit up and the floor is on a slope. Using the analogy of the shape of a glass, it slopes to the very bottom. The air one breathes is pulled down through shafts to a refrigeration plant where it is cooled and sent out to the mine face for the operators to breath. The accepted technique for mining is to place a leg mounted jackhammer against the rock face and drill holes for blasting. Ingersoll-Rand designed a pick miner to supplement this traditional system.

The miner was in a housing which sat on a track that could travel along the working face of the mine. Protruding from this box was the pick itself, an arm with several joints, and an impact mechanism. The arm could reach out and chip off chunks of rock comprising the mine seam. Our assignment was to design the controller for this system. We needed a box about 18 inches square to house the electronics and mechanisms. Because of the rugged environment and the operator's nonchalant attitude toward any and all equipment, we knew the controller would receive an unbelievable amount of rough handling. The box itself was to be constructed of fibrous glass and resin. The walls of the box would need to withstand the equivalent impact of a 50 caliber bullet. Even so, we chamfered and removed corners all to resist the impact that the controller was surely to receive. We even mounted runners or skids to the bottom of the box so that it could be dragged over the rock and floor debris. The box would have an emergency on/off switch on top. The two sides would have recessed panels for safety, warning lights and lighted on/off switches. On the back of the box would be the umbilical cord which would reach back to the miner itself. The opposite end would be a hand control for the operator. The hand control was a joystick and when moved about, transmitted electric signals to the miner. In turn the miner's arm would mimic the direction and action that the operator employed. Keep in mind that the environment, with all the moisture, was highly acidic and we had to be very careful in our choice of materials. For example, the runners and all metal parts were made of stainless steel. Once the operator was satisfied with the placement of the pick, his thumb would activate a switch on the control handle. This would start the pick to chip at the rock. As the rock is chipped away from the face it falls in front of the miner and then is worked down the slope to awaiting cars which move the rock to elevators for removal from the mine.

## The Importance of Human Factors in Product Design

The engineers who outlined the design specifications for us impressed upon me the importance of understanding the native psychology regarding the concept of "on/off." The native operators believed that the harder they hit an off switch, the more the mechanism is "turned off." So again, on the top of our controller box we made a big fibrous glass cover over the on/off switch so that an operator could hit it with his fist and be sure to turn off the controller but would not damage or

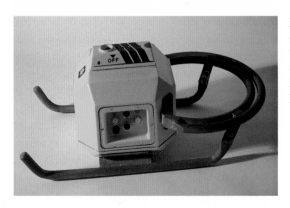

**FIGURE 9.35.** Prototype of pick- miner controller with armrests and skids, side view. Notice the emergency stop switch with protective cover on top.

FIGURE 9.36. Ingersoll-Rand's early engineering model of its hydraulic crawler drill, 1977. This model was developed to prove the concept. Photograph courtesy of Ingeroll-Rand.

break the switch (Figure 9.35). Then to turn the controller back on the operator must put his finger in a hole in the on/off cover to reactivate the switch. Last we knew, this was one of the final pieces of equipment that went to South Africa from the United States prior to the American embargo.

## Surface Rock Drill

Returning to the surface of the earth, the Rock Drill Division in around 1977—which had its headquarters in a quarry north of Easton, Pennsylvania—wanted us to look at a new concept, a portable-crawler, hydraulic blast-hole drill. My friend, Ewald Kurt, described to me what this product does. For example, try to recall driving along a modern expressway and passing through or by a rock cut along side the road. You often will see parallel grooves about two inches in diameter and spaced about a foot to a foot and a half apart in the rock. These are generated by a standard pneumatic crawler drill. Now the idea of a fluid driven or hydraulic driven drill was introduced. Such a drill, which is on a tracked vehicle, crawls up onto the top of the rock then proceeds to drill a series of holes perpendicular to the road. Dynamite is then placed in the holes and the rock is blasted away. Our job was to build a housing for the engine and hydraulic system, review the product for potential safety problems, and make the large number of controls easy to understand and use regardless of the language of the operator. The product was part of a system. For instance, the drill normally tows

behind a portable air compressor for hole cleaning purposes (Figure 9.36). These products function as a team.

To accomplish the design we used traditional sheet metal manufacturing techniques to make the side and top. We elected to make the front and back end caps of thermoformed plastic. We designed the shape and the general appearance of this housing to reflect the shape and form of portable compressors which we had previously designed. The product system looked very compatible and efficient and reinforced Ingersoll-Rand's corporate image (Figure 9.37).

To understand the myriad of hoses that pass between the hydraulic pumps and the drill itself, we built an accurate scale model and a cover system to protect the hoses as they passed down the boom and into the drill. To surmount the control housing problems we made a thermoformed cover that went over the hydraulic levers or controls, and then developed symbolic pictographs above each control which enabled the operator, regardless of his language, to safely control and manage the equipment (Figures 9.38 and 9.39).

**FIGURE 9.37.** Ingersoll-Rand's vertical grinder in use. Photograph courtesy of Ingersoll-Rand.

**FIGURE 9.38.** A close-up of the hydraulic valve bank on the ECM-450 after our design service. To identify the function of each control, we developed a series of symbols.

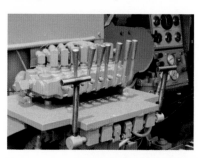

**FIGURE 9.39.** The hydraulic valve control bank on the ECM-450 before our design service.

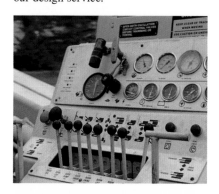

## Vertical Grinder

During this same period of time, a staff member from the Power Tool Division of Ingersoll-Rand called and asked me to stop by to discuss the design of a vertical grinder. I had wanted to work for this division for a couple of years and had consulted with its engineering manager and members of his staff who had worked for Chicago Pneumatic Tool Company years ago. These staff members remembered me from that early time in my career. At last I was being given an opportunity to work for this special division. The product the engineers wanted me to look at was reasonable in appearance but unfortunately workers who used this tool would remove the guard and the grinding wheel would wear thin and often shatter. The centrifugal force of the wheel was so great that it would send pieces of the wheel into the operator's body (Figure 9.40). The Chairman of the Board, William Wearly, instructed the division to design this product so that if an operator removed the safety guard the product would fall apart. I, being concerned about safety, highly approved of this feature.

To begin the project I instructed the division to set up space in the product test laboratory for me to spend a day operating Ingersoll-Rand products, as well as those of its competitors. I discovered an interesting law of physics. The closer the operator brought his hands together when operating the grinder, the greater control he has over the product's centrifugal forces. This makes it possible to work longer while experiencing less opposing forces, thus less fatigue and ultimately greater productivity and safety. This dictated the shape of the design (Figures 9.41 and 9.42). The client, at that time, chrome plated the castings and the product turned out to be quite handsome. We were very happy with the results.

## Horizontal Grinders

The success of this product led to the design of two horizontal grinders. In this case we put an angle on the back of the grinder, about 45 degrees, which provided for greater control. The traditional handles had a 90 degree angle. We did several other products for this division, all of them successful.

**FIGURE 9.40.** Ingersoll-Rand's vertical grinder before redesign. Photograph courtesy of Ingersoll-Rand.

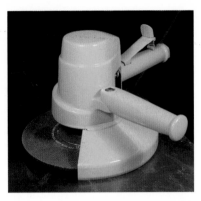

**FIGURE 9.41.** Our appearance model of the new vertical grinder design for Ingersoll-Rand, 1976.

**FIGURE 9.43.** Model of Cameron multistage pump, 1979.

**FIGURE 9.42.** Ingersoll-Rand's vertical grinder in use. Photograph courtesy of Ingersoll-Rand.

**FIGURE 9.44.** Blue and white porcelain Ming Dynasty vase, c. mid-15th century, 13-1/2" high, 7" diameter. Photograph courtesy of The Avery Brundage Collection, Asian Art Museum of San Francisco, (c) 1996.

FIGURE 9.45. Ingersoll-Rand's glass reinforced polymer pump, before.

FIGURE 9.46. Ingersoll-Rand's glass reinforced polymer pump, after our design service, 1977.

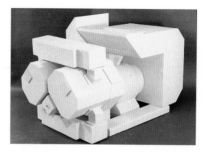

FIGURE 9.47. Dri-lobe compressor, styrofoam model, 1978.

FIGURE 9.48. Dri-lobe compressor housing. The top compartment is thermoformed plastic. Side panels are sheet metal and thermoformed plastic.

## Pumps

We also contacted the pump divisions of Ingersoll-Rand. Its Cameron Division in Phillipsburg, New Jersey was one of its original companies. Ingersoll-Rand also had a new pump division which we worked for, the Standard-Aldrich Division in Allentown, Pennsylvania. For the Cameron Division we designed a bearing housing and leg support system for a complex multistage pump system (Figure 9.43). We discovered one interesting problem as a result of all of our pump designs. Regardless of how much effort we applied to the design of a pump, the installation engineer was not particularly interested in the pump's aesthetics. He was more interested in the pump's capacity, space around it for maintenance, and easy, efficient plumbing and cost. Somehow these factors visually destroyed whatever aesthetics we applied to the product. However, the aesthetics were important because this product is pictured in reports and catalogs and this type of product is bought by purchasers from pictures in the catalog.

We did, however, have the assignment of designing a series of fiberglass-reinforced polymer pumps which could extend the life of a pump when transporting highly corrosive fluids. We had the opportunity of making this series of pumps really beautiful to look at. I recall studying the forms of Ming vases (Figure 9.44). I found the shape of these pumps somewhat reminiscent of the vases and was anxious to build on these shapes (Figures 9.45 and 9.46). Designing these pumps was fun!

## Stationary Air Compressors

Over the years I worked for several different stationary compressor divisions. We developed a nice looking housing for the Air Power Division. The compressor was called a Dri-Lobe (no oil in the system) compressor (Figure 9.47). Most compressors run with oil throughout the system for lubrication. However, in hospitals and places where the air must be clean and breathable, a product like a Dri-Lobe is needed. The product never achieved its intended expectations due to the small dimensional space requirements between parts. However, our housing was well received. We combined a large thermoformed top or cover and break formed sheet metal side panels to form a housing for the compressor (Figure 9.48). We also designed a couple of small compressor housings.

## Road Construction Equipment

Some of the final designs we did for Ingersoll-Rand were large road construction equipment. It seems that Ingersoll-Rand was one of the first companies to construct road rollers using the vibratory compaction principle. In essence, the product while vibrating compacts the ground or asphalt into a more compressed state. Because of the vibration, the product does not have to be as heavy as the old fashioned road rollers but can achieve comparable or better results. The Compaction Division started with two basic products, the DA-30 and

FIGURE 9.49.
Ingersoll-Rand's
DA-30 compaction
machine used to
smooth asphalt,
before redesign.
Photograph courtesy
of Ingersoll-Rand.

the DA-50. We worked on both of these products, but particularly enjoyed the results we got from our efforts of the DA-30 (Figure 9.49). We provided better human factors. The operator could see the highway where he was working better than the previous design. The profile of the product became very business like and we added material around the deck which provided a great deal of safety for the operator's feet (Figures 9.50 and 9.51). We contributed to the cost reduction of these products while at the same time enhancing their appearance, human factors, and safety.

## An Aircraft Tractor

In 1986 the Simmons-Rand division of Ingersoll-Rand asked me to look at its new aircraft tractor in development. This was a battery-powered vehicle used to push the aircraft from its berth out onto the runway. Our assignment was to design a pleasing appearance for the product. Safety was a serious concern since the push or pull bars would occasionally buckle and fracture, sending the broken bar into the operator's compartment. We accomplished our assignment and developed an attractive and safe product (Figures 9.52 and 9.53).

I am grateful for having the opportunity to work on this diverse assortment of products which went into some unique environments. When people drive along the highway and see compactors, down-hole crawler drills, and compressors, I am sure they do not think too much about the designer's work that goes into this equipment. It is far different than sculpting the body of an automobile. We are limited in the quantities manufactured which impacts product and design cost. We are also confined in our choice of materials and fabrication. All restrict the designer as compared to the freedom that an auto designer has when thinking in terms of thousands of units to manufacture. To do a good job in many of these areas, one must work hard, but I always appreciated the challenge. ∎

**FIGURE 9.50.** Rendering of the DA-30's new design, 1979.

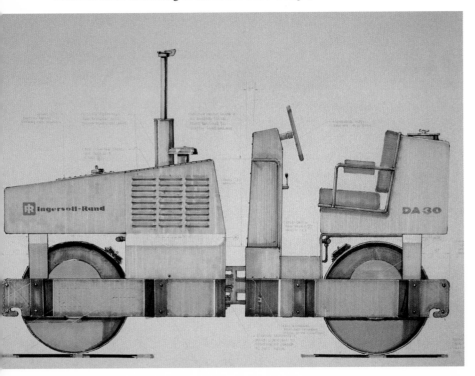

**FIGURE 9.51.**
DA-30, front view
of final design.
Photograph courtesy
of Ingersoll-Rand.

**FIGURE 9.53.**
Aircraft tractor,
rear view.

**FIGURE 9.52.** A scale model of an aircraft tractor for Simmons-Rand, front view, 1986.

## Corporate Design Philosophy

While a brief description of Ingersoll-Rand has been made, I would like to explore its design philosophy. (It may be inappropriate to call it a design philosophy; it is more like its corporate design policy.) The corporate staff of Ingersoll-Rand wanted industrial design offered to its divisions, but only if industrial design could help it achieve its goals. The practice of a corporate staff forcing design on a division was not even considered appropriate. The division had to see a need for it. Carl Horten, the corporate vice president in charge of engineering, invited me to visit the assorted divisions to speak to them about the value of industrial design.

My design philosophy was simple. Since all products need to be designed, then do the best that can be afforded, but do it! If the design service is coordinated carefully with engineering, then the cost and effort is negligible. By carefully coordinating the design development program between engineering and design, the work is efficiently accomplished with little or no duplication, thus saving development funds. It is true that some Ingersoll-Rand products are rarely seen by the public. So, why design? Because a rarely seen product still will be seen at times! If a product functions well and the corporation is proud of it, then make it great to look at and tell the world! An ugly product shows inconsistency in the corporate design philosophy.

I have discussed companies that employed me and described some of the projects completed for my clients. In the next chapter I will discuss design, especially good design and its designers, and how its development can be sustained. The future of industrial design in relation to world needs is important and the direction the profession should be going is explored.

### CHAPTER TEN

# GOOD DESIGN
# AND THE FUTURE OF DESIGN

*He's a man out there in the blue,
ridin' on a smile and a shoeshine…
a salesman has got to dream, boys.*

Arthur Miller

## GOOD DESIGN

### What is it?

What is good design? Museum warehouses are filled with special collections of objects identified as "good design." Companies have done well manufacturing and selling products that are labeled "good design." Many industries and designers have worked very hard to get their products identified as aesthetically pleasing. Everyone wants his or her designs or products identified as examples of good design. Following World War II the Museum of Modern Art in New York City started a movement toward the appreciation and identification of products of good design and exhibited examples of what it considered to be outstanding design.

Everyday here in America the staffs at periodicals and newspapers have discovered that the general public wants to know what is "good design." The general public likes to identify with it. It is chic. For example, television programs and automobile magazines have expended great effort on this subject. Magazines like *Popular Mechanics, Popular Science,* and *Consumer Reports,* among others, take products such as automobiles, appliances, electronic entertainment products, sporting goods, power tools, etc., and competitively evaluate them from a cost, mechanical, safety, and a human factors point of view as well as analysis of owner satisfaction. They give the reader their honest opinion of what they consider most valuable and, very possibly, which will be most acceptable. Such evaluations may take into consideration cost, durability, safety, the impact on the environment, human factors, and sometimes, snob appeal.

In the Philadelphia Museum of Art's book, *Design Since 1945,* contributing author Herbert J. Gans describes appreciation for good design as an "upper-middle class culture." He believes that people's tastes are affected by their incomes. In *Design Since 1945,* he expresses this opinion (page 32):

...[U]pper-middle culture can be divided further, into progressive and traditional wings, on the assumption that a liking for contemporary art, architecture, and furniture go together, as does a liking for traditional versions of each. Of course, some people like both; others swear by contemporary art but like traditional furniture, or vice versa; and yet others select combinations of each, for example, "good design" enthusiasts may also collect Shaker furniture.

In terms of social class, the people who prefer "good design" and other aspects of progressive upper-middle culture are mostly upper-middle class. Many work as professionals and are probably found especially in the symbolic professions: in design, of course, the arts and communications (broadly defined), and in academia.

Many manufacturers are aware that their products will be scrutinized to great depth and, in design and development, strive for excellence. If this works it can turn out to be good for the consumer/user, the manufacturer, the designer, and above all, the employees who make the product. On the other hand, if a product receives a negative review, it is discouraging and can be to the designer's disadvantage, but a great and lasting teaching experience evolves.

### Criteria for Good Design

In any presentation and product review, industrial designers should identify the product specification given them and discuss the end result. It should be evident that the specification was achieved, in other words, the design should look like it meets its specification. Now, what is good design? After spending much time and frustration with other designers and design critics, my description of good design includes the following:

- a product that looks as though it does what it is supposed to do

- a product with an outstanding, distinctive, and appealing appearance
- a product manufactured from new, appropriate materials and perhaps by an innovative, effective process
- a product that is pleasant, safe, and comfortable for a human being to use

In the book *Modern Masterpieces: The Best of Art, Architecture, Photography and Design since 1945,* edited by Udo Kultermann, Richard Hayhurst discusses the design qualities of the "Thunderball" chair by Eero Aarnio, a Finnish designer. Hayhurst identifies eight critical elements which make any product an outstanding design:

1. A genius or bravery to be different
2. The designer showed the courage to enter "fantasy" land
3. Logical in the evolution of the design
4. Needed something spectacular
5. Use of new materials
6. Material eventually became an acceptable material
7. The result brought shock and was labeled as garish at first
8. "Natural use" of an unnatural substance

## Tom Peters' View of What Makes Good Design

How to think to create good design? In *The New Business of Design,* author Tom Peters (who is not a designer), spoke at the Forty-Fifth International Design Conference in Aspen and identified 35 key points to what he calls "design mindfulness." Peters believes that institutions must exhibit these traits in order to overcome the glut of look-alike, poorly designed products on the market today. Here are excerpts from Peters' 35 characteristics of "design mindfulness":

1. Design mindfulness is a core competence, which becomes effective if (and only if) it becomes a culture of design. …[D]esign can become a way of life, an avenue for competitive advantage.

2. Design mindfulness/a culture of design is arguably the number one antidote to the commoditization of products and services. What have we been up to for the last ten, madcap years? …We have sped up product development immeasurably. Still, or more than ever, we are awash in products and services that are boring. …A jillion new products arriving faster than ever; and the quality of almost all of them is good. But do they sparkle…?

3. Design mindfulness looms ever larger as the economy grows ever softer. The end of the industrial era came, unheralded, on a day in early 1992.

4. Design mindfulness is a "numerator issue." "Lean, mean …and then what?" is the way one executive put it. …[T]he time has come to focus on the top line. The revenue line. …Competing effectively is about doing good things, making good things, creating good things. It is clearly a numerator issue. Design, too, is just that: a numerator issue.

5. Design mindfulness is a pervasive notion. Designer Michael Shannon, in a letter to me, said it as well: "Design is how a company looks, feels, tastes, wears, rides …what the company is that customers care about."

6. Design mindfulness is a matter of character.

7. Design mindfulness flows from leaders who love stuff (and vice versa). …[T]hat abiding passion, that love, that unnatural obsession with the product.

8. Design mindfulness is a passion for artistic expression at age eighteen or sixty-eight.

9. Design mindfulness can be thoroughly populist. …I've read the debates, …about the role of elitism in art. Sure, I think elitism has a role. [But] design mindfulness for the masses is no pipe dream.

10. Via design mindfulness you can wildly differentiate a 79 cent product as well as a $79,000.00 product. …That is, "high-end" (distinguished) does not equal high price. It's a matter of attitude, or call it design mindfulness.

11. There is a vast, mass market for good design. In the late 1940s, the designer George Nelson fought conventional wisdom and brought the idea of a big market for good design to Herman Miller. He was right, then and now.

12. Design mindfulness is as potent a tool for small companies as for large ones, for high-tech firms as for low-tech, for service enterprises as for manufacturers. The tragedy is that most small companies, in particular, don't get it. They don't understand that design clearly is the principal path to standing out from the crowd.

13. Design mindfulness is a big deal. Historically design has time and again transformed entire industries.

14. Design mindfulness applies to the accounting and purchasing and logistics and training departments as well as to engineering, R & D, marketing, and design itself.

15. Design mindfulness is abetted by the presence of great designers on the payroll, hanging about, and so forth. …[P]ay the talent. …[T]here is a difference between a superstar and a nonstar. Recognize it. Hire it. Pay it.

16. Design mindfulness is reflected in formal as well as informal arrangements. …Design may be an intangible, but if the designer is not even invited to the table, then that all-important intangible is going to have a difficult time making itself known.

17. Design mindfulness translates into playfulness and an abiding appreciation of the role of emotion in corporate life. …Emotion: in our business schools and in our businesses, we tend to downplay the role of passion, engagement, and emotion. It's a mistake. With the world brimming with new competitors and look-alike products, how do you stand out? The answer is products and services that are distinct. Special. …Products, that is, which are *emotional*.

18. Design mindfulness and daring-to-be-different are handmaidens. …Dare to be different.

19. Design mindfulness strikes a blow against boredom. … Screw things up. Shake things up. …Forget "good." Love "crazy." Stomp out the Great Blight of Dullness. Wipe out boredom. Disrupt the status quo.

20. You want design mindfulness? Then hire (and reward and promote) design mindfulness.

21. Design mindfulness is perpetual curiosity. … [P]erpetual curiosity, spunk, spirit, and a touch of madness are the essence of long-term success.

22. Design mindfulness means that all decisions must pass the DMT, or *Design Mindfulness Test*. In companies where quality reigns supreme, every issue, related or unrelated to quality per se, must go through the quality sieve.

23. Design mindfulness and diversity are identical twins.

24. Design mindfulness is about usability, manufacturability, and commercial viability. Design is what makes you shout "Holy smokes!" …Design is beauty. …Design mindfulness is multidimensional—period.

25. Design mindfulness is a thirst for personal renewal. …[A] premium, as never before, is being placed on creativity.

26. I know it—design mindfulness—when I see it, or there are limits to measurement. …[W]hether the issue is quality or service or design mindfulness, it is something that we "get." We know it's there or not. Trusting our gut and putting intuition and holism, rather than standard, analytic-center reductionism, at the top of management "tool" list is imperative.

27. Design mindfulness is impossible to pin down and easy to spot. It's another plea to trust that gut feeling.

28. Design mindfulness flows from autocratic leadership. ... [W]hen it comes to character there needs to be a strong, clear voice from the top.

29. Design mindfulness is abetted by ignoring your customer. "The customer is a rearview mirror," says George Colony of Forrester Research, "not a guide to the future."

30. If you are serious about design/design mindfulness, it will consume you. ...If design mindfulness is to be the essence of the enterprise, then leadership will eat it, sleep it, walk it, talk it.

31. Design mindfulness is strategy—an encompassing way of life.

32. Design mindfulness as core competence requires constant reinvention. The world is changing fast, absurdly fast.

33. Design mindfulness is more or less of TQM and reengineering and customer-is-king.

34. Design mindfulness equals love. ...[D]esign mindfulness is about being special.

35. Design mindfulness is living life out loud. ...We are in positions of responsibility, positions of opportunity, at the time of the biggest change in the ways of commerce and business— indeed, of life itself—in the past several hundred years.

## Acquiring Products in the Future

Never in the history of man have so many products been made available to consumers. This is evidenced by the excess of catalogs which seem to fill our mail boxes everyday illustrating and offering well-designed products. The products range in cost from low to extremely expensive and in usefulness from the practical to the merely decorative. Quality in design seems to be a requirement and a common theme running throughout these product offerings. Through a computer, the internet, and television consumers can now find assorted products evaluated and offered for sale. It is only logical that through a computer one can make detailed product reviews on his own. Just as the amount of time it takes to order a product from a catalog house is shortened, so is the amount of time between a "hot" product idea and the availability of the product itself. What next? Does this mean that when we order our clothes or cars in the future we will be able to sit in front of a computer screen and design the product we want? In other words, will we be able to arrange the placement of pockets, collars, buttons, etc. on clothing or the engine, tires, seat, and storage space on the car we want to purchase, thus bypassing salespeople and going directly to the manufacturer? It appears so.

## Judging Designs

The problem is how do we determine what is a well-designed product as compared to one that simply is not well designed? Having been on both sides of this issue, as a designer and a judge, I feel it is important to discuss it. In the case of skis, each year prominent ski magazines retain ski instructors to evaluate next year's equipment. They evaluate goggles, boots, bindings, poles and the skis themselves. With 10 to 20 such experts skiing and evaluating the equipment at the same time, it is possible to achieve a degree of unanimity on the performance of the equipment. As a consumer I find this approach quite satisfactory.

When I was a partner in the firm Stevens-Chase Design Associates, we liked having our designs selected by a museum or published as examples of "good designs." We won two "Master Design Awards" from McGraw Hill's magazine, *Product Engineering*

**FIGURE 10.1.** Philip Stevens (standing, second from right) receiving Master Design Award for Itek Corporation's 1824 Reader/Printer in 1962. Photograph courtesy of McGraw-Hill.

for our design of the SCM model 200 electric typewriter and Itek microfilm 1824 reader/printer (Figure 10.1). This made wonderful publicity and our peers accepted us as outstanding designers. We were then invited to become judges of *Product Engineering*'s annual contest.

Eventually, two other products we designed were selected by IDSA, PDC (Plastics Design Council), and the Department of Commerce for an international exhibit of outstanding American products and package design which were held in the U.S. Trade Center in London. All were shown as examples of well-designed American products. The exhibition demonstrated to emerging industrial countries the value industrial design has been to a modern industrial society like the United States. The two products we submitted were the SCM model 400 electric office typewriter and the Scott Aviation Executive Mark III portable oxygen system used on board small, four passenger aircraft that would fly at high altitude. Later, after I was established in Philip Stevens Associates and had testified on behalf of IDSA before Congress and a Presidential Commission, I was invited to be a judge at the annual product design review for *Industrial Design Magazine*.

There is much prestige, but also much responsibility that goes along with judging a design contest. The biggest problem with judging design competitions is that judges rarely have the opportunity to take the product home and use it. Judges do not, therefore, always evaluate a product from the point of view of the consumer. How do you evaluate a tractor or a crane? Magazines such as *Consumer Reports, Popular Science, Popular Mechanics,* and many automobile magazines do field test and evaluate the products they feature. I recall, as a typewriter designer, requesting a couple of different Olivetti typewriters to evaluate. One of the products given me to evaluate did not type correctly—its alignment was out of order. I found myself evaluating the design just like art critics/judges do—on looks alone.

## The Necessity for Good Design for Survival

Up until now I have described standard products with which most people are familiar, such as products that go into the home or office environment. There is a another type of product which is manufactured and evaluated in a desperate fashion. For instance, in the 1930s, Great Britain, Germany, and the United States felt that their countries needed better fighter aircraft to protect themselves. Designers in these countries were very impressed by Supermarine's *S.6B* designed by Reginald Mitchell (discussed later in this chapter) and its performance at the Schneider aircraft race in 1931. They felt that if a racer aircraft could go at this speed, why couldn't fighter aircraft. All these countries developed excellent fighter aircraft and I will discuss five of them. Please keep in mind that there were many other outstanding aircraft developed at this time, such as the American Army's *P-47* and the German-developed *Folk-Wolfe 190*. It is interesting to note that all five of the aircraft discussed here had almost the same design specification, i.e., speed over 400 mph, reaching 20,000 feet in eight minutes or less. Examples of achieving good design can be seen in World War II era aircraft design: the German *Bf 109* aircraft, designed by Willy Messerschmidt; the British Hawker *Hurricane,* designed by Sidney Camm; the British Supermarine *Spitfire* aircraft, designed by Reginald J. Mitchell; the North American *P-51 Mustang* aircraft, designed by Raymond Rice and Edgar Schmued; and the American Lockheed *P-38 Lightening,* designed by Clarence Kelly Johnson.

## The Design of the German *Bf 109* Aircraft

Willy Emil Messerschmitt was a genius in aeronautical engineering versus structural engineering. He had one love and that was the design of efficient, fast military aircraft. Besides designing against the Allied designers, he felt keen competition from his fellow German designers. He also had the ever-present design problem of making a faster, safer product which could approach closer and closer to the mysterious environment of supersonic speed. Once he conceived of such an aircraft, he had to make it lighter through the use of exotic materials. Trying to integrate manufacturing, fabrication, safety and reliability into a single design became an exceedingly difficult problem for Messerschmitt. As if these challenges were not enough, he was working for a totalitarian regime which thrived on distrust, intrigue, paranoia, and humiliation.

In 1933 the Nazi party came to power and Messerschmitt's company, the Bayerische Flugzeugwerke A.G., resumed operation. The company received a contract to design a competitive aircraft for participation in the 1934 "Challenge de Tourisme Internationale." This four passenger aircraft was called the *Bf 108*. Aesthetically, it was a very successful design. It was a monowing plane with a retractable landing gear, all sheet metal structure, an enclosed cabin with leading edge slots and baggage storage. However, before the *Bf 108* ever flew, and with no military aircraft design experience, Messerschmitt started the famed *Bf 109* design which looked much like the *Bf 108* (Figure 10.2).

The *Bf 109* was born on the drawing board to meet a Luftwaffe specification. Although Messerschmitt was the brains behind the *Bf 109* and coordinated the project, others were involved in its development. Walter Rethel, Messerschmitt's chief of design development, developed the original blueprints for the *Bf 109*. Much work was done by Robert Lusser and his office as well as Richard Bauer, Messerschmitt's chief design engineer.

In the development of the *Bf 109,* three very important design decisions were made which had far-reaching consequences. First, it was traditional in aircraft design to "over design" the plane's structure. This was done simply because there was little knowledge of aircraft structural engineering. An over-designed structure, while strong, added unnecessary weight. The structure's weight had to be reduced to enhance performance, even if the aircraft fell apart in intense aero-

## AIRCRAFT COMPARISON*

|  | German Bf 109E | Hawker Hurricane | Supermarine Spitfire | N. American P-51D Mustang | Lockheed P-38 Lightening** |
|---|---|---|---|---|---|
| **WING SPAN** | 32' | 40' | 36' | 37' | 52' |
| **LENGTH** | 28' | 32' | 29' | 32' | 38' |
| **RANGE** | 412 miles | 505 miles | 395 miles | 950 miles | 460 miles |
| **SPEED** | 357 mph | 328 mph | 362 mph | 437 mph | 414 mph |
| **FIRST FLOWN** | Sept. 1935 | Nov. 1935 | March 1936 | Oct. 1940 | Jan. 1939 |

*These figures were appropriate at different times. Models were continually being updated and changed.

**This aircraft had two engines.

**FIGURE 10.2.** The German *Bf 109,* designed by Willy Messerschmitt, 1935. Photograph courtesy of The Plane Picture Company, Hertfordshire, England, John M. Dibbs, photographer.

batics or critically tight combat maneuvers. Second, the design incorporated many of the best features of all fast aircraft known at that time. This specific approach was not seen again until the American design for the British of the *P-51* in 1940. Third, the advantages of aerodynamic engineering were beginning to be appreciated. For example, the fewer appendages that protrude from an aircraft's fuselage or wing, avoid air resistance, and thus allow the aircraft to travel faster. The *Bf 109* was rated at a speed of 357 miles per hour. That is why the cockpit of this aircraft was so narrow. Everything is trying to hide behind the engine which cannot be made smaller in the front view. That is also why the landing gear is retracted into the wing. Messerschmitt received a lucrative contract to manufacture this aircraft. At 40 years old, he was the foremost aircraft designer in the world!

The *Bf 109* was not without its problems, however. Some of Messerschmitt's fellow designers were jealous of his prominence and the Nazis never hesitated to antagonize him when his designs needed attention. For instance, the undercarriage wheels were too close together and the aircraft had a tendency to do ground loops, that is spin around when landing or taking off. It seemed that Messerschmitt wanted the landing gear supported directly up and into the fuselage and not penetrating the wing. Thus, during wing repair, the wing could be removed without jacking up the aircraft, saving time. Messerschmitt solved this ground loop problem by locking the tail wheel, thus putting greater drag on the back of the aircraft.

The *Bf 109* looked awkward on the ground with a nose too high which restricted visibility during taxying, but was handsome and efficient in the air. The canopy was slab-sided with squared corners which detracted from the nice carved sloping sides of the aircraft. The canopy looks like an afterthought. The aircraft was a monoplane design with a single-seat, all-metal construction, and took advantage of the latest aerodynamic and structural engineering techniques. It had slotted trailing edge flaps and leading edge slots plus a retractable

landing gear with an enclosed cockpit. This aircraft, like the British *Spitfire* and later the *Mustang,* was easy to service and upgrade with new and better features without disrupting the assembly line.

Upon seeing the *Bf 109,* Britain became alarmed and began to take notice of German aircraft design and technical developments. Yet it was British designers like Sir Sydney Camm of the Hawker Company (designer of the *Hurricane*) and Reginald J. Mitchell of Supermarine who almost single-handedly rebuffed their military's leaders ideas of future military aircraft and went beyond the specification to develop aircraft that could compete against the German *Bf 109*. These men wanted to create winning designs. They had professional pride!

## The Design of the British Hawker *Hurricane*

Sir Sydney Camm, one of Britain's most famous aircraft designers, started his career doing what many boys do, building model aircraft. This was done prior to World War I. It appears he gained his aircraft engineering experience on the job. Camm joined the H.G. Hawker Company in 1923 and designed his first aircraft in 1925. He designed many aircraft during his career. His outstanding aircraft included the *Hornet* in 1929 and the Hart two-seat bomber with a Rolls-Royce Kestrel engine (which was eventually used in the first Messerschmitt *Bf 109*). This aircraft was in production for a decade. Later, in the 1930s, Camm developed the *Fury*. He then turned his attention to the *Hurricane* with its retractable landing gear, eight machine guns, and enclosed canopy. It first flew in 1935. This outstanding aircraft played a magnificent role in the Battle of Britain. Camm went on to design many more great aircraft for the Hawker Company and the British Royal Air Force.

When aircraft armaments became much more powerful, stressed-skin construction began to be adapted as a new technique, replacing fabric. This allowed for easier aircraft repair and simplified construction. Camm's single-engine Hawker *Hurricane* used these

**FIGURE 10.3.** The British Hawker *Hurricane,* designed by Sir Sydney Camm, 1935. Photograph courtesy of The Plane Picture Company, Hertfordshire, England, John M. Dibbs, photographer.

**FIGURE 10.4.** The British Supermarine *Spitfire,* designed by Reginald J. Mitchell, 1936. Photograph courtesy of The Plane Picture Company, Hertfordshire, England, John M. Dibbs, photographer.

techniques (Figure 10.3). The *Hurricane* was the first fighter aircraft to exceed 300 mph at that time. During the Battle of Britain, *Hurricane*s shot down more enemy aircraft than all other aircraft and antiaircraft combined. It was easy to fly and repair. Its design was simpler than its sister ship, the single-engine Supermarine *Spitfire,* but its performance at that time was inferior to both the German *Bf 109* and the *Spitfire.* It should be noted that the *Hurricane* could be manufactured more rapidly than the *Spitfire.* Looking at the Hawker *Hurricane,* one gets the feeling that the canopy is too high compared to the aircraft's length. It had a purpose, enabling the pilot to better see his target over the nose of the aircraft. The canopy looks more modern than the slab-sided *Bf 109.* The tail, an undefinable form, does not quite fit into the fuselage with grace as compared to the *Spitfire* or the *Bf 109.*

## The Design of the British Supermarine *Spitfire*

The designer of the Supermarine *Spitfire,* Reginald J. Mitchell, was born in 1895. Mitchell became an engineer at the age of 21. He designed a racing flying boat, the *S.6B,* for which he won the coveted Schneider Trophy in 1931. To accomplish this it was necessary to design a sleek monoplane seaplane with floats. All of the experience that he acquired building this seaplane qualified him to respond to the Royal Air Force's request for a new fighter aircraft. The specification was too limiting for Mitchell, however. He was dissatisfied with his entry and developed his own specification. At that time Mitchell was suffering from cancer, having one lung operated on. During his recuperation he went to Germany and talked with some German pilots, probably about the performance and design of the new *Bf 109.* He sensed that his country may well be facing a formidable foe if war began, and he had better get a good design developed, and soon! He believed that through his work he might be able to influence the outcome of any future war. Mitchell developed his own aircraft which the government named the *Spitfire* (Figure 10.4). The completed design satisfied him and eventually the Royal Air Force and helped save a nation. Winston Churchill paid tribute to the Royal Air Force in the House of Commons on August 20, 1940 when he said, "Never in the field of human conflict was so much owed by so many to so few."

In Alfred Price's book, *The Spitfire Story* (page 16), he reveals an interesting observation about Mitchell's working style. On Mitchell's way of doing things, his chief draughtsman, Joe Smith says:

> He was an inveterate drawer on drawings, particularly general arrangements. He would modify the lines of an aircraft with the softest pencil he could find, and then remodify over the top with progressively thicker lines, until one would finally be faced with a new outline of lines about three-sixteenths of an inch thick. But the results were always worth while, and the centre of the line was usually accepted when the thing was redrawn.

The *Spitfire* flew in 1936 with a top speed of 362 miles per hour. It was a beautiful aircraft to look at. The *Spitfire* had almost straight lines parallel to the axis of the aircraft starting from the tail and progressing toward the nose, reminiscent of his racing seaplane the *S.6B* and the Italian *Macchi MC.72*. The cockpit appears to be lower than the *Hurricane*'s, which makes it more difficult to see over the nose for aiming purposes as well as taxying about the airfield. The plastic canopy aft of the windshield gives good visibility to the rear. The tail integrates into the fuselage nicely; it is a simple form. The belly of the aircraft is uncluttered compared to the *Hurricane,* the *Bf 109,* and the *Mustang.* Its elliptical, very thin wing tips, so important in turning, and the tail look beautiful when viewing the aircraft from the top or bottom. In his book, *Fighter: The True Story of The Battle of Britain,* Len Deighton talks about the appearance of the aircraft:

> The Spitfire's curved wing is said to have been influenced
> by the Heinkel He 70. Whether or not this is specifically true,

Mitchell, along with the rest of the world of aviation, must have found Heinkel's superb combination of aesthetic line and aerodynamic efficiency inspiring.

Viewing the *Spitfire* on the ground, the undercarriage appears as though the wheels are too close together and lacks stability (and is subject to ground looping like the *Bf 109*) as compared to the *Hurricane* or the *Mustang.*

However, the *Spitfire*'s performance from the start was outstanding. In fact, here is what the Supermarine test pilot said after landing (from *Chronicle of Aviation,* page 334, published by Jacques Legrand):

> Southampton, England, March 5
>
> Chief test pilot "Mutt" Summers expressed delight today at Southampton's Eastleigh aerodrome when he landed the prototype of Supermarine's latest fighter, to be known as the Spitfire. "Don't touch anything," he said after a highly successful first flight. The aircraft is not just a joy to fly but also a joy to behold: small and powerful, with superb, clean lines, it looks like a thoroughbred fighting machine.

The basic design structure and fabrication lent itself to infinite alterations without disrupting production progress. At Hawker Aircraft, Sidney Camm designed new planes from the wheels up, while Supermarine stuck to and continually upgraded the *Spitfire.* My research has not revealed a comparative analysis of the human factors qualities of the cockpits of both Allied and Axis fighters. I do not even believe that the concept of developing a cockpit to satisfy the 5 to 95 percentile, which has become almost an international standard, was even considered. I have heard stories that those who were particularly large were uncomfortable or actually rejected from flying the aircraft because of the limiting size of the cockpit. In Len Deighton's book, *Blood, Tears and Folly,* he comments about the cockpit:

The cockpit—let's say it's a Spitfire—fits you like a glove. It just about touches your shoulders on either side. The perspex canopy almost touches your head above. You can move your booted feet a few inches in either direction; you can stretch your arms right forward or down, but need to bend your elbows if you pull them back or up. No matter; you can control a fighter with just a few inches' movement of hands and feet.

This aircraft far exceeded the government's expectations and could compete favorably with the *Bf 109*. Yet, William Green criticizes the *Bf 109* in his book, *War Planes of the Third Reich* (page 542):

> The general consensus of opinion among R.A.F. pilots who had an opportunity to evaluate the Bf 109E-3 in flight was that it provided a formidable opponent to be treated with respect. Its excellent handling and response at low and medium speeds, good low-speed climb angle, gentle stall, lack of any tendency to spin, short take-off run, and draught-free canopy opening were commended, but among criticisms voiced were control heaviness at the upper end of the speed range, the poor view for taxying, the absence of a rudder trimmer necessitating the continuous and tiring application of rudder to fly straight at high speeds, the uncomfortably cramped cockpit offering insufficient headroom, and the large angle through which the aircraft had to be rotated on touch down due to its ground attitude.

## The Design of the North American *P-51 Mustang* Aircraft

After the war started, the United States discovered that while it was capable of high production, it had not designed a suitable single-engine competitive fighter like the *Spitfire* or the Messerschmitt *Bf 109*. North American Aviation, responding to a British specification in 1940, started designing a unique, beautifully proportioned fighter aircraft. The company offered a better design which combined the best features of all fighter aircraft designs known at that time. It

**FIGURE 10.5.** The North American *P-51 Mustang,* designed by Raymond Rice and Edgar Schmued, 1940. Photograph courtesy of The Plane Picture Company, Hertfordshire, England, John M. Dibbs, photographer.

became known as the *P-51,* called the *Mustang* (Figure 10.5). It was engineered and designed by Raymond Rice, Chief Engineer, and Edgar Schmued, Chief Designer. This was at least six years after the *Bf 109* had been designed. Through evolution, the *P-51D Mustang* was presented with a beautiful, one piece tear drop canopy that sat on top of, but blended well into the fuselage. A tail with a transitional dorsal fin had been added to the fuselage. The aircraft with the weight and placement of an added fuel tank behind the pilot tended to "wag its tail." The fin helped reduce this problem. The radiator scoop just aft and under the cockpit was a visual detraction, but vital for the great performance of the aircraft. This aircraft was big compared to the *Bf 109* and the British fighters. It had far greater fuel capacity, with drop gas tanks, which made it possible to escort American bombers from England to Germany and back. The *P-51 Mustang,* with the sound of

**FIGURE 10.6.** The Lockheed *P-38 Lightening,* designed by Clarence Kelly Johnson, 1939. Photograph courtesy of Ethell Enterprises, Front Royal, Virginia.

the Merlin engine, completed the aesthetic experience of viewing and hearing this aircraft. The aircraft was highly successful—first flying in 1940—one of the finest fighters of the war with maximum speed of 437 mph and a range of 1,710 miles. It had outstanding maneuverability, handsome both in performance and appearance. Other than the windshield, the *P-51D* had a full Plexiglas sliding canopy which worked well and provided excellent visibility. The lines to the engine were straight. The United States Air Force used the *Mustang* during the postwar for many years.

## The Design of the American Lockheed *P-38 Lightening*

An American aircraft which appears to have an excellent cockpit arrangement was the Lockheed *P-38* (Figure 10.6). It looked like it had a regular automotive steering wheel instead of the usual joystick.

The space provided for comfortable seating and superb visibility. The cockpit windows came down almost to elbow height. In 1936, Kelly Johnson, a California aircraft designer for the Lockheed Corporation, developed a twin-engine fighter. Lockheed began to build the prototype *XP-38* in 1937, soon after the Supermarine *Spitfire* and Hawker *Hurricane* first flew. Lockheed was the winner of a twin engine competition in June of that year. In his book, *The Lockheed P-38 Lightning* (page 20), Warren M. Bodie spoke about the popularity of the P-38:

> A minimum of 15 completely different two-engine, single-seat fighter aircraft attained at least prototype status in no fewer than five nations during the war. Only one, the P-38 Lightning, was ever given the production status of a true first line combat fighter, i.e., ordered into and committed to mass production.

The first flight of Johnson's *P-38* took place January 1939, ultimately attaining a maximum speed of 414 miles per hour. This unusually designed aircraft had twin booms extending and supporting the engines in front through the wing to the tail. The aircraft, 38 feet long and 13 feet high, had a range on internal fuel tanks of 460 miles and a wing span of 52 feet. The pilot's compartment and armaments were built into the center of the wing between the two engines. Having every detail carefully thought out made the aircraft unusually attractive. The tail, a modified symmetrical ellipse, was attached to the end of the booms. Having no transition from the fins to the booms, made the aircraft reminiscent of an organic form, like a leaf. The air scoops on the side of the booms and the super charger on top of the booms detract somewhat as one gets closer to the aircraft from the overall aircraft aesthetics. When introduced in January 1939, this aircraft was a commanding contribution to the impending war effort from an outstanding American designer.

## What Motivates Designers to Create Good Designs?

Why did all of these designers, including the Wright brothers, design such outstanding products at this critical time in history? Were they compelled or driven by patriotic ideology? Did their countries establish these high requirements for them? It seems that these men sensed that greater performance could be achieved than what was called for and they were determined to achieve it. Perhaps this is pride. It would be easy to say Messerschmitt loved Nazism, but seeing the work that he did in aviation over his lifetime one senses he transcended inclination in this direction. Why did the Wright brothers, Messerschmitt, Camm, Mitchell, Edgar Schmued, and Kelly Johnson all basically ignore the current specification or current assumption that it cannot be done and drive themselves to design and accomplish the seemingly impossible while developing superior designs? This initiative is unique in product engineering. We rarely see this in other fields of design.

As an industrial designer and an ex-aircraft engineer, I would like to discuss why I think they were successful. All of these strong, creative aircraft designers loved the challenge of modern technology and the competition among themselves. Additionally, they thrived on making progress while obeying the strict laws of physics. They loved the beauty of flight, speed, and technology and also the publicity and professional respect. Little was sweeter and more soul satisfying than obeying these physical laws while trying to actually fly or break the sound barrier and winning previously unwon design victories. We should be eternally indebted to the British designers Camm and Mitchell! These designers sensed that war was imminent and their patriotic feelings only added to their drive for design excellence. If they had not designed the appropriate fighters when they did there is little doubt that we would have lost the Battle of Britain. Hitler more than likely would have invaded and captured Britain and then it would have been a superhuman effort to win the war against Germany.

**FIGURE 10.7.** Burt and Dick Rutan's two-seat aircraft, *Voyager,* 1986. Photograph courtesy of CORBIS, New York.

Today some other young aircraft designers need to be recognized for their innovation and forward thinking. One is sailplane designer Paul MacCready. MacCready developed the *Gossamer Albatross,* a human-powered aircraft which looked much like a bicycle. In June of 1979 his aircraft flew across the English Channel in just over three hours. He and his pilot won the famed Kremmer prize. They were awarded 100,000 pounds.

The brothers Burt and Dick Rutan took the challenge of designing an energy-efficient aircraft that would circumnavigate the earth on one tank of fuel. They designed the *Voyager,* a two-person aircraft (Figure 10.7). Harold Rabinowitz describes the *Voyager's* record-breaking flight in his book, *Conquer The Sky: Great Moments in Aviation,* (page 203):

> The flight of the Voyager, the two-seat, twin engine
> airplane that circumnavigated the globe, taking off from

**FIGURE 10.8.** Clarence "Kelly" Johnson (1910-1990), creator of Lockheed's Skunkworks, c. 1980. Photograph courtesy of Lockheed Martin Skunkworks, Palmdale, California.

**FIGURE 10.9.** Lockheed's SR-71 *Blackbird,* 1966. Photograph courtesy of Lockheed Martin Skunkworks, Palmdale, California; Denny Lombard, photographer.

**FIGURE 10.10.** Lockheed's *U2 High Altitude Reconnaissance Spy Plane,* 1955. Photograph courtesy of Lockheed Martin Skunkworks, Palmdale, California; Eric Schulzinger, photographer.

**FIGURE 10.11.** Lockheed's *F-117A Stealth Fighter.* 1982. Photograph courtesy of Lockheed Martin Skunkworks, Palmdale, California; Tom Reynolds, photographer.

Edwards Air Force Base on December 14, 1986, and landing there nine days later without stopping for midair refueling, captured the world's attention as few flights had done in fifty years. The plane was designed by Burt Rutan and flown by his brother, Dick Rutan, and Jeanna Yeager. The aircraft was just big enough for the pilots to take turns popping his or her head into the raised bubble while the other lay flat and slept or ate. The pair had oxygen for flights higher than sixteen thousand feet, but the Voyager was not pressurized, so they could not fly higher than twenty thousand feet which meant that they could not fly above harsh weather.

## Skunk Works Philosophy

Corporate officials are beginning to see the advantages of what is called a "Skunk Works" to design and develop products. This approach was developed by Lockheed in 1943, headed by Clarence "Kelly" Johnson, and was officially known as Lockheed's Advanced Development Projects (Figure 10.8). In fact, some believe that the development of the *P-38* was the real beginning of the famous Skunk Works. Many of the same people were involved in the *P-38*'s develop-

ment. The Skunk Works drew talent from existing Lockheed employees, "borrowing" whom ever was most qualified and available at the time.

Since its inception until his retirement in the mid 1970s, the Skunk Works was entirely Johnson's domain. He was a brilliant designer with forward thinking and the provocation to take risks—even daring. Johnson established the specifications for most of his projects himself. In other words, to best achieve what the Air Force wanted he would embellish the specification to ensure excellent performance was achieved. One example of Kelly Johnson's brave innovation can be seen in the development of the *SR-71* spy plane, called the *Blackbird* (Figure 10.9). In 1958 Johnson assembled a team to begin developing a new spy plane that would far exceed the capabilities of the *U-2* (Figure 10.10) spy plane (another aircraft of his development). In *Skunk Works: A Personal Memoir of my Years at Lockheed,* by Ben R. Rich and Leo Janos (page 193), Johnson's forward thinking philosophy is revealed. "It makes no sense," he said, "to just take this one or two steps ahead, because we'd be buying only a couple of years before the Russians would be able to nail us again.

No, I want us to come up with an airplane that can rule the skies for a decade or more." Johnson proposed an aircraft to cruise at more than three times the speed of sound, that could fly coast to coast in less than an hour on one tank of gas. Now that is daring, risky thinking!

This new aircraft required all its components to be developed from scratch. Nothing "off the shelf" existed because the design was so revolutionary—so unlike anything that had been developed before. After four years in development, seriously over budget and overdue, the first successful test flight of the *Blackbird* took place. Rich and Janos describe the new spy plane (*Skunk Works,* page 233): "The Blackbird so outmatched any other airplane in the world with its speed and altitude, it would dominate air warfare for at least a decade or more." During its run, the *Blackbird* established a new speed record of 2,070 miles per hour and an altitude of 80,257 feet (*Skunk Works,* page 240-1):

> The Blackbirds flew 3,500 operational sorties over Vietnam and other hostile countries, had more than one hundred SAM SA-2 missiles fired at them over the years, and retired gracefully in 1990 after twenty-four years of service as the only military airplane never to be shot down or lose a single crewman to enemy fire. Which was truly amazing because the Blackbird and its crews continuously drew the most dangerous missions.

Johnson is truly a remarkable designer. Lockheed's Skunk Works is also responsible for the development of the *F-117 Stealth Fighter* (Figure 10.11). The characteristics of a Skunk Works are as follows:

- promotes strong leadership
- selects a small, hand picked, talented group of designers, engineers and related support personnel
- works toward very specific objectives
- gives the freedom and authority to take risks
- seeks high quality control, each member usually reporting to the person in charge, as well as continual self-checking

- allows each member of the Skunk Works the authority to reject parts not up to quality standards
- encourages team members to think imaginatively, to improvise and to try unconventional approaches to solve problems
- sticks to reliable suppliers and builds a long term relationship with them
- works closely with other key engineering and design personnel
- places each team member near the production line and the model laboratory

## FORD MOTOR COMPANY

### The *Mustang*

Other manufacturers are catching on to the Skunk Works approach to product development. Ford Motor company used this technique to develop a new model of its *Mustang.* In *Skunk Works,* Ford's *Mustang* project is described as follows (page 319):

> For many years the idea of reopening that once popular line of cars was rejected by company executives as being prohibitively expensive. Development costs were projected at more than $1 billion. But in 1990, management put together an ad hoc Skunk Works operation called Team Mustang, comprised of designing and marketing executives and expert shop people, swore them to secrecy, then instructed them to design and produce a new Mustang for 1994. Most important, management allowed Team Mustang to do the job with a minimum of second-guessing and management interference. The result: the group took three years and spent $700 million to produce a new vehicle that was extremely well received and became one of Ford's hottest sellers. That represents 25 percent less time and 30 percent less money spent than for any comparable new car program in the company's recent history.

General Motors is now following Ford and has started a separate and secret development group of its own for future projects. Four or five aerospace companies now claim to have a Skunk Works. McDonnell Douglas calls its group Phantom Works, and it apparently emulates …Lockheed.

Foreign manufacturers have long seen the advantage of this type of product development. Japanese automobile manufacturers know that switching suppliers based on the lowest bid can prove costly in the long run. Skunk Works' philosophy is that keeping trouble-free relationships with old suppliers with proven quality parts will ultimately keep the price of products lower.

## The *Taurus*

Another example of innovative thinking in design can be seen by examining Ford Motor Company's development of the *Taurus*. In the late 1970s, Ford, along with other American automobile companies, had a reputation for outdated, ugly, and unreliable cars. Consumer confidence in Ford vehicles was nonexistent. Foreign competition began to intensify and the person who in the past might have purchased a Ford looked at Japanese and German-made cars. In his book *Taurus: The Making of the Car That Saved Ford,* Eric Taub explains what was happening (page 92):

**FIGURE 10.12.** A 1986 Ford *LTD.* This car was replaced with the *Taurus* in model year 1986. Photograph courtesy of Ford Motor Company.

American drivers were beginning to demand a different kind of experience in their automobiles. They did not want to feel as isolated from the road, and to get that feeling, they had to buy foreign cars. But the American companies sluffed off those buyers as fringe consumers. "Detroit's blind insistence at looking at every BMW owner as a cult person driving a cult car is nuts," Lou Ross said. "Certainly, the good old-fashioned American car is not the one that people now want to drive."

About 1979 Ford began developing a new vehicle known then as the Sigma project, later to be named *Taurus*. This car was to appeal to trend setters and be touted as a family vehicle. It ultimately replaced the unpopular and unappealing Ford *LTD* (Figure 10.12). Ford's strategy was a unique, team-work approach. For the first time, all divisions involved in a car's production—engineering, design, sales, marketing, manufacturing, public relations—were involved in the design process from the very beginning. Regular meetings were scheduled so that everyone involved in the process would be up to date on the progress and problems evolving in the design. This is quite a departure from each individual department, i.e., engineering, design, manufacturing, etc., working independently without consideration for how their work would relate to the work of the department next to them. Eric Taub writes about the advantages of this approach to design (page 49):

Manufacturers could no longer claim that an engineer had wasted months designing an engine no one could build, because the manufacturer would be present during the design. Marketers could not argue that the public hated a car, because research would be carried out on every stage of the design process and reported back to the entire group before a vehicle was finally approved.

This type of team approach met resistance at Ford where most workers were accustomed to working independently, as specialists in their own domain. Preliminary work began on the car in early 1980. The decision was made to make the car front-wheel drive. This meant adding hundreds of millions of dollars in development costs to the project. A new transmission capable of working with a front-wheel-drive vehicle needed developing. Taub (page 53) describes other engineering problems encountered during the preliminary engineering phase of the project:

> ...[F]ront-wheel-drive cars were assembled and painted in a different order than rear-drive models. So the two assembly plants that would eventually make the Taurus would have to be shut down for at least two months to be retooled to accommodate a front-drive system.
>
> Before they would approve the project, top management wanted proof that front-wheel drive would be as technologically sound as the proven rear-wheel-drive system, because the costs of developing the new system were enormous. Upward of $1 billion, close to one-third of the cost of the entire program, would be spent just on front-drive development.

Up until this point in time, designers were not taken too seriously at Ford, and probably not at the other American automobile giants either. Every day designers would find their ideas thrown out the window by corporate executives frightened by new concepts (*Taurus,* page 105):

> The key question a designer asks is if a new concept immediately feels acceptable. If so, something is wrong. A fresh design has to scare the person who conceived it, because that car has to look fresh five years after it is originally drawn. "I want everybody to be a little uncomfortable with the car initially," Telnack [a Ford employee] said. "If they're not, it's the same old thing." Adds a former General Motors designer, "If the folks in the three-piece suits smile and say, 'Yeah, I'm comfortable with that,' then you're in trouble."

Americans had not only lost the lead in automotive design to Japanese and Europeans, but in all product design. For years the way a commodity looked was of little importance to U.S.

## Good Product Development

Here are some conclusions that can be drawn from the case studies discussed in this chapter:

1. Good product development is dependent upon careful corporate commitment, both in will and resources.
2. Strong leadership is imperative!
3. Delegation of responsibility is fine if authority is given commensurate to the responsibility.
4. Project research or careful research into the user's needs and wants is essential.
5. The sharing of information, ideas, objectives, and failures along with frustrations among development team members is crucial. It is surprising who can help solve a problem by suggesting solutions.
6. Know your competition.
7. Have a mock-up, model area nearby. Building prototypes and models to prove ideas is essential.
8. If you use consultants or outside suppliers, take them into your confidence. Work closely with them. They may be expensive but they sometimes can save the day.
9. Stay close to the assembly line and product test area. This is where many product problems occur. They must become evident to be solved.

manufacturers; its functionality was all that mattered. While Germans were designing sleek automatic coffee makers, Americans were producing bulky units that had no integrity of form. While Japanese and Europeans were experimenting with new pastels and fluorescent colors for their products, Americans used plastic wood applique on toaster ovens and televisions and produced avocado green refrigerators.

**FIGURE 10.13.** A 1986 Ford *Taurus*—a car five years in development! The *Taurus* became the best-selling car in American history. Photograph courtesy of Ford Motor Company.

**FIGURE 10.14.** A 1998 Ford *Taurus*. In 1996, after ten years in production with only minor modifications to its original design, Ford introduced a redesigned appearance for its popular *Taurus*. Photograph courtesy of Ford Motor Company.

Good design was not an element that interested most American manufacturers. Even those intimately involved in the process often failed to keep up with trends, unaware of their competition.

This philosophy was about to change with the *Taurus*. First, Ford did extensive research on the consumers' opinion of Ford and their preferences in automobiles. They studied how people buy cars—what their behavior was while shopping, do they look under the hood, take a test drive, sit in the driver's seat, or bring their spouses along. Some of Ford's specifications for the *Taurus* were as follows:

- create a family vehicle, not a sporty sedan.
- include good human factors—placement of all instruments was to be logical. Switches were to be "user friendly" and easy to turn on at night without looking at them (tactile switches). To accomplish this, extensive research was required.
- follow German-influenced design, i.e., produce automobiles that appear robust and solid. This implies a stable, dependable car.
- take into consideration the needs of female drivers. This is the first time an American car manufacturer developed a car specifically for female drivers. It felt that if it met the human factors requirements of women, it could satisfy all drivers.
- design the car as front-wheel driven.
- achieve 0 to 60 miles per hour in 11.5 seconds.
- generate 130 horsepower.
- require oil changes only every 7,500 miles.
- survive 100,000 miles without major repairs or maintenance.

After test cars were developed, the *Taurus* was evaluated for looks, driveability, interiors, and exteriors. Ford rented a large room and showed over 300 people photographs of life-size clay models of the new car along with competitive cars.

All of this effort paid off in the long run. The Ford *Taurus* went on sale December 26, 1985 for model year 1986 and became the best-selling vehicle in American history (Figure 10.13). It represented a startling shift toward more aerodynamic car designs. In 1996, Ford redesigned and updated the appearance of its *Taurus,* but the integrity of the original design is proven by the fact that Ford did not make any major changes to the car's design for a full ten years (Figure 10.14).

# R. BUCKMINSTER FULLER:
## AN INFLUENTIAL ARCHITECT

R. Buckminster Fuller has much in common with the designers discussed above. He believed that elegant design was the most efficient design using the minimum of world energy and natural resources. In *Design Discourse* (page 269), Victor Margolin makes a reference to Fuller and his many writings and philosophy:

> …[I]n… 1960,… many young people rejected their elders' dreams of material prosperity and sought to build an alternative culture based on community life and reduced consumption. The model designer of this movement was R. Buckminster Fuller, the brilliant engineer who had tried to industrialize the American building industry in the late 1920s, and whose geodesic domes were widely adopted by many after initial applications by the U.S. Marine Corps and several large corporations.

> …Fuller was also the inspiration for Stewart Brand's *The Whole Earth Catalog* (Menlo Park, Calif.: Portola Institute, 1969-1971), a semiannual publication dedicated to the tireless inventor and featuring a collection of low-tech tools for living, as well as publications intended to foster a multifaceted alternative lifestyle.

Fuller visited my design school and gave many lectures. The design school's faculty and students were moved by his philosophy. He preached energy conservation long before the oil shortages of 1975. He wanted us to think about all the oil that was wasted every time we stopped at a traffic signal. Who can fault such "ultra green" thinking? In my opinion, he was the greatest minimal designer of the twentieth century.

Fuller was not only a designer and philosopher, but also a great architect of the twentieth century. Some people are critical of his work for not being terribly aesthetic, but he looked at the world and concluded that we as people must change our treatment of the environment and the way we think if we are to survive. Looking back over all the designers we have talked about in this book, no group or individual was as comprehensive as Fuller and sensitive to the needs of the people. He lectured at many schools and probably had more impact on design faculties and students than any other visiting lecturer. In John McHale's book, *R. Buckminster Fuller: Makers of Contemporary Architecture,* he writes (page 15-6):

> From the outset, Fuller's thinking is comprehensive: each development proceeds from consideration of its largest and most universal context, then goes on to local and more immediate aspects which present themselves.

> …He proceeds from the initiation and statement of a problem to a review of the means available for its solution, and to the analysis of these in relation to over-all requirements—then, and only then, does he pass to actual design and reduction to practice.

Fuller once designed a house which he called the "Dymaxion House" in 1927. It was a prefabricated unit costing then about $23,000.00 if mass produced, not including tooling cost. The design incorporated Fuller's philosophy. Designed not only for mass production, the house was deliverable by aircraft (helicopter) and could be used anywhere throughout the world. Fuller's design was far beyond his time and he incorporated many concepts which were deemed impractical then but that are now considered standard in today's home construction. For example, he created flexible dividers for internal spaces, storage through a system of revolving shelves and hangers, automatic laundry and dishwashing devices, garbage disposal unit, and built-in vacuum units for cleaning and dusting. In *R. Buckminster Fuller: Makers of Contemporary Architecture,* John McHale describes Fuller's house design (page 18): "This was not simply an aesthetic 'machine to live in' but a machine like the auto or airplane, designed to extend the potential of living—either in or out! …[T]he Dymaxion House was far in advance of its time, compared to other architectural work about 1927."

Fuller became very concerned about the energy that is necessary to make and support our modern way of life and our products, particularly automobiles. He was one of the first to begin thinking in terms of recycling products. His imagination hardly knew any limit. For example, he was enthralled by the sphere as a form and components and portions of a sphere. He believed that portions of cities could be weather-proofed under a giant dome. John McHale discusses Fuller's fascination with the sphere (*R. Buckminster Fuller,* page 31):

> …In an all-motion universe, all phenomenon interactions are precessional; lines of force are not straight but tend to curvilinear paths. These paths are inherently "geodesic," i.e., the shortest distance between points on a curved or spherical surface. With the automatic tendency of energy in networks to triangulate, Fuller assumed that the most economical structural energy web might be derived through the fusion of tetrahedron and sphere. (The sphere encloses most space with least surface and is strongest against internal pressure, the tetrahedron encloses least space with most surface and is strongest against external pressure.) This may be accomplished via the icosahedron, a multiphase tetra, all of whose vertexes lie on the surface of a sphere. By exploding this form onto the sphere and symmetrically subdividing its faces, we arrive at the three-way great-circle grid of the geodesic structure.

> …It is important to note that there are no inherent size limitations. As the system gets larger, the number, or frequency, of triangulation is increased.

In the latter phase of Fuller's career, at the International Congress of Architects held in London in 1961, *Architectural Design* editors asked him to contribute his views on the world environmental situation. Fuller suggested a plan for all architectural departments at universities the world over. He urged them to spend the next 10 years studying the problem and seeking solutions on how to make the world's resources serve 100 percent of humanity through design. How refreshing it is to see and hear a designer/architect talk about our environmental needs and responsibilities. He felt that the practice of having first year architectural students focus on local and small problems, working up to larger problems in subsequent years, was inadequate and shortsighted. He believed that students should be involved in total world planning from the beginning of their training. Below is an excerpt from his speech (from *R. Buckminster Fuller* by John McHale, page 120-1) which is reminiscent of Bok's writings discussed in Chapter 4:

> The first year's total world planning by the students and its designed implementation may be expected to disclose great amateurishness and inadequacies, but not only will the criticism come from the architectural profession, but it will also be evoked from the politicos, from the economists, the industrialists, excited by its treading on their doorsteps, out of which criticism the next year's round of world designing by the students may be greatly advantaged. The second, third, and fourth years should show swift acceleration in the comprehension of the problem and the degree of satisfaction of the problem.

> …It is clearly manifest, however, in this Sixth Congress of the International Union of Architects that the architects are able

to think regarding such world planning in a manner transcendental to any political bias. My experience around the world and amongst the students tells me that the students themselves tend always to transcend political bias and that all of them are concerned with the concept of making the world work through competent design.

In much investigation and inquiry I have had no negative response to the programme of organization of the student capability to the raising of the performance of the world resources to serve 100 percent of humanity by peaceful, comprehensive laboratory experiment and progressive design evolution.

…What will appear will unquestionably be world news of the first order, and not only world news but the news that men all around the earth have waited for. The common goals for all to work toward will be reduced from empty words to simple physical objectives.

## OTHER INFLUENTIAL ARCHITECTS OF THE 20TH CENTURY

It is regrettable that we cannot go into detail about all of the great and influential architect/designers of the twentieth century. Obviously, Frank Lloyd Wright must be included as one of the most outstanding American architects along with the great French/Swiss Le Corbusier. The German/American Walter Gropius must also be included, not only for his architectural and design ability, but also for his teachings at the Bauhaus. Besides these leaders, other distinguished men, such as Marcel Breuer, Mies van der Rohe from the Bauhaus, and the architectural engineers Pier Luigi Nervi of Italy, and Robert Maillart of Switzerland, should be recognized.

This book is not intended to be about architecture or architects, but since they are of one profession and are asked to help in the design of products and solving critical urban design problems, it is only natural that they should be discussed. It is regrettable that more

designs illustrating the work of each of these architects could not be included. The designs tell a great deal about the architects and their philosophies.

In the final analysis, one must ask—whether an engineer, industrial designer, or architect—have I and my profession left this world a better place than when we entered it? Is our time in history as significant as the Industrial Revolution or the Renaissance period, and is mankind better off? Is this not what design is all about?

## THE FUTURE OF DESIGN

### A New Design Culture and A New Theory of Design

So what does the future hold for industrial design? This question has been asked by design historians not only here in America but also in Europe. Many designers want it to change believing that the modern period of design and art has come and gone. Some designers have called this time we are now in the minimalist period. This simply means that anything we design is reduced to its simplest form and economical shapes. Personally, I feel it is unfair of those who never fully appreciated or practiced the minimal approach in design to criticize it. I see the work of some architects interjecting classical symbolism into modern design. It seems to me that designers should strive to achieve true minimal design before we agree to accept symbols of past design eras.

Maurizio Vitta believes there is a need for a new design theory. In his essay *The Meaning of Design* (from *Design Discourse*, page 31), he writes:

A general theory of "the culture of design" does not yet exist. But it is discussed so much because a need for it is felt and because designers today are called upon to face problems that, in practice, involve cultural questions that are rather broad and remote from the traditional scope of design.

Some critics sincerely believe that design culture must change. They suggest we live in a new period or post modern era. Other thoughtful critics say that with all the problems facing the world today and the fact that we as designers claim to have creativity and problem-solving capabilities, we should work on more and more meaningful problems. In the book *Discovering Design,* Richard Buchanan and Victor Margolin (page xi) discuss the problems facing designers today:

> Professional design practice is vulnerable in a way that it has never been before. Based on the past success of the design professions, designers are now invited to participate in the early stages of the product development process because of a belief that they can contribute something special that others cannot provide in forming the concept of a new product or design problem solution. In the past, however, designers often prevailed through personal charisma and the vividness of their proposed solutions, without directly joining issues with the technical challenge of competing professionals who rely on various forms of "objective" proof of the validity of their ideas. Now, designers must work closely and persuasively with other participants, often including representatives of the general population expected to use a new product. Indeed, designers must often play the subtle and informal role of facilitator in such groups, quietly guiding the process of deliberation and encouraging the integration of sound contributions by other professionals.

All aspects of design should be interrelated. Currently, design is divided into forms of practice such as, industrial design, graphic design, engineering, interior design, or fashion design. For the most part, this is to separate artistically oriented designing from technologically based designing (engineering, computer science, etc.).

## The Designer and the Changing World

Who can predict when change is upon us? Like it or not, change does come about! I believe that if a designer (or anyone) is dissatisfied with his or her work, a change should be made if possible. Thankfully, an industrial-design education does include a liberal arts background. I have seen designers leave the profession to become entrepreneurs or product manufacturers. I had one employee who went off to become an antique and junk dealer. Several acquaintance designers have selected model making and industrial-design marketing as their work. Some believe that training and retraining, job hopping and even career hopping will become commonplace in the twenty-first century.

## What does the future hold for design?

Design as we know it cannot change very much. How we design can change. I look upon the design process as a three-cornered structure. It has been this way since Christopher Dresser's era. In one corner of the structure is the designer. In another corner is the client, including its management, marketing, sales, and engineering. In the third corner is the user and/or consumer.

Many forward thinking design historians or critics envision dramatic changes in the above structure. They envision more sophisticated research processes regarding the consumer and careful inspection of the client himself. Finally, as we have seen, industrial design has made itself more efficient with the use of computer-aided design (CAD) and the computer. However, I believe the three cornered structure of design service will remain the same. Industrial design is finding more efficient means of production and new ways of seeing the customer while becoming more sensitive to the client's needs and wants. The way designers communicate their designs, however, will change. Design service will accelerate because of technological advances in model development and manufacturing tooling. Designers of the future will basically change little from today's practitioner. In the future:

1. Designers will still be concerned with their ethical relationship with their colleagues and clients.

2. Design consultants will find increasing competition to gain clients. They will have to find new techniques for finding work.

3. Designers will need to be proficient with computer skills, enabling them to do research, prepare reports, and begin designs all using the computer. A few additional comments regarding the computer are necessary. First, it is a tool that every designer must master. However, the computer is no better than the information put into it. It will help immensely in providing different perspectives of a product system. This can save designers much time and clients design costs. At last, designers can take complex products, add or subtract elements of the design and concurrently evaluate the aesthetics, and in some cases, the human factors, manufacturing complexities, and the ramifications of such potential changes. There is a down-side to this. If a product has been developed to interface with a user, a model or mock-up must be constructed to evaluate and duplicate the design. If the design is acceptable after being evaluated, it must then be transposed onto a document (a drawing) to guarantee the human factors or ergonomics. Achieving this transposition is the frustration. A computer cannot "feel" or evaluate the product and appropriately record dimensions. Very accurate dimensions are critical in the design of power and hand tools, business machines, transportation vehicles, and even firearms.

4. The computer will become increasingly necessary for efficient design communication but the design tools of the past will also remain important.

5. The speed in which designers work will increase in the future because of the computer and other technological advances. Designers can receive immediate feedback on their designs from clients and users. Concepts, suggestions, and criticism will be communicated quickly from designer to client and vice versa.

6. The overall quality of graphics in our society will improve because the designer will be computer proficient.

7. Designers may well be involved with industrial-design schools which are near them by working with students of industrial design.

8. Designers will probably remain in touch with their universities after graduation and may even seek an affiliation with the faculties.

9. With continuing global business opportunities, designers in the future will be working in foreign cultures. This may necessitate designers speaking a couple of different languages. Design clients will be worldwide, and not necessarily regional.

10. More than likely, designers will find themselves more successful if they specialize in their design service.

11. Designers will be forced to work more closely with their lawyers due to our increasing awareness of safety issues and product liability, plagiarism concerns, proprietary rights, and patents.

12. As companies become increasingly aware of the value design brings them, designers will continue to earn a good living.

So, where does this leave the future of design? Today we separate the design of objects (products) from immaterial products like techniques and consulting services. However, all types of designers, engineers, architects, etc. must work together in the future to help solve the critical problems facing the world today. Designers should be challenged with solving world problems, such as, lack of education, awkwardness of helping the handicapped, pollution of the environment, overpopulation, starvation, incarceration, etc. Good design should help solve social and environmental problems, not create them. New methods of training designers needs to be explored and implemented. Because of the trend toward service industries, designers are no longer simply creators of objects but of complete environments as well. This puts the spotlight on the capabilities and contributions of industrial designers. To identify problems and work toward solutions, designers must become masters of psychology and statistics. They must be able to write persuasively and intelligently. To illustrate, when I was working for SCM on a wide variety of office products, I felt that there must be some integration of these products. This led to our firm selling the SCM Corporation on letting us explore the possibility of an integration of the products and their functions as discussed in Chapter 6.

Before the question about industrial design and the next century can be fully explored, other important considerations must be made. If our world continues to go around as it has for the past 50 years, do we expect the desire and need for design to continue? Yes, we can expect the same desires and needs thanks to our security and way of life. Yes, we may be attacked by small countries with weapons of mass destruction out of sheer envy or greed. Following my military experience in Italy during World War II, Italy had been reduced to the status of a Third World country facing failure. Since then, peace has prevailed throughout the land for over 53 years. I have visited Italy off and on over the past 20 years and witnessed the return of its status as an important country. Today, the villages, ports, and industries have been rebuilt to their pre-war condition. None of this could have been accomplished without this long period of peace. I can only hope that other countries can experience the same peaceful longevity to develop themselves. It is important to remember that if a country becomes involved in war, the arts—whether it be music, architecture or industrial design—will come to a halt.

The world will continue to experience global warming, destruction of our forests to make more toilet paper and wasteful depletion of our natural resources to make tasteless, foolish products. Life expectancy will probably continue to rise, while crime, drugs, and disease will continue to plague the world's society. Obviously, the continuation of a healthy industry is of extreme importance. In order for design to thrive, there is a need for economic stability for continued development of design. Throughout my career America has experienced a recession every decade. This puts undue pressure upon manufacturers, which in turn slows or compromises new product development.

Paul Kennedy, in his book *Preparing for the Twenty-First Century,* identifies four significant problems threatening world peace:

- lack of mass education
- tribal ignorance including intolerance of others
- overpopulation
- rising imbalance of income between rich and poor

Kennedy later comments that many successful companies, recognizing the need to think globally, project themselves onto the international economic stage. They simply have little choice. If they do not expand and try to serve world markets, some other company in some other country will. It should be remembered that just as there must be a company headquarters with executives making decisions, there likewise needs to be design and engineering departments responding to corporate needs. While a company's location is irrelevant, the fact is that something must be done to meet the desire for new products. New and better products will always be wanted as long as there is peace.

The concept of a product being one-hundred-percent American made will continue to fade, as it is now. Products today may be controlled by a management residing in one country, with engineering and design from another country, while the manufacture, assembly, and distribution from yet another country.

In the book, *Bold New World,* William Knoke speaks about the future (page 95-6):

> The abundance of new "raw materials" in the next twenty years will completely revolutionize manufacturing and construction by making products more functional at less cost.
>
> …Aircraft manufacturers may yet obtain their El Dorado "unobtanium"—a mythical material with lilliputian weight, gargantuan strength, and an unreachable melting point. Japanese, European, and American scientists are working on a new generation of ceramics able to withstand up to 4,000 degrees Fahrenheit, a temperature that turns nearly all materials into liquid. These ceramics will be used for the turbine blades of the new generation of jet engines. Such hyper-hot engines will be feather-weight, burn fuel more cleanly, and turn everyday hypersonic jet travel into reality. Aircraft designers will use composites and plastics to make the fuselage and wings so that, twenty years from now, the commercial jet will scarcely contain any metal at all.
>
> Glass fibers, plastics, and ceramics are rendering copper wire obsolete. Fiber-optic cables made from these materials are replacing uncounted tons of copper telephone cabling beneath the streets of Manhattan and in office buildings everywhere.

Knoke also believes that smart companies in the future will track their customers in order to satisfy their needs (page 124):

> Perhaps the quintessential company providing top quality postpurchase customer support is WordPerfect Corporation, which developed one of the most successful application programs in the history of the computer. With corporate offices close to no major metropolitan center, in Orem, Utah, WordPerfect's customer service telephone system can handle up to 1,300 calls at any one time. Technicians are immediately at customers' desks, anywhere in the world, taking them through difficult problems. The results has earned WordPerfect one of the highest ratings of all word processing packages; but it has also given technicians insight into every conceivable product glitch, and ideas for future product designs and improvements. WordPerfect could not have become a dominant player in word processing without such intimate contact with its customers. The competitive battles of the twenty-first century will be those of service.

The current trend toward service industries versus manufacturing will continue in the United States as well as in most every other industrialized country. Designers will, more and more, become creators of systems and *environments* rather than *things*. Yet I believe that careful arrangement of *things* creates the *environment*. Somebody will still need to design products to fit the environment and meet the task at hand.

I had an interesting experience when a client asked me to design a microscope for inspecting the quality of microchips used in the computer industry. It soon became apparent to me that to do a better job, the stand the microscope sits on along with the operator's chair and lights were all part of the system and must be designed in concert with the microscope. In other words, the design assignment should have been how can we better inspect microchips? The total process including the environment should have been examined. For too long industrial designers have been content sitting on the sidelines, holding out their hands, hoping industries will give them work. If something is given to them, rest assured it will be to the client's specification. Getting the project properly oriented, whereby the industrial designer can manage the assignment, is often a herculean job. I am convinced that industrial designers must find a way to better explain to everybody what they do, for whom they do it, and why they are good at it.

## Politics

Naturally, it is the responsibility of all citizens to be concerned about their government and exercise their civic responsibilities. This is usually done by serving in the Armed Forces, Peace Corps, or Americorps (an organization in which young people can work to earn money for college), or by working for such organizations as Habitat for Humanity or United Way or become a government intern or join a political party. There are many organizations that yearn for volunteers, like hospitals, schools, and nursing homes.

The Green Party, a political party concerned with environmental issues, is concerned with such problems as preserving the landscape and recycling used products. It views the earth as (from *Green Products by Design: Choices for a Cleaner Environment* by the Office of Technology Assessment, Congress of the United States, page 45) "a closed ecological system" and stresses the "co-evolution of human society and ecosystems on an equal basis." The Sierra Club in the United States has a similar cause. Any sensitive designer will take these principles into consideration when designing products and exercising his civic obligations.

## Design vs. Service

In *Bold New World,* Knoke comments on the upsurge in the service industry (page 125):

> Today, 80 percent of the US labor force is in service, and over the next few decades almost all new jobs will likely be in service.
>
> ...In every case, workers are no longer making things, but contributing by helping solve specific human needs. For the aged, we have a phalanx of nurses, physical therapists, and cardiac surgeons. For the two-earner households, we have battalions of child-care providers, cleaning crews, and even professional shoppers. For design work we have legions of architects, engineers, and programmers. Investment advisers, aerobic instructor, tort attorneys, insurance adjusters, interior decorators, even movie stars—these and a thousand more like them no longer make a living by growing or by making, but by *doing.* We have risen above an economy driven by *things* to an economy driven more and more by *actions.*

How do I see the future of industrial design? More people are enjoying the fruits of life now than ever before in the history of mankind. This type of world encourages those with the desire and/or means to seek out and use design to enrich their lives. Newsstands have row upon row of magazines on how to enhance readers' environment and lifestyle through design. This helps human beings adjust their environments to make life more productive, enjoyable, and aesthetically rewarding. While most people are not designers themselves, they are becoming much more selective and critical of the products they chose to have in their environment.

Other countries understand that to penetrate our markets their goods must be professionally developed. In other words, the product must look appropriate in our environment, be useful, safe, meet a genuine human need, and have value. Who will design such products?

In this chapter I have described the ingredients necessary to make good design. I have looked at the use of design in the survival of countries themselves, and I have explored the designers who design these beautiful and critical products. Lastly, I have identified critical problems facing the world today and have presented solutions that can be achieved by industrial designers. I have talked about some of the world's seemingly unsolvable problems and the need to channel the talent we (designers) have toward solving these problems. I am optimistic that industrial design can contribute to the resolution of some of these difficult problems. Having been associated with design for almost 50 years, having grown up in the Great Depression, having served in World War II, having seen our country maintain its responsibility toward world peace, as well as having operated a successful design partnership and corporation—and designed good products, I sincerely believe there is a need for industrial design that will continue well into the twenty-first century and beyond.

## APPENDIX A

### IDSA Code of Ethics and Articles of Ethical Practice

The Industrial Designers Society of America
45195 Business Court, Suite 250, Dulles, VA 20166-6717
Phone: 703/707-6000  Fax: 703/787-8501
E-mail: idsa@idsa.org  Web: www.idsa.org

The following is from the Industrial Designers Society of America *2002 Directory of Industrial Designers* (page 5):

> Recognizing that industrial designers affect the quality of life in our increasingly independent and complex society; that responsible ethical decision making often requires conviction, courage, and ingenuity in today's competitive business context: We, the members of the Industrial Designers Society of America, will endeavor to meet the standards set forth in this code, and strive to support and defend one another in doing so.

### Fundamental Ethical Principles

We will uphold and advance the integrity of our profession by:

1. supporting one another in achieving our goals of maintaining high professional standards and levels of competence, and honoring commitments we make to others;
2. being honest and fair in serving the public, our clients, employers, peers, employees, and students regardless of gender, race, creed, ethnic origin, age, disability, or sexual orientation;
3. striving to maintain sufficient knowledge of relevant current events and trends so as to be able to assess the economic and environmental effects of our decisions;
4. using our knowledge and skill for the enrichment of human well-being, present and future; and
5. supporting equality of rights under the law and opposing any denial or abridgement of equal rights by the United States or by any individual state on account of gender, race, creed, ethnic origin, age, disability, or sexual orientation.

### Articles of Ethical Practice

The following articles provide an outline of ethical guidelines designed to advance the quality of our profession. They provide general principles in which the "Ethics Advisory Council" can resolve more specific questions that may arise.

**Article I:**  We are responsible to the public for their safety, and their economic and general well-being is our foremost professional concern. We will participate only in projects we judge to be ethically sound and in conformance with pertinent legal regulations; we will advise our clients and employers when we have serious reservations concerning projects we have been assigned.

**Article II:**  We will provide our employers and clients with original and innovative design service of high quality; by serving their interests as faithful agents; by treating privileged information with discretion; by communicating effectively with their appropriate staff members; by avoiding conflicts of interest; and by establishing clear contractual understandings regarding obligations of both parties. Only with agreement of all concerned will we work on competing products lines simultaneously.

**Article III:**  We will compete fairly with our colleagues by building our professional reputation primarily on the quality of our work; by issuing only truthful objective and non-misleading public statements and promotional materials; by respecting competitors' contractual relationships with their clients; and by commenting only with candor and fairness regarding the character of work of other industrial designers.

**Article IV:**    We will be responsible to our employees by facilitating their professional development insofar as possible; by establishing clear contractual understandings; by maintaining safe and appropriate work environments; by properly crediting work accomplished; and by providing fair and adequate compensations for salary and overtime hours.

**Article V:**    We will be responsible to design education by holding as one of our fundamental concerns the education of design students; by advocating implementation of sufficiently inclusive curricula and requiring satisfactory proficiency to enable students to enter the profession with adequate knowledge and skills; by providing opportunities for internships (and collaboratives) with and observation of practicing designers; by respecting students' rights to ownership of their designs; and by fairly crediting them for work accomplished.

**Article VI:**    We will advance the interests of our profession by abiding by this code; by providing a forum within the Society for the ongoing review of ethical concerns; and by publishing, as appropriate, interpretations of this Code.

Any member wishing advice on professional ethics or interpretation of the IDSA Code should contact the IDSA Executive Director.

# APPENDIX B

## Office Policy Manual Outline

### 1. General Information

1.1 Description of the employer (in this case, me)

1.2 Industrial Designers Society of American (IDSA)

1.3 Human Factors and Ergonomics Society (HFES)

1.4 Other professional organizations

### 2. General Policies and Benefits Pertaining to All Employees

2.1 Name of company lawyer and accountant

2.2 Office hours

2.3 Vacation schedule

2.4 List of paid holidays

2.5 Housekeeping

   a. Food

   b. Garbage

   c. Work surfaces

   d. Smoking

2.6 Security

2.7 Procedure for closing the office

   a. Lights

   b. Security lights

   c. Appliances

   d. Locks, etc.

2.8 Procedure for acquiring supplies

2.9 Paychecks (when paid)

2.10 Pay and performance reviews

2.11 Overtime

2.12 Travel expenses

2.13 Termination

2.14 Use of facilities during nonworking hours

2.15 Health and life insurance

### 3. Guidelines and Policies for Industrial Designers

3.1 The firm's objective

3.2 The firm's image

3.3 The firm's philosophy

3.4 Ideas

3.5 Credits

3.6 Communication problems

3.7 The firm's ethics

3.8 IDSA's Code of Ethics and Professional Practices for Industrial Designers

3.9 Professional ethical principles

3.10 Self-education

3.11 Work area

3.12 Dress code

3.13 Use of secretary

3.14 Vendors and salesmen

3.15 Safety

3.16 Record keeping

3.17 Slides

3.18 List of outside associates (engineers, prototypers, plastic experts, etc.) we call upon for assistance

3.19 Sample time book

3.20 Sample "Weekly Project Progress Report"

### 4. Guidelines and Policies for Secretary/Bookkeeper

4.1 Definition of Industrial Design

4.2 Summary of our service

4.3 Important names and phone numbers (vendors, services, etc.)

4.4 Mail

4.5 Telephone

4.6 Visitors

## 5.  Job Descriptions

## 6.  Sample Forms (This section was updated by each secretary)

While it is time consuming to establish a document like this, it has saved me an unbelievable amount of time. I made a point of reviewing this manual with every potential new employee for the express purpose of avoiding problems and misunderstandings in the future. I have found it very useful.

# APPENDIX C

## Sample Employment Agreement

This Agreement entered into by and between
(Company) _____
and (Employee) _____ :

The Company has retained the services of the Employee for the performance of work related to the field of Industrial Design, and

The Employee desires to formalize this relationship with the Company and assume the responsibilities set forth in the Office Policy Manual and individual job description.

In consideration of this, the parties agree as follows:

## Employment

The Company employs the Employee and the Employee accepts employment upon the terms and conditions outlined in this Agreement.

## Duties

The Employee shall be employed by the Company and shall faithfully and to the best of his/her ability perform and render services and perform duties directed by the Company, and shall devote all of his/her working time to such services and duties.

## Remuneration

For services rendered, the Employee will receive a yearly salary of $_____, paid vacation time, paid holidays, and medical and life insurance as outlined in the Office Policy Manual.

## Term

The term of employment shall commence on _____ (starting date), and continue indefinitely, however, either party may terminate this Agreement at any time upon four weeks written notice. In such event, the Employee will render services during the residual period of employment at the discretion of the Company, but the Employee's compensation will continue during this residual period whether or not services are rendered.

## Expenses

The Company will reimburse the Employee for all expenses incurred which are incidental and necessary to the performance of the Employee's duties (except commuting expenses between the Employee's home and the office). These expenses will be paid at actual cost and mileage will be paid for the use of the Employee's personal vehicle at _____ per mile.

## Disclosure of Information

"Confidential Information" means information disclosed to the Employee or known by the Employee through his/her employment by the Company, but not generally known by the public, such as information about the Company's clients, financial position, marketing, services, etc.

Except as required in his/her duties to the Company, the Employee will never directly or indirectly use, disseminate, disclose, lecture upon, or publish articles concerning any confidential information.

## Termination

Upon termination of his/her employment with the Company, all documents, notebooks, time books, calendars, drawings, renderings, slides, sketches, photographs, models, etc. will be left with the Company.

In certain cases the Employee may duplicate slides and photographs for his/her portfolio, but only with the express written permission of the Company.

## Subsequent Employment

The Employee will not engage himself/herself as an employee, consultant, or in any other way contract to provide service to any of the clients of the Company for a period of one year following the termination of the Employee's position with the Company. For purposes of interpretation, a client is any person, organization, or company for which the Company has performed services within a period of three years prior to the effective date of the termination of the Employee. Upon request, a list of such persons, organizations, or companies will be provided to the Employee.

## Notices

Any notice required to be given under this Agreement shall be in writing.

## Waiver of Breach

A waiver by the Company of a breach of any provision of this Agreement by the Employee shall not operate as a waiver of any subsequent breach by the Employee.

## Entire Agreement

This instrument and the Office Policy Manual contain the entire Agreement of the parties and they may be changed only by a written agreement.

## Binding Effect

This Agreement is binding upon the Company and the Employee and upon their respective executors, administrators, legal representatives, and successors.

## Assignment by Employee

This Agreement can in no way be transferred by the Employee.

## Applicable Law

This Agreement is governed by the laws of New York State. If any provision in this Agreement is declared void, such provision will be deemed severed from this Agreement and the Agreement will otherwise remain in full effect.

**IN WITNESS WHEREOF,** the parties have agreed to the terms and conditions set forth in this Agreement.

Date: _____ Signed: _____
(employer)

Date: _____ Signed: _____
(employee)

# APPENDIX D

## Considerations for Establishing a Consulting Firm

### 1. Location

1.1 Physical location of your office

Being in, near, or within a reasonable drive to a large city can be advantageous. If frequent or overseas air travel is a consideration, then a location near a major airport is a plus.

Do you want to work and live in the same community? If not, how far away is your office from your home?

1.2 Location compared to that of your clients' facilities.

I have found that if you are good, you can be located almost any place and cultivate clients. Obviously working from a remote area makes it more difficult to service clients in large metropolitan areas. With the advent of the fax machine and computers, communication problems are diminished. However, I have found that when starting out in business, thinking about the work potential of a certain area is critical.

If one is considering hiring employees, one may wish to research the labor force of a particular area. Being near a university with a design school can be an advantage. Having a large library and experts nearby is an advantage, likewise.

### 2. Facility

2.1 Type of work environment—consider the following when selecting the physical work location:

A. Buy or lease

B. How much square footage is required

C. Is there room for future expansion

2.2 Space required to start up a design consulting firm

A. Office/Reception area—for posting critical information, chairs for awaiting clients and/or sales people, area to hang coats, display of one's work (make it informative of what you do). An effective office needs this minimum of equipment, fixtures, and supplies to function:

1. Desk and chair
2. Filing cabinet(s)
3. Telephones
4. Computer and printer
5. Fax machine
6. Typewriter
7. Photocopier
8. Adding machine or calculator
9. Office supplies
10. Library of books and photographs
11. Radio (perhaps) for entertainment and news

B. Conference Room—should contain a table and chairs, adjoin reception area and model and mock-up display area.

C. Drawing Room—drawing tables, chairs, equipment, supplies storage, computer.

D. Mock-up and model lab—mock-ups and models should be on display. Model lab should contain all necessary tools to construct models.

### 3. Type of entity

3.1 Sole Proprietorship

3.2 Partnership (consult a lawyer)

3.3 Corporation (consult a lawyer)

### 4. Name

4.1 Why personalize, add what you do

4.2 Ltd., Inc., Co., Associates—pros and cons

Why call yourself "associates"? The word "associates" suggests that you have a variety of experts just waiting to help a potential client. Such experts can be marketing experts, researchers, report writers, designers, photography and video experts, model makers, etc. If you do not have these experts available, are you deceiving potential clients, your competition, and your staff? For this reason, IDSA frowns on firms that claim they have associates.

4.3  Logo
     A. Typestyle
     B. Color
     C. Firm's identity

## 5.  Staff

5.1  Principle(s)—owner, partner or stockholder—primarily responsible for running the company
5.2  Secretary—correspondence, telephone calls, filing, sometimes bookkeeper
5.3  Chief Designer—a design specialist
5.4  Model Development Manager—mock-up specialist
5.5  Bookkeeper—day-to-day financial obligations along with record keeping and tax reporting
5.6  Researcher/product planner—report writer, interviewer
5.7  Designer
5.8  Maintenance—cleaning and repairs

## 6.  Consultants to the design firm

6.1  Model and materials specialists
6.2  Market researcher—understands statistics
6.3  Accountant—tax preparation and financial advice
6.4  Lawyer—legal advice
6.5  Board of Directors (if a corporation)

## 7  Public Relations (how to get clients)

7.1  Telemarketing
7.2  Brochures
     A. illustrates the firm's strengths
     B. new accounts
     C. employees
     D. case studies of successful designs
7.3  Advertising
7.4  Write articles—value in publishing
7.5  Write books
7.6  Announcements—who has joined the firm or retired
7.7  Trade shows (visit and display)

## 8.  New Business and plans

## 9.  Competition—how to deal with

## 10.  Income and Rates

10.1  Rates must be based on your expenses, but also must be a realistic assessment of what the market will bear

## 11.  Estimating

## 12.  Contracts

## 13.  Office Policy Manual—See Appendix B

## 14.  Design workbooks and timebooks

14.1  What they should be
      A. a diary of information involved with the evolution of a design,
      B. minutes of meetings the designer participates in,
      C. data that is difficult to remember

14.2  What purpose
      A. provides documentation as to the originality of a design
      B. patent information

# APPENDIX E

## Sample Proposal

PROPOSAL #: _____

DATE: _____

CLIENT:  ABC Tool Company
P.O. Box 225
Anytown, NY 10000

PROJECT:  The industrial design for a new, high-quality precision line of screwdrivers. The system consists of:

1. a pistol grip model,
2. a pistol grip model with a right angle rear attachment, and
3. a vertical straight model.

This project can start (Date) _____.

DESIGN SCOPE:  The designer has been asked to apply ergonomics (human factors) to the three new products.

The image of ABC Tool Company as a manufacturer of high-quality products using ergonomics in tool design is to be generated. This will be accomplished by placing emphasis on developing the best possible ergonomics in conjunction with the best appearance design.

The products are to have a strong product identity, relating to one another while being identified as examples of new, high-quality products offered by ABC Tool Company.

PHASE I:  The designer will begin the project by:

1. studying any market research reports available from the client,
2. visiting the client's facility and using any competitive screwdrivers for comparative ergonomic analysis,
3. interviewing engineering and marketing experts at ABC Tool Company, and
4. visiting one or two manufacturing installations using competitive screwdrivers to canvass their engineers who specify tools and also observe and interview users of pneumatic screwdrivers.

After studying the reports, completing on-site inspections of the screwdrivers in use, and using competitive tools, the designer will prepare a brief report discussing his views and observations as they relate to the design assignment. This report will contain a product ergonomic specification as well as product design ideas. This material will be presented to the client for review and opinions.

This phase will be completed a day or two following the last task outlined above.

PHASE II:  The designer will begin the design of the three products concurrently with Phase I, however, revisions will be made following the completion of Phase I incorporating this research.

Using the product ergonomic specification and any product design ideas developed in Phase I as a guide, the designer will develop a concept or concepts for the products and present the ideas to the client in orthographic drawing and/or mock-up form. Consideration will be given to:

1. Human factors as it relates to the grip, throttle, exhaust, size, center of gravity, etc. Consideration for the relief of carpal tunnel syndrome, white fingers disease, and other occupationally related diseases and injuries will be made.
2. The appearance of the product will be studied and compared with competitive products.
3. Corporate and product identity will be examined.
4. Manufacturing process, materials, and finishes will be explored.

The results of this phase will be presented to the client at its facility. At that time, comments, criticism, and suggestions from the client will be taken into consideration.

This phase will be completed within 30 days of completion of Phase I.

Phase III:  Based on the results of Phase II, the designer will incorporate the client's suggestions and ideas and refine the designs in drawing form. The designer will commence to build final appearance models which will resemble production units as much as possible with all necessary corporate identity. This completes the design service outlined in this proposal.

The results of this phase will be presented at the client's facility within 30 days following the completion of Phase II.

COST:  The cost of the design service as outlined in this proposal will not exceed ($ .00), excluding expenses.

A retainer fee of $2,000.00 will commence the service. This retainer fee will be credited to the first $2,000.00 of design service rendered.

TERMS:  The designer will bill the client twice monthly and the client will pay the designer within fifteen (15) days after receipt of invoice. Expenses such as long-distance telephone calls, travel, special model materials, and other directly related expenses are considered extra and will be billed to the client.

All Confidences, Exclusivity of Service, Term of Agreement, etc. as outlined or implied in Philip Stevens Associates, Ltd. Agreement shall apply.

# APPENDIX F

## Sample Agreement

This Agreement, made on this _____ day of _____, 20____ by and between

_____
(Client)                                    of (Address)

and

_____
(Designer)                                  of (Address)          .

## Recitation

(Designer) _____ is a design firm engaged in the field of industrial design. The client desires to engage the services of the designer as provided for in this Agreement.

## Services

The designer shall provided services set forth in our proposal #_____ dated _____.

## Assurances

The client shall provide the designer at the commencement of this assignment, all information specified by the designer and/or required to properly fulfill the project assignment.

## Exclusivity

During the term of this Agreement, the designer shall not be actively engaged in any designs of a competitive nature with those products and/or services now being offered by the client, without the written approval of the client.

## Term of Agreement

The term of this Agreement shall be from _____ to _____.

## Information Disclosed in Confidence

The designer shall hold in strict confidence all information received from the client during the term of this Agreement.

## Proprietary Rights

The designer gives to the client, and the client accepts from the designer, all rights, title and interest to and ownership of all designs, discoveries, and inventions made. The designer undertakes that he and the personnel engaged on the client's project shall execute such applications, assignments, and affidavits and shall furnish such information, testimony, and assistance as the client may require for prosecuting at the client's expense, through the client's attorneys, applications for letters of patent for such discoveries, designs, and/or inventions.

The client shall, in any published article which has reference to the design service provided by the designer, give credit to the designer for such service.

## Remuneration

The client shall pay the design fee as provided for in the proposal #_____ dated _____.

The designer will bill the client as outlined in the proposal and the client will pay the designer as outlined in the proposal.

## Modification or Change of Agreement

This agreement is the entire understanding between the parties and no modification or change in this Agreement shall be effective unless in writing and executed by both parties.

## Successors

This Agreement shall bind the parties and their respective heirs, administrators, executors, successors, and assigns.

The parties have executed this Agreement on this _____ day of _____, _____.

Designer: _____ Signed: _____
(name and title)

Client: _____ Signed: _____
(name and title)

# APPENDIX G

## Additional Thoughts for Curriculum

### Chapter 1

- What is your definition of industrial design?
- Do you personally know some industrial designers who practice design? What do they say about their profession? Do you want to be like them? If not, why? What do you want to do?

### Chapter 2

- What can be done to build a greater appreciation for engineering among industrial designers?
- What can industrial designers do to instill a greater appreciation for their work among engineers?
- What types of problems faced by society can be helped by industrial design?
- Can you name four outstanding practicing industrial designers not identified in this book? What is outstanding about their work?
- What other events not listed in the timeline do you think impacted the development of industrial design? Why?

### Chapter 3

- What visual media do you consider most effective at communicating ideas and why?
- In your opinion, what artists are best at modern communications?
- In this chapter some elements (i.e., letterhead, packaging, etc.) of corporate identity have been identified. What other elements come to your mind?

### Chapter 4

- Can you think of other techniques for discovering talent?
- Identify your own "crystallizing experiences."
- What creative processes do you use in solving design problems?
- What products or environments have you designed?
- How important is self-confidence? How do you get it?

### Chapter 5

- Besides the qualifications mentioned in the chapter, can you think of other qualifications a designer should possess?
- What pre-college courses or experiences were most influential in helping you decide to become an industrial designer?
- Do you think a master's degree would be helpful to you?
- Before you settled on the school of your choice, how many other schools did you consider? Why?
- How do you feel about ethics being practiced in school?
- Do you support the idea of the Industrial Designers Society of America as a professional organization? Should it do more or less?
- What courses do you feel should be added or eliminated from the industrial design curriculum?
- In your opinion, which is the best choice working for a consulting firm or go working in industry? Support your views with pros and cons.
- Have you thought about what type of industry or field of work you wish to pursue? What is it and why?
- What techniques could a designer use to contact those in industry that might be interested in a designer's services?

## Chapter 7

- What type of business entity do you feel is the best? Why?
- I gave an illustration of losing a client. What would you have done differently to prevent this loss?
- What do you think the value is of having a board of directors?
- What is the value of establishing a budget? Have you ever worked within the confines of a budget?

## Chapter 8

- What other techniques for acquiring design contracts could be used besides the ones described in this chapter?
- Can you think of other areas where designers and/or their firms can serve their communities?

## Chapter 9

- Can you name other products that were developed and demonstrate innovative, forward thinking on the part of its designer(s)?
- Who makes the policies to sustain, develop, and promote innovation in a company? Is this the designer's responsibility?

## Chapter 10

- Make your own list of products displaying "good design" (see page 3-5).
- What other categories would you add?
- What about the future? How do you see it evolving?
- Do you feel design is getting better? Has it gotten worse? If so, how?
- In what areas do you expect the next big design breakthrough to be?
- Are we:
  1. Encountering stricter enforcement of our professional code of ethics?
  2. Witnessing our designers being trained to function as corporate executives and leaders? Are they acquiring such roles.
  3. Making our designs more user-friendly toward children and older citizens?
  4. Establishing a trend toward licensing our profession? If electricians and plumbers have to be licensed in some municipalities, then why shouldn't designers be required when we are involved in product safety?
  5. Cooperating with other professionals, particularly engineers and architects?
  6. Growing at a rate comparable to other professional groups? Should we be? How do we evaluate such growth?
  7. Seeing better products simply because there are more designers practicing today than ever before?

# SELECTED BIBLIOGRAPHY

Abercrombie, Stanley. *George Nelson: The Design of Modern Design.* Cambridge: The M.I.T. Press, 1995.

Apostolos-Cappadona, Diane and Bruce Altshuler. *Isamu Noguchi Essays and Conversations.* New York: Harry N. Abrams, Inc., 1994.

Bartinique, A.Patricia. *Gustav Stickley… His Craft.* Parsippany: The Craftsman Farms Foundation, 1992.

Bayer, Herbert. *Herbert Bayer: painter, designer, architect.* New York: Reinhold Publishing Corporation, 1967.

Bel Geddes, Norman. *Horizons.* Little, Brown, and Company, Boston, MA , 1932.

Bodie, Warren M. *The Lockheed P-38 Lightning.* Hiawassee, GA: Widewing Publications, 1991.

Bok, Derek. *Higher Learning.* Cambridge, MA: Harvard University Press, 1986.

Booth-Clibborn, Edward and Daniele Baroni. *The Language of Graphics,* New York: Harry N. Abrams, Inc., Publishers, 1980.

Brohan, Torsten and Thomas Berg. *Avantgarde Design, 1880-1930.* Bonn, Germany: Benedikt Taschen, 1994.

Buchanan, Richard and Victor Margolin, editors. *Discovering Design: Explorations in Design Studies.* Chicago: The University of Chicago Press, 1995.

Caton, Joseph Harris. *The Utopian Vision of Moholy-Nagy.* Ann Arbor, Michigan: UMI Research Press, 1984.

Deighton, Len. *Fighter: The True Story of the Battle of Britain.* New York: Harper Collins Publishers, 1977.

Deighton, Len. *Blood, Tears and Folly: An Objective look at World War II.* New York: Harper Collins Publishers, 1993.

Doordan, Dennis P., editor. *Design History: An Anthology.* Cambridge: The M.I.T. Press, 1995.

Dreyfuss, Henry. *Designing For People.* New York: Simon and Schuster, 1955.

Droste, Magdalena. *Bauhaus, 1919-1933.* Germany: Benedikt Taschen, 1990.

Durant, Stuart. *Christopher Dresser.* Ernst & Sohn, London, 1993.

Flurscheim, Charles H., editor. *Industrial Design in Engineering, a Marriage of Techniques.* New York: Springer-Verlag, 1983.

Ford, Edward R. *The Details of Modern Architecture.* Cambridge: The M.I.T. Press, 1990.

Forty, Adrian. *Objects of Desire: Design & Society from Wedgwood to IBM.* Pantheon Books, New York, 1986.

Gardner, Howard. *To Open Minds: Chinese Clues to the Dilemma of Contemporary Education.* New York: Basic Books, Inc., 1989.

Gardner, Howard. *Art, Mind and Brain: A Cognitive Approach to Creativity.* New York: Basic Books, Inc., 1982.

Gardner, Howard. *The Unschooled Mind: How Children Think & How Schools Should Teach.* New York: Basic Books, Inc., 1991.

Gardner, Howard. *Creating Minds: An anatomy of creativity seen through the lives of Freud, Einstein, Pacasso, Stravinsky, Eliot, Graham, and Gandhi.* New York: Basic Books, Inc. 1993.

Gardner, Howard. *Multiple Intelligences: The Theory in Practice.* New York: Basic Books, Inc., 1993.

Gardner, Howard. *Frames of Mind.* New York: Basic Books, Inc. 1983.

Giedion, S. *Walter Gropius: Work and Teamwork.* New York: Reinhold Publishing Corporation, 1954.

Gies, Joseph & Frances. *The Ingenious Yankees, The men, ideas, and machines that transformed a nation, 1776-1878.* New York: Thomas Y. Crowell Company, 1976.

Green, William. *The Warplanes of the Third Reich.* New York: Galahad Books, 1970.

Grove, Nancy and Diane Botnick, foreword by Isamu Noguchi. *The Sculpture of Isamu Noguchi, 1924-1979.* New York: Garland Publishing, Inc., 1980.

Grun, Bernard. *The Timetables of History: A Horizontal Linkage of People and Events,* 3rd revised edition. New York: Simon & Schuster/ Touchstone, 1991.

Gunston, Bill, editor. *Chronicle of Aviation.* Paris: Jacques Legrand International Publishing, 1992.

Halen, Widar. *Christopher Dresser.* Oxford: Phaidon Christies Limited, 1990.

Hauffe, Thomas. *Design: An illustrated historical overview.* New York: Barron's Educational Series, Inc., 1996.

Heskett, John. *Industrial Design.* London: Thames and Hudson, 1995.

Hochman, Elaine S. *Bauhaus: Crucible of Modernism.* New York: Fromm International, 1997.

Hollingsworth, Brian and Arthur Cook. *The Great Book of Trains.* New York: Crown Publishers, Inc., 1987.

Hughes, Thomas P. *American Genesis, a Century of Invention and Technological Enthusiasm.* New York: Penguin Books USA Inc., 1989.

Hunter, Sam. *Isamu Noguchi.* New York: Abbeville Press, Inc., 1979.

Industrial Designers Society of America. *Comprehensive Description of Industrial Design.* Great Falls, VA: 1999.

Industrial Designers Society of America. *1996 Compensation Study.* Great Falls, VA: 1996.

International Design Conference in Aspen. *The New Business of Design.* New York: Allworth Press, 1996.

Kantowitz, Barry H. and Robert D. Sorkin. *Human Factors, Understanding People-System Relationships.* New York: John Wiley & Sons, Inc., 1983.

Keegan, John. *Warpaths: Travels of a Military Historian in North America.* London: Hodder and Stoughton, 1995.

Kennedy, Paul. *Preparing for the Twenty-First Century.* New York: Vintage Books, 1993.

Kepes, Gyorgy, editor. *The Visual Arts Today.* Middletown, Connecticut: Wesleyan University Press, 1960.

Klamkin, Marian. *Hands to Work: Shaker Folk Art and Industries.* New York: Dodd, Mead & Company, 1972.

Knoke, William. *Bold New World: The essential road map to the twenty-first century.* New York: Kodansha America, Inc., 1996.

Koether, George. "The Building of Men, Machines, and a Company." *Compressed Air Magazine,* 1971.

Kuh, Katharine. *Leger.* Urbana: The University of Illinois Press, 1953.

Kultermann, Udo, editor. *St. James Modern Masterpieces: The Best of Art, Architecture, Photography and Design since 1945.* Detroit: Visible Ink Press, 1998.

Lambert, Anthony, editor. *The Railroad Encyclopedia.* Ann Arbor: Longmeadow Press, 1996.

Lichtenstein, Claude and Franz Engler, editors. *Streamlined: A Metaphor for Progress.* Baden, Switzerland: Lars Muller Publishers.

Lorenz, Christopher. *The Design Dimension, Product Strategy and the Challenge of Global Marketing.* New York: Basil Blackwell, Inc., 1986.

Lucie-Smith, Edward. *A History of Industrial Design.* Van Nostrand Reinhold Company, New York, 1983.

Margolin, Victor, editor. *Design Discourse: History, Theory, Criticism.* Chicago: The University of Chicago Press, 1989.

Massey, James and Shirley Maxwell. *Arts & Crafts.* New York: Abbeville Press,.

Mayer, Barbara. *In The Arts & Crafts Style.* San Francisco: Chronicle Books, 1992.

Maynard, Dr. Fredelle. *Guiding Your Child to a More Creative Life.* New York: Doubleday & Company, Inc., 1973.

McHale, John. *R. Buckminster Fuller: Makers of Contemporary Architecture.* George Braziller, Inc., New York, 1962.

Meadows, Donella H. and Dennis L. and Jorgen Randers. *Beyond the Limits: Confronting Global Collapse, Envisioning a Sustainable Future.* Post Mills, Vermont: Chelsea Green Publishing Company, 1992.

Meadows, Donella H. and Dennis L., Jorgen Randers and William W. Behrens III. *The Limits to Growth.* New York: Universe Books, 1972.

Meikle, Jeffrey L. *Twentieth Century Limited: Industrial Design in America, 1925-1939.* Temple University Press, Philadelphia, 1979.

Morison, Elting E. *From Know-how to Nowhere, The Development of American Technology.* New York: Basic Books, Inc., 1974.

Nervi, Pier Luigi, preface and Ernesto N. Rogers, introduction. *The Works of Pier Luigi Nervi.* Frederick A. Praeger, New York, 1957.

*The New Yorker Album of Drawings 1925-1975.* New York: The Viking Press, 1975.

*The New Yorker Book of Cat Cartoons.* New York: Alfred A. Knopf, Inc., 1990.

Paepke, C. Owen. *The Evolution of Progress: The End of Economic Growth and the Beginning of Human Transformation.* New York: Random House, 1993.

The Patricia and Phillip Frost Collection. *American Abstraction, 1930-1945.*

Philadelphia Museum of Art. *Design since 1945.* Philadelphia: 1983.

Price, Alfred. *The Spitfire Story.* Revised second edition. London: Arms and Armour Press, 1995.

Pulos, Arthur J. *Opportunities in Industrial Design Careers.* New York: Universal Publishing and Distributing Corporation, 1970.

Pulos, Arthur J. *The American Design Adventure.* Cambridge, MA: The MIT Press, 1988.

Pye, David. *The Nature and Aesthetics of Design.* Bethal, CT: Cambium Press, 1978.

Rabinowitz, Harold. *Conquer the Sky: Great Moments in Aviation.* New York: Friedman/Fairfax Publishers, 1996.

Reynolds, Donald Martin. *Monuments and Masterpieces: Histories and Views of Public Sculpture in New York City.* New York: Macmillan Publishing Company, 1988.

Rich, Ben R. and Leo Janos. *Skunk Works: A Personal Memoir of My Years at Lockheed.* New York: Little, Brown and Company, 1994.

Rodengen, Jeffrey L. *The Legend of Ingersoll-Rand.* Fort Lauderdale, FL: Write Stuff Syndicate, Inc., 1995.

Schmeckebier, Laurence. *Ivan Mestrovic, sculptor and patriot.* Syracuse: Syracuse University Press, 1959.

Seuphor, Michel. *The Sculpture of this Century.* New York: George Braziller, Inc., 1960.

Smith, Mary Ann. *Gustav Stickley: The Craftsman.* New York: Dover Publications, Inc., 1983.

*The Inventive Yankee.* Dublin: Yankee Books, 1989.

Taub, Eric. *Taurus: The Making of the Car That Saved Ford.* New York: The Penguin Group, 1991.

Ulrich, Karl T. and Steven D. Eppinger. *Product Design and Development.* New York: McGraw-Hill, Inc., 1995.

Wang, Penelope. "The Smartest Ways to Invest for College." *Money,* September 1996, page 120.

*Webster's New Collegiate Dictionary.* Springfield, MA: G. & C. Merriam Company, 1977.

Weston, Richard. *Modernism.* London: Phaidon Press, Ltd., 1996.

White, Peter T. "Gold, The Eternal Treasure." *National Geographic,* January 1974, page 1-27, 41-50.

Whitford, Frank. *Bauhaus.* New York: Thames and Hudson, Inc., 1984.

# INDEX

*page number in italics is reference to a photo*

page number in *italics* is reference to a photo